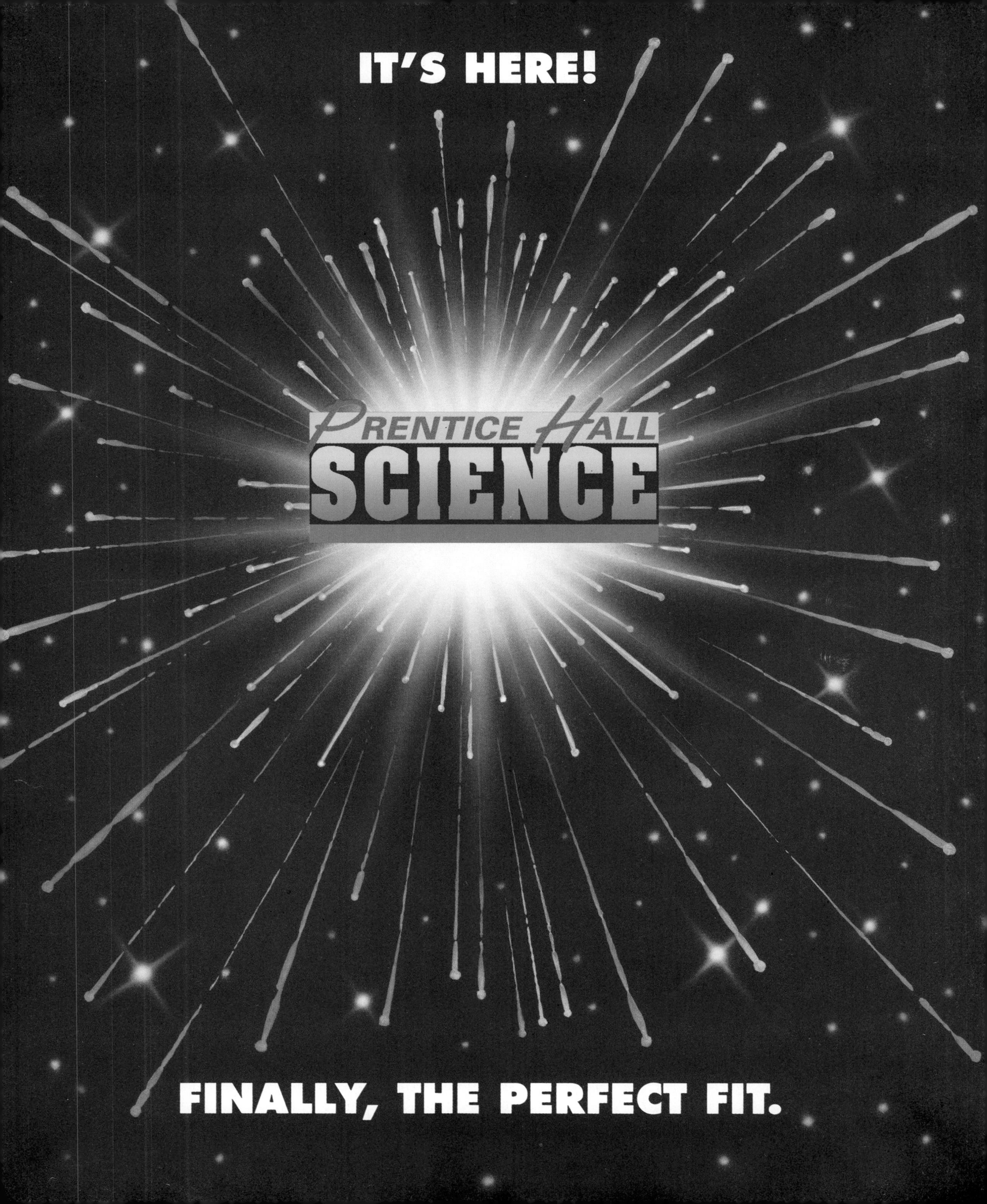
IT'S HERE!
PRENTICE HALL
SCIENCE
FINALLY, THE PERFECT FIT.

NOW YOU CAN CHOOSE THE PERFECT FIT FOR ALL YOUR CURRICULUM NEEDS.

The new Prentice Hall Science program consists of 19 hardcover books, each of which covers a particular area of science. All of the sciences are represented in the program so you can choose the perfect fit to *your* particular curriculum needs.

The flexibility of this program will allow you to teach those topics you want to teach, and to teach them *in-depth*. Virtually any approach to science—general, integrated, coordinated, thematic, etc.—is possible with Prentice Hall Science.

Above all, the program is designed to make your teaching experience easier and more fun.

ELECTRICITY AND MAGNETISM
Ch. 1. Electric Charges and Currents
Ch. 2. Magnetism
Ch. 3. Electromagnetism
Ch. 4. Electronics and Computers

HEREDITY: THE CODE OF LIFE
Ch. 1. What is Genetics?
Ch. 2. How Chromosomes Work
Ch. 3. Human Genetics
Ch. 4. Applied Genetics

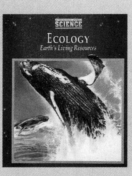

ECOLOGY: EARTH'S LIVING RESOURCES
Ch. 1. Interactions Among Living Things
Ch. 2. Cycles in Nature
Ch. 3. Exploring Earth's Biomes
Ch. 4. Wildlife Conservation

PARADE OF LIFE: MONERANS, PROTISTS, FUNGI, AND PLANTS
Ch. 1. Classification of Living Things
Ch. 2. Viruses and Monerans
Ch. 3. Protists
Ch. 4. Fungi
Ch. 5. Plants Without Seeds
Ch. 6. Plants With Seeds

EXPLORING THE UNIVERSE
Ch. 1. Stars and Galaxies
Ch. 2. The Solar System
Ch. 3. Earth and Its Moon

EVOLUTION: CHANGE OVER TIME
Ch. 1. Earth's History in Fossils
Ch. 2. Changes in Living Things Over Time
Ch. 3. The Path to Modern Humans

EXPLORING EARTH'S WEATHER
Ch. 1. What Is Weather?
Ch. 2. What Is Climate?
Ch. 3. Climate in the United States

THE NATURE OF SCIENCE
Ch. 1. What is Science?
Ch. 2. Measurement and the Sciences
Ch. 3. Tools and the Sciences

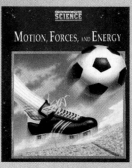

ECOLOGY: EARTH'S NATURAL RESOURCES

Ch. 1. Energy Resources
Ch. 2. Earth's Nonliving Resources
Ch. 3. Pollution
Ch. 4. Conserving Earth's Resources

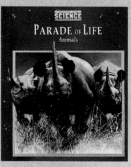

MOTION, FORCES, AND ENERGY

Ch. 1. What Is Motion?
Ch. 2. The Nature of Forces
Ch. 3. Forces in Fluids
Ch. 4. Work, Power, and Simple Machines
Ch. 5. Energy: Forms and Changes

PARADE OF LIFE: ANIMALS

Ch. 1. Sponges, Cnidarians, Worms, and Mollusks
Ch. 2. Arthropods and Echinoderms
Ch. 3. Fish and Amphibians
Ch. 4. Reptiles and Birds
Ch. 5. Mammals

CELLS: BUILDING BLOCKS OF LIFE

Ch. 1. The Nature of LIfe
Ch. 2. Cell Structure and Function
Ch. 3. Cell Processes
Ch. 4. Cell Energy

DYNAMIC EARTH

Ch. 1. Movement of the Earth's Crust
Ch. 2. Earthquakes and Volcanoes
Ch. 3. Plate Tectonics
Ch. 4. Rocks and Minerals
Ch. 5. Weathering and Soil Formation
Ch. 6. Erosion and Deposition

MATTER: BUILDING BLOCK OF THE UNIVERSE

Ch. 1. General Properties of Matter
Ch. 2. Physical and Chemical Changes
Ch. 3. Mixtures, Elements, and Compounds
Ch. 4. Atoms: Building Blocks of Matter
Ch. 5. Classification of Elements: The Periodic Table

CHEMISTRY OF MATTER

Ch. 1. Atoms and Bonding
Ch. 2. Chemical Reactions
Ch. 3. Families of Chemical Compounds
Ch. 4. Chemical Technology
Ch. 5. Radioactive Elements

HUMAN BIOLOGY AND HEALTH

Ch. 1. The Human Body
Ch. 2. Skeletal and Muscular Systems
Ch. 3. Digestive System
Ch. 4. Circulatory System
Ch. 5. Respiratory and Excretory Systems
Ch. 6. Nervous and Endocrine Systems
Ch. 7. Reproduction and Development
Ch. 8. Immune System
Ch. 9. Alcohol, Tobacco, and Drugs

EXPLORING PLANET EARTH

Ch. 1. Earth's Atmosphere
Ch. 2. Earth's Oceans
Ch. 3. Earth's Fresh Water
Ch. 4. Earth's Landmasses
Ch. 5. Earth's Interior

HEAT ENERGY

Ch. 1. What Is Heat?
Ch. 2. Uses of Heat

SOUND AND LIGHT

Ch. 1. Characteristics of Waves
Ch. 2. Sound and Its Uses
Ch. 3. Light and the Electromagnetic Spectrum
Ch. 4. Light and Its Uses

A COMPLETELY INTEGRATED LEARNING SYSTEM...

The Prentice Hall Science program is an *integrated* learning system with a variety of print materials and multimedia components. All are designed to meet the needs of diverse learning styles and your technology needs.

THE STUDENT BOOK
Each book is a model of **excellent writing and dynamic visuals**—designed to be exciting and motivating to the student *and* the teacher, with relevant examples integrated throughout, and more opportunities for many different activities which apply to everyday life.

Problem-solving activities emphasize the thinking process, so problems may be more open-ended.

"Discovery Activities" throughout the book foster active learning.

Different sciences, and other disciplines, are integrated throughout the text and reinforced in the "Connections" features (the connections between computers and viruses is one example).

TEACHER'S RESOURCE PACKAGE
In addition to the student book, the complete teaching package contains:

ANNOTATED TEACHER'S EDITION
Designed to provide **"teacher-friendly"** support regardless of instructional approach:

■ **Help is readily available** if you choose to teach thematically, to integrate the sciences, and/or to integrate the sciences with other curriculum areas.

■ **Activity-based learning** is easy to implement through the use of Discovery Strategies, Activity Suggestions, and Teacher Demonstrations.

■ Integration of all components is part of the teaching strategies.

■ For instant accessibility, all of the teaching suggestions are wrapped around the student pages to which they refer.

ACTIVITY BOOK
Includes a **discovery activity for each chapter**, plus other activities including problem-solving and cooperative-learning activities

THE REVIEW AND REINFORCEMENT GUIDE
Addresses **students' different learning styles** in a clear and comprehensive format:

■ Highly visual for visual learners

TEACHER'S RESOURCE PACKAGE

FOR THE PERFECT FIT TO YOUR TEACHING NEEDS.

■ Can be used in conjunction with the program's audiotapes for auditory and language learners.

■ More than a study guide, it's a guide to comprehension, with activities, key concepts, and vocabulary.

ENGLISH AND SPANISH AUDIOTAPES
Correlate with the Review and Reinforcement Guide to aid auditory learners.

LABORATORY MANUAL ANNOTATED TEACHER'S EDITION
Offers **at least one additional hands-on opportunity per chapter** with answers and teaching suggestions on lab preparation and safety.

TEST BOOK
Contains **traditional and up-to-the-minute strategies for student assessment.** Choose from performance-based tests in addition to traditional chapter tests and computer test bank questions.

STUDENT LAB MANUAL
Each of the 19 books also comes with its own Student Lab Manual.

ALSO INCLUDED IN THE INTEGRATED LEARNING SYSTEM:

■ Teacher's Desk Reference
■ English Guide for Language Learners
■ Spanish Guide for Language Learners
■ Product Testing Activities

■ Transparencies
■ Computer Test Bank (IBM, Apple, or MAC)
■ VHS Videos
■ Videodiscs
■ Interactive Videodiscs (Level III)
■ Courseware

All components are integrated in the teaching strategies in the Annotated Teacher's Edition, where they directly relate to the science content.

THE PRENTICE HALL SCIENCE
INTEGRATED LEARNING SYSTEM

The following components are integrated in the teaching strategies for
MATTER: BUILDING BLOCK OF THE UNIVERSE.

■ **Product-Testing Activities:**
Testing Paper Towels
Testing Yogurt
Testing Disposable Cups
Testing Bottled Water
Testing Glues

■ **Transparencies:**
Molecules
Rutherford's Experiment
Structure of the Atom
Isotopes of Carbon
Energy Levels
The Periodic Table

■ **Videos/Videodiscs:**
Elements, Compounds and
  Mixtures
Periodic Table and
  Periodicity
Acids, Bases and Salts

■ **Annotated Teacher's
Edition**

■ **Activity Book**

■ **Review and
Reinforcement Guide**

■ **Laboratory Manual,
Annotated Teacher's Edition**

■ **Test Book**—including
Performance-Based Tests

■ **Laboratory Manual**

■ **English/Spanish
Audiotapes**

INTEGRATING OTHER SCIENCES

Many of the other 18 Prentice Hall Science books can be integrated into **MATTER: BUILDING BLOCK OF THE UNIVERSE.** The books you will find suggested most often in the Annotated Teacher's Edition are:
EXPLORING THE UNIVERSE; ECOLOGY: EARTH'S LIVING RESOURCES; PARADE OF LIFE: ANIMALS;
DYNAMIC EARTH; EXPLORING EARTH'S WEATHER; EXPLORING PLANET EARTH; ECOLOGY:
EARTH'S NATURAL RESOURCES; CELLS: BUILDING BLOCKS OF LIFE; EVOLUTION: CHANGE OVER
TIME; and PARADE OF LIFE: MONERANS, PROTISTS, FUNGI, AND PLANTS.

INTEGRATING THEMES

Many themes can be integrated into **MATTER: BUILDING BLOCK OF THE UNIVERSE.**
Following are the ones most commonly suggested in the Annotated Teacher's Edition: PATTERNS OF
CHANGE, SCALE AND STRUCTURE, SYSTEMS AND INTERACTIONS, and STABILITY.

For more detailed information on teaching thematically and integrating
the sciences, see the Teacher's Desk Reference and teaching strategies throughout
the Annotated Teacher's Edition.

For more information, call 1-800-848-9500 or write:

P R E N T I C E   H A L L

Simon & Schuster Education Group
113 Sylvan Avenue Route 9W
Englewood Cliffs, New Jersey 07632
Simon & Schuster A Paramount Communications Company

Annotated Teacher's Edition

Prentice Hall Science

Matter
Building Block of the Universe

Anthea Maton
NSTA National Coordinator
Project Scope, Sequence,
   Coordination
Washington, DC

Jean Hopkins
Science Instructor and Department
   Chairperson
John H. Wood Middle School
San Antonio, Texas

Susan Johnson
Professor of Biology
Ball State University
Muncie, Indiana

David LaHart
Senior Instructor
Florida Solar Energy Center
Cape Canaveral, Florida

Charles William McLaughlin
Science Instructor and Department
   Chairperson
Central High School
St. Joseph, Missouri

Maryanna Quon Warner
Science Instructor
Del Dios Middle School
Escondido, California

Jill D. Wright
Professor of Science Education
Director of International Field
   Programs
University of Pittsburgh
Pittsburgh, Pennsylvania

Prentice Hall
A Division of Simon & Schuster
Englewood Cliffs, New Jersey

ISBN 0-13-986126-2

1 2 3 4 5 6 7 8 9 10   95 94 93 92 91

Contents of Annotated Teacher's Edition

To the Teacher

Welcome to the *Prentice Hall Science* program. *Prentice Hall Science* has been designed as a complete program for use with middle school or junior high school science students. The program covers all relevant areas of science and has been developed with the flexibility to meet virtually all your curriculum needs. In addition, the program has been designed to better enable you—the classroom teacher—to integrate various disciplines of science into your daily lessons, as well as to enhance the thematic teaching of science.

The *Prentice Hall Science* program consists of nineteen books, each of which covers a particular topic area. The nineteen books in the *Prentice Hall Science* program are

The Nature of Science
Parade of Life: Monerans, Protists, Fungi, and Plants
Parade of Life: Animals
Cells: Building Blocks of Life
Heredity: The Code of Life
Evolution: Change Over Time

Ecology: Earth's Living Resources
Human Biology and Health
Exploring Planet Earth
Dynamic Earth
Exploring Earth's Weather
Ecology: Earth's Natural Resources
Exploring the Universe
Matter: Building Block of the Universe
Chemistry of Matter
Electricity and Magnetism
Heat Energy
Sound and Light
Motion, Forces, and Energy

Each of the student editions listed above also comes with a complete set of teaching materials and student ancillary materials. Furthermore, videos, interactive videos and science courseware are available for the *Prentice Hall Science* program. This combination of student texts and ancillaries, teacher materials, and multimedia products makes up your complete *Prentice Hall Science* Learning System.

About the Teacher's Desk Reference

When you purchase a textbook in the *Prentice Hall Science* program, you also receive a copy of the *Teacher's Desk Reference*. The *Teacher's Desk Reference* includes all the standard information you need to know about *Prentice Hall Science*.

The *Teacher's Desk Reference* presents an overview of the program, including a full description of each ancillary available in the program. It gives a brief summary of each of the student textbooks available in the *Prentice Hall Science* Learning System. The *Teacher's Desk Reference* also demonstrates how the seven science themes incorporated into *Prentice Hall Science* are woven throughout the entire program.

In addition, the *Teacher's Desk Reference* presents a detailed discussion of the features of the Student

Edition and the features of the Annotated Teacher's Edition, as well as an overview section that summarizes issues in science education and offers a message about teaching special students. Selected instructional essays in the *Teacher's Desk Reference* include English as a Second Language (ESL), Multicultural Teaching, Cooperative-Learning Strategies, and Integrated Science Teaching, in addition to other relevant topics. Further, a discussion of the Multimedia components that are part of *Prentice Hall Science*, as well as how they can be integrated with the textbooks, is included in the *Teacher's Desk Reference*.

The *Teacher's Desk Reference* also contains in blackline master form a booklet on Teaching Graphing Skills, which may be reproduced for student use.

Integrating the Sciences

The *Prentice Hall Science* Learning System has been designed to allow you to teach science from an integrated point of view. Great care has been taken to integrate other science disciplines, where appropriate, into the chapter content and visuals. In addition, the integration of other disciplines such as social studies and literature has been incorporated into each textbook.

On the reduced student pages throughout your Annotated Teacher's Edition you will find numbers within blue bullets beside selected passages and visuals. An Annotation Key in the wraparound margins indicates the particular branch of science or other discipline that has been integrated into the student text. In addition, where appropriate, the name of the textbook and the chapter number in which the particular topic is discussed in greater detail is provided. This enables you to further integrate a particular science topic by using the complete *Prentice Hall Science* Learning System.

Thematic Overview

When teaching any science topic, you may want to focus your lessons around the underlying themes that pertain to all areas of science. These underlying themes are the framework from which all science can be constructed and taught. The seven underlying themes incorporated into *Prentice Hall Science* are

Energy
Evolution
Patterns of Change
Scale and Structure
Systems and Interactions
Unity and Diversity
Stability

A detailed discussion of each of these themes and how they are incorporated into the *Prentice Hall Science* program are included in your *Teacher's Desk Reference*. In addition, the *Teacher's Desk Reference* includes thematic matrices for the *Prentice Hall Science* program.

A thematic matrix for each chapter in this textbook follows. Each thematic matrix is designed with the list of themes along the left-hand column and in the right-hand column a big idea, or overarching concept statement, as to how that particular theme is taught in the chapter.

The primary themes in this textbook are Scale and Structure, Stability, Systems and Interactions, and Patterns of Change. Primary themes throughout *Prentice Hall Science* are denoted by an asterisk.

CHAPTER 1

General Properties of Matter

ENERGY	
EVOLUTION	
*PATTERNS OF CHANGE	• Due to inertia, all objects resist a change in motion unless acted upon by a force.
*SCALE AND STRUCTURE	• All objects, no matter how large or small, are made of matter.
*SYSTEMS AND INTERACTIONS	• Objects with a density less than water will float, whereas those with a density greater than water will sink.
UNITY AND DIVERSITY	• Characteristics common to all matter can be described by the general properties of matter. • Specific properties can be used to distinguish one type of matter from another.
*STABILITY	• The mass of an object is constant unless matter is added to or taken away from the object. Weight, however, is dependent on both mass and location and is not constant.

CHAPTER 2

Physical and Chemical Changes

ENERGY	• Substances can be made to change phase by adding or taking away energy.
EVOLUTION	
***PATTERNS OF CHANGE**	• Matter can exist in four phases: solid, liquid, gas, and plasma.
***SCALE AND STRUCTURE**	• The properties of solids, liquids, and gases are related to the arrangement of particles that make up the substance.
***SYSTEMS AND INTERACTIONS**	• During a chemical reaction, new substances with different physical and chemical properties are produced.
UNITY AND DIVERSITY	• The general properties of matter—such as weight, volume, and density—are physical properties.
***STABILITY**	• When a substance undergoes a physical change, its physical properties are altered but the substance remains the same kind of matter.

CHAPTER 3

Mixtures, Elements, and Compounds

ENERGY	• Heat and electric energy can be used to separate some compounds into their elements.
EVOLUTION	
*PATTERNS OF CHANGE	• Atoms of different elements can be chemically combined to form compounds. • The compounds have properties different from the elements that formed them.
*SCALE AND STRUCTURE	• The particles in a heterogeneous mixture are large enough to be seen and to separate from the mixture. • The particles in a homogeneous mixture are too small to be seen and cannot easily be separated from the mixture.
*SYSTEMS AND INTERACTIONS	• During a chemical reaction, substances can be changed into new and different substances through a rearrangement of their atoms.
UNITY AND DIVERSITY	• Matter can exist as elements, compounds, mixtures, and solutions.
*STABILITY	• Elements—the simplest pure substances—cannot be broken down any further without losing their identity.

CHAPTER 4

Atoms: Building Blocks of Matter

ENERGY	• The energy content of an electron (which can increase or decrease) determines its energy level in an atom.
EVOLUTION	
*PATTERNS OF CHANGE	• Each increase in the number of protons in an atom results in a new kind of atom.
*SCALE AND STRUCTURE	• Atoms are made of smaller particles. • The three main subatomic particles are the proton, the neutron, and the electron. • The number of protons in the nucleus of an atom is called the atomic number of the element.
*SYSTEMS AND INTERACTIONS	• The forces that govern the behavior of subatomic particles are electromagnetic, strong, weak, and gravity.
UNITY AND DIVERSITY	• The atom is the smallest piece of matter. • Atoms of different elements have different numbers of protons, neutrons, and electrons.
*STABILITY	• The modern atomic model shows that an atom has a positively charged nucleus surrounded by a region in which there are enough electrons to make the atom neutral.

CHAPTER 5

Classification of Elements: The Periodic Table

ENERGY	• The amount of energy needed to remove an electron from an atom shows a periodic increase from left to right across a period.
EVOLUTION	
*PATTERNS OF CHANGE	• The periodic law states that the physical and chemical properties of the elements are periodic functions of their atomic number.
*SCALE AND STRUCTURE	• Atomic size decreases as you move from left to right across a period. • The size of an atom and the number of its electrons determine the atom's reactivity.
*SYSTEMS AND INTERACTIONS	• The periodic law can be used to predict the properties of elements.
UNITY AND DIVERSITY	• The properties of elements in the same group, or family, are similar to one another.
*STABILITY	• The number of valence electrons can be used to predict an element's reactivity. • Elements whose outer energy shell of electrons is full are inert.

Comprehensive List of Laboratory Materials

Item	Quantities per Group	Chapter
Balance	1	4
Broom	1	1
Bunsen burner	1	5
Candle, small	1	2
Candle holder or small empty food can	1	2
Chloride test solutions (LiCl, CaCl$_2$, KCl, CuCl$_2$, SrCl$_2$, NaCl$_2$, BaCl$_2$, unknown)	5 mL each	5
Cork	1	5
Food coloring (red, yellow, blue, green)	1 small bottle each	3
Hydrochloric acid, dilute	1 small bottle	5
Magnet	1	4
Marshmallows, large	25	3
Matches	1 book	2
Metric ruler or meterstick	1	1, 2
Objects of various masses	several	4
	1 set of 3	1
Sand	small amount	2
Shoe box with lid	1	4
	several	1
Test tubes	8	5
Test-tube rack	1	5
Toothpicks	1 box	3
Water, distilled	5 mL	5
Wire, nichrome or platinum, 30 cm	1 piece	5

MATTER
Building Block of the Universe

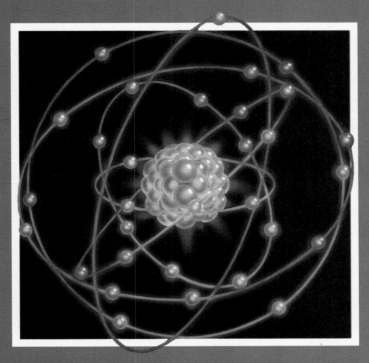

Anthea Maton
NSTA National Coordinator
Project Scope, Sequence, Coordination
Washington, DC

Jean Hopkins
Science Instructor and Department Chairperson
John H. Wood Middle School
San Antonio, Texas

Susan Johnson
Professor of Biology
Ball State University
Muncie, Indiana

David LaHart
Senior Instructor
Florida Solar Energy Center
Cape Canaveral, Florida

Charles William McLaughlin
Science Instructor and Department Chairperson
Central High School
St. Joseph, Missouri

Maryanna Quon Warner
Science Instructor
Del Dios Middle School
Escondido, California

Jill D. Wright
Professor of Science Education
Director of International Field Programs
University of Pittsburgh
Pittsburgh, Pennsylvania

Prentice Hall
Englewood Cliffs, New Jersey
Needham, Massachusetts

Prentice Hall Science

Matter: Building Block of the Universe

Student Text and Annotated Teacher's Edition
Laboratory Manual
Teacher's Resource Package
Teacher's Desk Reference
Computer Test Bank
Teaching Transparencies
Science Reader
Product Testing Activities
Computer Courseware
Video and Interactive Video

The illustration on the cover, rendered by Keith Kasnot, shows the nucleus of an atom with its protons and neutrons, surrounded by electrons in the electron cloud.

Credits begin on page 160.

FIRST EDITION

ISBN 0-13-981036-6

1 2 3 4 5 6 7 8 9 10   95 94 93 92 91

Prentice Hall
A Division of Simon & Schuster
Englewood Cliffs, New Jersey 07632

STAFF CREDITS

Editorial:	Harry Bakalian, Pamela E. Hirschfeld, Maureen Grassi, Robert P. Letendre, Elisa Mui Eiger, Lorraine Smith-Phelan, Christine A. Caputo
Design:	AnnMarie Roselli, Carmela Pereira, Susan Walrath, Leslie Osher, Art Soares
Production:	Suse Cioffi, Joan McCulley, Elizabeth Torjussen, Christina Burghard, Marlys Lehmann
Photo Research:	Libby Forsyth, Emily Rose, Martha Conway
Publishing Technology:	Andrew Grey Bommarito, Gwendollynn Waldron, Deborah Jones, Monduane Harris, Michael Colucci, Gregory Myers, Cleasta Wilburn
Marketing:	Andy Socha, Victoria Willows
Pre-Press Production:	Laura Sanderson, Denise Herckenrath
Manufacturing:	Rhett Conklin, Gertrude Szyferblatt

Consultants

Kathy French	National Science Consultant
William Royalty	National Science Consultant

Contributing Writers

Linda Densman
Science Instructor
Hurst, TX

Linda Grant
Former Science Instructor
Weatherford, TX

Heather Hirschfeld
Science Writer
Durham, NC

Marcia Mungenast
Science Writer
Upper Montclair, NJ

Michael Ross
Science Writer
New York City, NY

Content Reviewers

Dan Anthony
Science Mentor
Rialto, CA

John Barrow
Science Instructor
Pomona, CA

Leslie Bettencourt
Science Instructor
Harrisville, RI

Carol Bishop
Science Instructor
Palm Desert, CA

Dan Bohan
Science Instructor
Palm Desert, CA

Steve M. Carlson
Science Instructor
Milwaukie, OR

Larry Flammer
Science Instructor
San Jose, CA

Steve Ferguson
Science Instructor
Lee's Summit, MO

Robin Lee Harris Freedman
Science Instructor
Fort Bragg, CA

Edith H. Gladden
Former Science Instructor
Philadelphia, PA

Vernita Marie Graves
Science Instructor
Tenafly, NJ

Jack Grube
Science Instructor
San Jose, CA

Emiel Hamberlin
Science Instructor
Chicago, IL

Dwight Kertzman
Science Instructor
Tulsa, OK

Judy Kirschbaum
Science/Computer Instructor
Tenafly, NJ

Kenneth L. Krause
Science Instructor
Milwaukie, OR

Ernest W. Kuehl, Jr.
Science Instructor
Bayside, NY

Mary Grace Lopez
Science Instructor
Corpus Christi, TX

Warren Maggard
Science Instructor
PeWee Valley, KY

Della M. McCaughan
Science Instructor
Biloxi, MS

Stanley J. Mulak
Former Science Instructor
Jensen Beach, FL

Richard Myers
Science Instructor
Portland, OR

Carol Nathanson
Science Mentor
Riverside, CA

Sylvia Neivert
Former Science Instructor
San Diego, CA

Jarvis VNC Pahl
Science Instructor
Rialto, CA

Arlene Sackman
Science Instructor
Tulare, CA

Christine Schumacher
Science Instructor
Pikesville, MD

Suzanne Steinke
Science Instructor
Towson, MD

Len Svinth
Science Instructor/
Chairperson
Petaluma, CA

Elaine M. Tadros
Science Instructor
Palm Desert, CA

Joyce K. Walsh
Science Instructor
Midlothian, VA

Steve Weinberg
Science Instructor
West Hartford, CT

Charlene West, PhD
Director of Curriculum
Rialto, CA

John Westwater
Science Instructor
Medford, MA

Glenna Wilkoff
Science Instructor
Chesterfield, OH

Edee Norman Wiziecki
Science Instructor
Urbana, IL

Teacher Advisory Panel

Beverly Brown
Science Instructor
Livonia, MI

James Burg
Science Instructor
Cincinnati, OH

Karen M. Cannon
Science Instructor
San Diego, CA

John Eby
Science Instructor
Richmond, CA

Elsie M. Jones
Science Instructor
Marietta, GA

Michael Pierre McKereghan
Science Instructor
Denver, CO

Donald C. Pace, Sr.
Science Instructor
Reisterstown, MD

Carlos Francisco Sainz
Science Instructor
National City, CA

William Reed
Science Instructor
Indianapolis, IN

Multicultural Consultant

Steven J. Rakow
Associate Professor
University of Houston—
Clear Lake
Houston, TX

English as a Second Language (ESL) Consultants

Jaime Morales
Bilingual Coordinator
Huntington Park, CA

Pat Hollis Smith
Former ESL Instructor
Beaumont, TX

Reading Consultant

Larry Swinburne
Director
Swinburne Readability
Laboratory

CONTENTS

MATTER: BUILDING BLOCK OF THE UNIVERSE

Reference Section

Features

CONCEPT MAPPING

Throughout your study of science, you will learn a variety of terms, facts, figures, and concepts. Each new topic you encounter will provide its own collection of words and ideas—which, at times, you may think seem endless. But each of the ideas within a particular topic is related in some way to the others. No concept in science is isolated. Thus it will help you to understand the topic if you see the whole picture; that is, the interconnectedness of all the individual terms and ideas. This is a much more effective and satisfying way of learning than memorizing separate facts.

Actually, this should be a rather familiar process for you. Although you may not think about it in this way, you analyze many of the elements in your daily life by looking for relationships or connections. For example, when you look at a collection of flowers, you may divide them into groups: roses, carnations, and daisies. You may then associate colors with these flowers: red, pink, and white. The general topic is flowers. The subtopic is types of flowers. And the colors are specific terms that describe flowers. A topic makes more sense and is more easily understood if you understand how it is broken down into individual ideas and how these ideas are related to one another and to the entire topic.

It is often helpful to organize information visually so that you can see how it all fits together. One technique for describing related ideas is called a **concept map**. In a concept map, an idea is represented by a word or phrase enclosed in a box. There are several ideas in any concept map. A connection between two ideas is made with a line. A word or two that describes the connection is written on or near the line. The general topic is located at the top of the map. That topic is then broken down into subtopics, or more specific ideas, by branching lines. The most specific topics are located at the bottom of the map.

To construct a concept map, first identify the important ideas or key terms in the chapter or section. Do not try to include too much information. Use your judgment as to what is really important. Write the general topic at the top of your map. Let's use an example to help illustrate this process. Suppose you decide that the key terms in a section you are reading are School, Living Things, Language Arts, Subtraction, Grammar, Mathematics, Experiments, Papers, Science, Addition, Novels. The general topic is School. Write and enclose this word in a box at the top of your map.

SCHOOL

Now choose the subtopics—Language Arts, Science, Mathematics. Figure out how they are related to the topic. Add these words to your map. Continue this procedure until you have included all the important ideas and terms. Then use lines to make the appropriate connections between ideas and terms. Don't forget to write a word or two on or near the connecting line to describe the nature of the connection.

Do not be concerned if you have to redraw your map (perhaps several times!) before you show all the important connections clearly. If, for example, you write papers for Science as well as for Language Arts, you may want to place these two subjects next to each other so that the lines do not overlap.

One more thing you should know about concept mapping: Concepts can be correctly mapped in many different ways. In fact, it is unlikely that any two people will draw identical concept maps for a complex topic. Thus there is no one correct concept map for any topic! Even

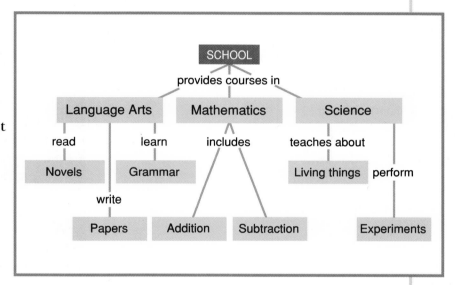

though your concept map may not match those of your classmates, it will be correct as long as it shows the most important concepts and the clear relationships among them. Your concept map will also be correct if it has meaning to you and if it helps you understand the material you are reading. A concept map should be so clear that if some of the terms are erased, the missing terms could easily be filled in by following the logic of the concept map.

Matter: Building Block of the Universe

TEXT OVERVIEW

In this textbook students are introduced to the nature of matter, which makes up everything in the universe. They learn about the general properties of matter (mass, weight, volume, density). They also explore the meaning of inertia.

Next, students study phases of matter (solid, liquid, gas, plasma) and phase changes. They also investigate the nature of chemical properties and changes. Then students learn to classify matter as mixtures, solutions, elements, or compounds. Students also read about the use of chemical symbols, formulas, and equations.

Next, students study the atomic model and subatomic particles. They also are introduced to the four forces (electromagnetic, strong, weak, gravity) that govern the behavior of subatomic particles.

Finally, students read about the development of the periodic table and about its design. They gain an understanding of metals, nonmetals, and metalloids. They also become familiar with the elements in the various families of the periodic table.

TEXT OBJECTIVES

1. Describe the general properties of matter.
2. Explain and give examples of physical properties and physical changes.
3. Explain and give examples of chemical properties and chemical changes.
4. Classify matter as elements, compounds, solutions, or mixtures.
5. Describe the structure of the atom.

MATTER

Building Block of the Universe

Five hundred years ago, Christopher Columbus began a perilous journey. This journey, financed by Queen Isabella of Spain, was designed to find a new route to the riches of the Far East. In those lands, valuable spices and other treasures could be found. The rest is history: In traveling west to find the East, Columbus bumped into a New World.

People have always explored the unknown and made journeys to distant places—if only in their dreams. But no matter how far the journey or how strange the place, one observation can always be made: The universe—as

 In 1492, Christopher Columbus and a brave crew crossed the Atlantic Ocean on a voyage of exploration. This is a woodcut of one of the ships.

Today's voyagers leave the comforts of city and country to begin to explore the vastness of space.

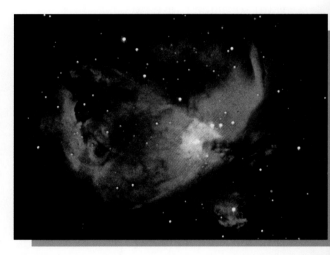

INTRODUCING MATTER: BUILDING BLOCK OF THE UNIVERSE

USING THE TEXTBOOK

Begin your introduction of the textbook by having students examine the opening photographs and captions. Before they read the introduction, ask them the following questions:

• **How are the voyages of Christopher Columbus different from our voyages into space?** (Encourage students to tell what they know about Columbus and space travel. Columbus crossed the ocean in wooden ships, looking for spices, gold, and treasure. We travel in space in sophisticated ships, looking for knowledge and new ways of life.)
• **How are the voyages alike?** (In each case, the explorers went into the unknown. It was just as frightening and exciting for Columbus to sail across an un-

known ocean then as it is for us to explore unknown space now. All explorers seek answers to questions, or perhaps they just want to satisfy their curiosity.)

Have students read the introduction.
• **Think about the idea that the same kinds of materials make up everything in the universe. How does that idea make you feel?** (Answers will vary. Some students might find it frightening, some comforting. Others may not believe it.)

CHAPTERS

near as one's feet and as far as the most distant star in a galaxy far, far away—is made of the same (and relatively few) kinds of materials.

In this textbook you will begin your own kind of voyage. Your goal is to discover the nature of materials that form you and your universe—the matter inside and around you.

Matter surrounds everyone—whether you share space with other people in a large city or live in a house on a quiet country road.

Discovery *Activity*

Is Something the Matter?

1. Make a list of all the things that are found in an aquarium. Describe each item on your list. If you like, you can set up a small aquarium in your classroom. If you do, however, keep in mind that you are responsible for caring for the animals and plants that live there.

2. As you learn more about the matter that makes up the world around you, add to your list of things that are found in your aquarium.

3. Compare your "before" and "after" lists.
   ■ Has matter taken on any new meanings for you?

DISCOVERY ACTIVITY

Is Something the Matter?

Begin your introduction to the textbook by having students perform the Discovery Activity. Students may use the ongoing activity to increase their understanding of what constitutes matter. You may wish to set up an aquarium as a class project and ask all students to contribute to the list as they proceed through the chapter. An alternative would be to divide the class into several groups, each with its own aquarium. Periodically, while studying the chapter, the groups can add to and compare their lists. Ask students to explain their reasons for adding things to their lists.

---

6. Explain the development and design of the periodic table.
7. Compare the properties of different families of elements and account for these properties.

CHAPTER DESCRIPTIONS

1 General Properties of Matter In Chapter 1 the nature of matter is examined. Mass and inertia are explained. Gravity and weight are related. Volume is introduced. A verbal and mathematical treatment of the concept of density is presented.

2 Physical and Chemical Changes Chapter 2 introduces the idea of physical phases and phase changes and relates them to changes in heat energy. The chapter concludes with an examination of chemical properties and chemical changes.

3 Mixtures, Elements, and Compounds Materials are classified on the basis of whether they are mixtures, solutions, elements, or compounds. The use of chemical symbols, formulas, and equations is also introduced.

4 Atoms: Building Blocks of Matter Chapter 4 first describes the development of the atomic model. The proton, the neutron, and the electron are presented as well as the concepts of mass number, atomic number, atomic mass, and isotopes. Finally, the four fundamental forces are described, and their role in atomic structure is analyzed.

5 Classification of Elements: The Periodic Table In Chapter 5 Mendeleev's development of the periodic table is discussed first. Next, the modern periodic table is analyzed. The properties of metals, nonmetals, and metalloids are contrasted. Many of the elements in the families in the periodic table are discussed.

Chapter 1 GENERAL PROPERTIES OF MATTER

SECTION	LABORATORY INVESTIGATIONS AND DEMONSTRATIONS
1–1 Matter pages N12–N14	**Teacher Edition** Observing Density, p. N10d
1–2 Mass and Weight pages N14–N20	**Student Edition** Inertia, p. N28
1–3 Volume and Density pages N20–N27	**Laboratory Manual** Determining Density Determining the Density of Liquids Determining Specific Gravity **Teacher Edition** Comparing Densities, p. N10d
1–4 Chapter Review pages N28–N31	

*All materials in the Chapter Planning Guide Grid are available as part of the Prentice Hall Science Learning System.

OUTSIDE TEACHER RESOURCES

Books

Gleasner, Diana C. *Breakthrough: Women in Science,* Walker.

Goodstein, D. L. *States of Matter,* Prentice-Hall.

Solomon, J. *Structure of Matter,* Halsted Press.

Audiovisuals

Investigations in Science: Properties of Matter Series, film loops, BFA Educational Media

It's Chemical: Density of Liquids, video, AIMS Media

Matter and Energy (2nd ed.), film, Coronet

Matter and Energy: Properties of Matter, filmstrip, SVE

Matter and Its Physical Condition, film, Macmillan

Newton's Laws of Motion: Demonstrations of Mass, Force, and Momentum, video, AIMS Media

OTHER ACTIVITIES	MULTIMEDIA
Activity Book Chapter Discovery! Discovering Properties of Matter **Student Edition** Find Out by Writing: Describing Properties, p. N13 **Review and Reinforcement Guide** Section 1–1	**Video** Heat, Temperature, and the Properties of Matter (Supplemental) **English/Spanish Audiotapes** Section 1–1
Activity Book ACTIVITY: Quick Weight Changes **Student Edition** Find Out by Doing: Demonstrating Inertia, p. N16 Find Out by Calculating: A Quick Weight Change, p. N19 **Product Testing Activity** Paper Towels **Review and Reinforcement Guide** Section 1–2	**English/Spanish Audiotapes** Section 1–2
Activity Book ACTIVITY: Density Drill ACTIVITY: Does It Float? ACTIVITY: Volume—Taking Up Space **Student Edition** Find Out by Doing: Volume of a Solid, p. N21 Find Out by Thinking: Archimedes and the Crown, p. N24 **Review and Reinforcement Guide** Section 1–3	**Video** Buoyancy (Supplemental) **English/Spanish Audiotapes** Section 1–3
Test Book Chapter Test Performance-Based Tests	**Test Book** Computer Test Bank Test

CHAPTER OVERVIEW

Everything in the world is made of matter. The Earth itself and the things of the Earth represent a bewildering variety of matter. Yet in all of this variety, there are general properties of matter that make all matter the same.

The general properties of matter are mass, weight, volume, and density. Using these properties, specific matter can be identified and its special features studied.

Mass and weight are not the same. Mass is the amount of matter in an object. Mass can be defined as a measure of inertia. Inertia is the property of a mass to resist changes in motion. The mass of an object does not change.

Weight is a force caused by the gravitational attraction between any two objects. On Earth, the weight of an object is a result of the gravitational pull between the planet and the object. The same mass has a different weight on a mountain, in a valley, or on the moon. Because it is a force, weight is measured in force units.

All matter takes up space. The amount of space a certain object takes up is called its volume. The volume and the mass of an object are related by the formula: Density = Mass/Volume, D = M/V, or density is mass per unit volume. All matter has density. The density of a specific kind of matter is a property that helps to identify and distinguish it.

1–1 MATTER
THEMATIC FOCUS

The purpose of this section is to introduce students to the term *matter*, in particular, the properties of matter. Students will learn that matter can be distinguished by specific properties such as color, texture, odor, and so on. The main thrust of the section, however, is to point out to students that there are general properties that apply to all forms of matter. The section ends with the key idea that there are several general properties of matter—mass, weight, volume, and density. These general properties of matter will be explored in subsequent sections of the chapter.

The themes that can be focused on in this section are scale and structure, unity and diversity, and stability. All these themes, as they relate to matter, are interconnected by the commonality that all objects are made up of some form of matter.

*Scale and structure: Stress that all objects, no matter their size, are made of matter. You may want to introduce the concept of the atom, pointing out to students that regardless of their size or structure, all objects are made of atoms.

Unity and diversity: As you discuss the general and specific properties of matter, make sure students understand that despite the many forms and types of matter both on Earth and throughout the universe (diversity), all matter is made of the same basic components (unity).

*Stability: It will be easy to demonstrate to students that forms of matter can change in terms of their specific properties. For example, a piece of wood is quite different after it has been burned in a fire than when it was a part of a living tree. Despite these overt changes, the basic properties of matter (mass, weight, volume, and density) are stable in that all matter has these properties regardless of what is done to the particular piece of matter.

PERFORMANCE OBJECTIVES 1–1

1. Describe matter in terms of specific properties.
2. Identify the general properties of matter.

SCIENCE TERMS 1–1

matter p. N12
property p. N12

1–2 MASS AND WEIGHT
THEMATIC FOCUS

The purpose of this section is to introduce students to the concepts of mass and weight, two important general properties of matter. Mass is the amount of matter in an object and is measured in grams (g) and kilograms (kg). An object has weight because its mass is attracted by the gravitational force of the Earth. The force of attraction between objects is called gravity.

The themes that can be focused on in this section are patterns of change, systems and interactions, and stability.

*Patterns of change Stress that unless matter is added or taken away from an object, the mass of that object remains constant. The weight of the object, however, can change as the object is moved farther from the center of the Earth. As such, gravitational forces between objects diminish when the distance between objects increases. In addition, students should clearly understand that due to inertia, an object will resist any change in motion unless acted upon by an outside force.

*Systems and interactions: All objects interact through gravitational forces between them. The strength of the gravitational force is dependent on the mass of the objects and the distance between them.

*Stability: The mass of an object remains constant, or stable, unless matter is added to or taken away from that object. Weight, however, is dependent on both mass and location and is not constant.

PERFORMANCE OBJECTIVES 1–2

1. Explain why the mass of an object is constant whereas weight can change.
2. Discuss the relationship between mass and inertia.
3. Define gravity.
4. Compare mass and weight.

SCIENCE TERMS 1–2

mass p. N14
inertia p. N15
weight p. N17
gravity p. N18

1-3 VOLUME AND DENSITY
THEMATIC FOCUS

The purpose of this section is to introduce students to the concepts of volume and density. Students will learn that volume measures the amount of space taken up by matter and that matter can be defined as anything that has mass and volume. They will also learn the units in which volume is measured. Students will then be introduced to the fact that mass and volume can be used to measure density, another important general property of matter. Density is then defined as mass per unit volume of an object. Finally, the concept of density will be used to explain why some objects float in water while other objects sink. Students will learn that objects with a density greater than 1 g/mL will sink in water, whereas objects with a density less than 1 g/mL will float.

The themes that can be focused on in this section are patterns of change, scale and structure, systems and interactions, and stability.

*Patterns of change: Make students aware that the volume of an object can change if matter is added to or taken away from the object. The density of an object, however, will not change if the same kind of matter is added to or taken away from an object. Demonstrate this fact using an example such as two wooden blocks of unequal size to show that their density is the same.

*Scale and structure: Tie the concept of scale and structure to patterns of change in that while the size (scale) of an object may change, its density will remain the same if the structure of the object (the kind of atoms in that object) does not change.

*Systems and interactions: After pointing out why an object floats or sinks in water, using the concept of density, make sure students understand that these same concepts can be used to determine if an object will float or sink in fluids (air or liquids) other than water. Stress that while the system (the fluid) and the interaction (object placed in the fluid) may change, the basic concepts that govern the interactions of matter based on density do not change.

Stability: You may want to use the theme of stability, rather than patterns of change, to demonstrate that the density of a particular type of matter does not vary despite any change in the volume of that matter. Again, using wooden blocks of unequal size would be a good way to demonstrate this important concept.

PERFORMANCE OBJECTIVES 1-3
1. Define volume and give the metric units used to measure volume.
2. Describe matter in terms of mass and volume.
3. Define density and compare the densities of various objects.
4. Describe why an object sinks or floats in water, using the concept of density.

SCIENCE TERMS 1-3
volume p. N21
density p. N21

Discovery Learning

TEACHER DEMONSTRATIONS
MODELING
Observing Density

Set a tall 500- to 1000-mL glass graduated cylinder on the demonstration table. Nearly fill the cylinder with clear, carbonated soda. Show the class a small pea-sized stone.
• **What do you predict will happen if the stone is dropped into the liquid?** (It will sink.)
Drop the stone into the liquid.
• **What happened?** (The stone fell to the bottom.)
• **What do you predict will happen if a raisin or a kernel of popcorn is dropped into the liquid?** (Students might guess that the raisin or corn kernel will float, sink completely, or sink only halfway to the bottom. The objects usually sink to the bottom, float upward, lose air bubbles, and then sink.)
Drop several raisins and/or popcorn kernels into the liquid.
• **What happened?** (They fell to the bottom and then floated up. Some floated only part of the way up.)

• **What change occurred in the objects to cause them to both float up and sink down?** (Students might suggest a change in weight, or magic, or they might notice that the air bubbles have something to do with the movement.)
Point out that students will be able to provide a more scientific explanation for their observations after completing the chapter.

Comparing Densities
Nearly fill a large liter beaker with water. Place the beaker on a tray. Show students a glass marble. Place the marble on top of the water.
• **What happened to the marble?** (It fell to the bottom.)
• **What happened to the level of the top of the water?** (It went up.)
• **Which substance has the greater density?** (The marble.)
• **How do you know that the density of the marble is greater than the density of water?** (The marble sinks in water.)
Place several rocks into a small bottle (be sure the bottle is small enough to float in the beaker). Point out that the glass bottle and the marble have about the same density.
• **What do you predict will happen if this bottle with rocks is placed upright in the beaker of water?** (Students may guess incorrectly that the bottle will sink, or correctly that the bottle will float.)
Place the bottle upright in the beaker of water.
• **What happened?** (Accept all logical answers. The bottle floated. The water overflowed.)
• **Why did the glass bottle with rocks float?** (Students should suggest that the total density of the air, bottle, and rocks is less than one.)

CHAPTER 1
General Properties of Matter

INTEGRATING SCIENCE

This physical science chapter provides you with numerous opportunities to integrate other areas of science, as well as other disciplines, into your curriculum. Blue numbered annotations on the student page and integration notes on the teacher wraparound pages alert you to areas of possible integration.

In this chapter you can integrate earth science and astronomy (pp. 12, 18, 25), language arts (pp. 13, 21), physical education (p. 14), life science and nutrition (p. 17), mathematics (pp. 19, 20, 23), life science and ecology (pp. 22, 26), social studies (pp. 24, 27), life science and fishes (p. 25), and mythology (p. 27).

SCIENCE, TECHNOLOGY, AND SOCIETY/COOPERATIVE LEARNING

The density of hot air inflates and keeps aloft hot-air balloons. Knowledge about hot-air balloons led to larger (dirigibles) airships that carried passengers from one point to another. The infamous *Hindenburg* and the well-known Goodyear Blimp are examples of airships that evolved from hot-air balloons. Today, buildings supported by columns of hot air have extended the Montgolfier brothers' application of density even further.

Air-supported buildings vary from temporary structures erected to protect people in areas hit by disasters to camping equipment and huge permanent domed

INTRODUCING CHAPTER 1

DISCOVERY LEARNING

▶ *Activity Book*

Begin your teaching of the chapter by using the Chapter 1 Discovery Activity from your *Activity Book*. Using this activity, students will discover that all forms of matter can be described through certain general properties.

USING THE TEXTBOOK

Have students observe the photograph on page N10.
• **What do you predict is happening in the picture?** (Students might suggest that the diver is looking for treasure, living organisms, or a sunken ship.)

Explain that the diver is examining the ruins of a ship called the *Mary Rose*. Have students read the chapter introduction.

Point out that from 1545 to 1970, a period of 425 years, the *Mary Rose* rested

on the ocean floor without anyone knowing what had happened. Tell students that according to the article, it took divers five years to find the *Mary Rose*.
• **Why do you think it took the divers so long to find the ship?** (Accept all answers. Lead students to suggest that the ship was lying deep in the ocean.)
• **How did the divers stay down near the bottom of the ocean?** (Students should remember that the divers wore lead belts.)

General Properties of Matter

Guide for Reading

After you read the following sections, you will be able to

1–1 Matter
- Explain what is meant by the term matter.
- List some general properties of matter.

1–2 Mass and Weight
- Define the term mass.
- Describe the connection between mass and weight.
- Explain how gravity and weight are related.

1–3 Volume and Density
- Define the term volume.
- Calculate the density of a substance when you know its mass and volume.

On July 19, 1545, a fleet of British warships sailed slowly out of Portsmouth Harbor, England, on its way to battle the French fleet. One ship, the *Mary Rose,* carried a crew of 415 sailors, 285 soldiers, and a number of very new, and very heavy, bronze cannons.

But the *Mary Rose* never met the French fleet. As the story goes, a gust of wind tipped over the *Mary Rose,* and in seconds the ship sank to the bottom of the sea. Was this the true story?

In 1965, teams of scuba divers began a search for the wreck of the *Mary Rose.* Some of the divers wore heavy weights on their belts so that they could hover above the sandy ocean bottom.

In 1970, the *Mary Rose* was found. And scientists uncovered the cause of the ship's sinking. The weight of the heavy bronze cannons had made the ship top-heavy. When the ship tipped over, water rushed into its open spaces, replacing the air. Without the air inside it, the *Mary Rose* had sunk like a stone.

But another mystery remains in this story—a mystery for you to solve. How can a diver wearing a weighted belt hover in the sea, while a ship weighted with cannons and excess water sinks to the bottom? You will uncover the solution as you read on.

Journal *Activity*

You and Your World Do you know how to swim? Think back to your first few attempts at floating in a pool or lake. What were your feelings as you moved through the water? Write your feelings in your journal. Have you ever swum in the ocean? Is it easier to remain afloat in salt water?

The secrets of the Mary Rose—*hidden for so long under water—are revealed by a flashlight's piercing beam.*

N ■ 11

---

stadiums that house athletic events. Regardless of their size, all air-supported structures have the same basic design elements as the hot-air balloon: a membrane to enclose and be supported by the hot air; a means of anchoring the air-supported membrane to the ground to counter the uplift force of the less dense air; a source of hot air; and a means of access that limits air loss.

Several large sports stadiums—the Hoosier Dome in Indiana and the B. C. Pavilion in Canada—use hot air to exert an upward thrust on a membrane to create an enclosed arena for athletic events. Future applications for structures supported by the density of hot air include "inflatable" furniture, equipment for space exploration, temporary bridges, protection of crops from extreme weather, office enclosures, and "fabridams" for water and sewage control.

Cooperative learning: Using preassigned lab groups or randomly selected teams, have groups complete one of the following assignments:
• Brainstorm a list of possible uses for air-supported structures. Each group should select a use and draw a picture of the air-supported structure best suited for that use. Ask students how they plan to meet the four basic elements of design for an air-supported structure.
• Design a series of air-supported structures that could be used as a base for a yearlong study of the moon by ten astronauts. Remind groups that they must keep in mind the basic elements of design for air-supported structures.

See Cooperative Learning in the *Teacher's Desk Reference.*

JOURNAL ACTIVITY

You may want to use the Journal Activity as the basis for a class discussion. As students offer their experiences with floating and swimming, lead them to the idea that the reason a balloon floats in the air is similar to how they can float in water. Point out that they will all understand this relationship after they have completed the chapter. Students should be instructed to keep their journal activities in their portfolios.

• **What did the lead belts do for the divers?** (Accept all logical answers. Students should suggest that the belts gave the divers extra weight.)
• **Without the belts, what do you predict would have happened to the divers?** (Most students will say that the divers would not have been able to reach the ocean floor or that they would have floated back to the surface of the ocean.)
• **If the divers would not naturally sink to the bottom of the ocean, why did the ship sink to the bottom?** (Accept all logical answers. Students might refer to water replacing the air in the ship's interior, or they might say the ship was heavier.)
• **What do you think causes objects to float or to sink?** (Accept all logical answers. Allow students time to use descriptive words in describing objects and in explaining why they sink or float.)

1-1 Matter

Conduct a property scavenger hunt to help students develop the vocabulary associated with describing properties. This will be especially helpful for limited English proficient (LEP) students in your class. Divide the class into pairs (you may wish to pair an LEP student with an English-speaking student. Give each pair a secret property (for example, brown, shiny, smooth). The students are to find five examples of the property. Then, without revealing the property to the class, they show their examples and see if their classmates can identify the property.

ESL STRATEGY 1-1

Verify that students understand the concept of matter. Ask them to name its general properties—mass, weight, volume, and density—and to give a brief definition of each. Have they encountered these terms in other contexts? For instance, the word *volume* may also refer to the loudness of a sound or to a book; the word *weight* may also mean "a burden."

Have students explain why mass and weight are not the same. Suggest that they use words such as *however, in contrast, on the other hand* in their explanations.

Guide for Reading

Focus on this question as you read.

▶ What are four general properties of matter?

Figure 1-1 *The moon is the first body in space to feel the footprints of a human being. In this photograph you can see the ultimate "dune buggy," a specially designed vehicle that is able to scoot along the moon's soft surface. What kinds of technology make a moon visit possible?*

1-1 Matter

Taking a bit of the Earth's air along, the astronaut you see in Figure 1–1 is walking over the surface of the moon. He and his fellow astronauts traveled a great distance on their journey to the moon and back, and, fortunately for us, they did not return home empty-handed. For along with tales of triumph, they brought back some of the moon itself: moon rocks for scientists to study in a laboratory and a special piece of moon rock for all to touch. This special rock, once part of the moon's surface, is now one of the great treasures on display at the Smithsonian Institution in Washington, DC. Touch this rock and your mind can journey to the moon with brave astronauts. Touch this rock and you can feel the stuff of the universe. But did you know that you can touch the stuff of the universe right here on Earth?

What Is Matter?

You see and touch hundreds of things every day. And although most of these things differ from one another, they all share one important quality: They are all forms of **matter**. Matter is what the universe is made of. Matter is what you are made of.

Through your senses of smell, sight, taste, and touch, you are familiar with matter. Some kinds of matter are easily recognized. Wood, water, salt, clay, glass, gold, plants, animals—even a piece of the moon—are examples of matter that are easily observed. Oxygen, carbon dioxide, ammonia, and air are kinds of matter that may not be as easily recognized. Are these different kinds of matter similar in some ways? Is salt anything like ammonia? Do water and glass have anything in common?

In order to answer these questions, you must know something about the **properties,** or characteristics, of matter. Properties describe an object. Color, odor, size, shape, texture, and hardness are properties of matter. These are specific properties of matter, however. Specific properties make it easy to tell one kind of matter from another. For example, it is

---

TEACHING STRATEGY 1-1

FOCUS/MOTIVATION

Prepare ahead of time several brown paper bags, each containing an everyday object. Objects such as a knife or a fork, a toothbrush, a sponge, a piece of fruit, and a sweater or a shirt will work well. Ask a student volunteer to take one of the bags and leave the room for a moment to determine what the object is. When the student returns, challenge him or her to describe the characteristics of the object to the class accurately enough so that the other students can guess what the object is without seeing it. The characteristics described can include size, shape, color, texture, heaviness, or lightness. Emphasize that the description should *not* include how the object is used—saying, for example, that a knife is used to cut food would be a dead giveaway! Repeat the activity several times, using different student volunteers.

CONTENT DEVELOPMENT

Point out that matter is all around us. Explain that the students themselves are matter. Have students look around the classroom and list some things that are made of matter.

Tell students that everything in the universe is made of matter. Explain that matter can be in the form of solids, liquids, or gases. Point out that when we talk about matter, we use words to describe that matter. We describe the characteristics of the

not hard to tell a red apple from a green one, or a smooth rock from a rough one.

Some properties of matter are more general. Instead of describing the differences among forms of matter, general properties describe how all matter is the same. **All matter has the general properties of mass, weight, volume, and density.**

N ■ 13

Figure 1-2 *Rocks carved by winds, cascading water, beautiful plants, and floating magnets are all made of matter. In fact, everything on Earth—and beyond—is made of matter.*

FIND OUT BY WRITING

Describing Properties

In a novel, the author describes the properties of the objects he or she is writing about. These details add interest to the story.

Collect at least six different kinds of objects. You might include rocks, pieces of wood or metal, and objects made by people. Identify each sample by its general properties and by its special properties. Now write a short paragraph that uses the descriptions you have developed. Be sure to include the following properties in your paragraph: color, density, hardness, mass, texture, shape, volume, and weight. Here is an example of the beginning of a paragraph:

It was a cold, wintry night as Jeff walked home from school. Small six-sided snowflakes fell to the ground. Walking past the Jefferson house, a three-story mansion with many pointed window frames, each of which had at least one broken pane of glass, Jeff was startled to see a huge shape. He had heard this house was haunted. . . .

matter that we are talking about. Point out that some of the characteristics are very specific, whereas others are very general.
• **What is a specific characteristic of this desk?** (Wood.)
• **What is a general characteristic of this desk?** (Accept all logical answers. Some students might point out that it is heavy.)

Explain that the characteristics of matter are called properties. Point out that all matter has common characteristics, or properties. Some properties are specific; they distinguish one form of matter from another. Some properties are general; they describe how all matter is the same.

● ● ● ● **Integration** ● ● ● ●

Use the discussion on lunar rocks to integrate astronomy into your lesson.

GUIDED PRACTICE

Skills Development

Skill: Making generalizations

Divide the class into teams of four to six students per team. Give each team a sealed bottle (half filled with air and half filled with water), a block of wood, a stone, a sheet of paper, a ball of plastic clay, a piece of cloth, and an inflated balloon. Have the teams examine the items and list all their general properties.
• **What are the general properties of all the items?** (Accept all logical answers. Students may suggest size, shape, and weight.)

Point out that the general properties of all matter are mass, weight, volume, and density.

1-2 Mass and Weight

Discuss with students the various uses of the word *mass*. Often students who are first learning a language will have difficulty with homonyms.

ESL STRATEGY 1-2

Let students examine a tennis ball and a golf ball. Ask them which of the two has more mass and inertia. Have students write a few short sentences to substantiate their answer. Then ask them to exchange their papers with a classmate and check each other's work for correctness. Volunteers can read their sentences aloud.

ECOLOGY NOTE
GARBAGE

Use the term *mass* to introduce the concept that an enormous amount of garbage accumulates each year. Students may want to research and report to the class the mass of the garbage each person in the United States produces each day. A class debate on how to reduce the amount of garbage students produce might prove to be a valuable lesson at this point.

1-1 (continued)

GUIDED PRACTICE

Skills Development

Skill: Analyzing relationships

Show students two small pieces of typing paper.

• **What do these two pieces of paper have in common?** (Students might suggest color, shape, size, kind of material, or other properties.)

Use a match to light and burn one of the pieces of paper. As the paper is burning, place it in a beaker.

• **What is in the beaker?** (Most students will say ashes.)

Show students the remaining piece of paper.

• **Now what do the pieces of paper have**

1-1 Section Review

1. What is matter?
2. Name four general properties of matter.

Connection—*Astronomy*

3. Imagine that you have voyaged to deep space, far beyond our known universe. There you have encountered a planet inhabited by people who are much like you and who understand your language. They are very curious about Planet Earth. Describe for them the matter that makes up your home.

Guide for Reading

Focus on this question as you read.

▶ *What is the difference between mass and weight?*

Figure 1–3 *You know that a bowling bowl has weight, for it is heavy to lift. The weight of a bowling bowl depends upon gravity. The weight can change if the force of gravity acting on it changes. Does the mass of a bowling ball ever change?*

14 ■ N

1-2 Mass and Weight

The most important general property of matter is that it has **mass. Mass is the amount of matter in an object.** The amount of mass in an object is constant. It does not change unless matter is added to or removed from the object.

Mass, then, does not change when you move an object from one location to another. A car has the same mass in Los Angeles as it has in New York. You have the same mass on top of a mountain as you do at the bottom of a deep mine. In fact, you would have that exact same mass if you walked on the surface

---

in common? (Students might suggest that they have nothing in common, which is incorrect, or that they might both still contain some tiny bits of the same kind of matter, which is correct.)

INDEPENDENT PRACTICE
Section Review 1-1
1. Matter is what all objects are made of.
2. Mass, weight, volume, and density.
3. Descriptions should use the terms introduced in the section accurately and in a well-written format.

REINFORCEMENT/RETEACHING

Monitor students' responses to the Section Review questions. If students appear to have difficulty understanding any of the concepts, review this material with them.

CLOSURE

▶ *Review and Reinforcement Guide*

At this point have students complete Section 1–1 in their *Review and Reinforcement Guide*.

Figure 1–4 *It is not really magic—just a demonstration of inertia. As the table on which this dinner is set (left) is moved quickly, the objects are suspended in midair, but only for an instant (right).*

of the moon! Later in this chapter you will discover for yourself why this is such an important concept.

Mass and Inertia

Scientists have another definition for mass. Mass is a measure of the **inertia** (ihn-ER-shuh) of an object. Inertia is the resistance of an object to changes in its motion. Objects that have mass resist changes in their motion. Thus objects that have mass have inertia. For example, if an object is at rest, a force must be used to make it move. If you move it, you notice that it resists your push or pull. If an object is moving, a force must be used to slow it down or stop it. If you try to stop a moving object, it will resist this effort.

Suppose you were given the choice of pushing either an empty shopping cart or a cart full of groceries up a steep hill. The full cart, of course, has more mass than the empty one. And as you might know from past experience, it is much easier to push something that is empty than it is to push something that is full. Now suppose the empty cart and the full

HISTORICAL NOTE
NEWTON'S LAWS

In the seventeenth century, Sir Isaac Newton published a book in which he set forth his three laws of motion. The first of these laws is often called the law of inertia. In modern language, the law of inertia states that an object at rest tends to remain at rest and that an object in motion tends to keep moving in a straight line unless acted on by an unbalanced force.

TEACHING STRATEGY 1–2

FOCUS/MOTIVATION

Divide the class into teams of four to six students per team. Have the teams find and list common classroom objects that have masses (a) less than their science textbook and (b) greater than their science textbook. The teams might exchange lists and check to see if they agree with the estimates of mass made by the other teams.

CONTENT DEVELOPMENT

Emphasize the idea that mass is the most important property of matter, as it describes the amount of matter present in an object or substance.

• **What instrument is used to measure mass?** (Balance scale.)

• **In what units is mass measured?** (Grams or kilograms.)

• **What does it mean if one object has a mass of 5 grams and another object has a mass of 20 grams?** (More matter is present in the second object than in the first.)

● ● ● ● **Integration** ● ● ● ●

Use the photograph of the bowling ball and pins to integrate physical education into your science lesson.

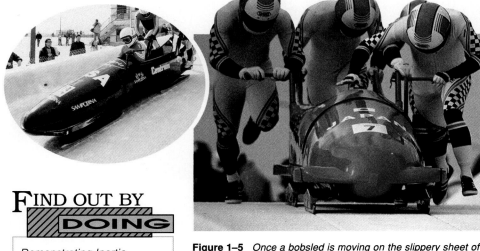

Figure 1–5 *Once a bobsled is moving on the slippery sheet of ice that makes up its run, it can reach high speeds. However, to overcome its inertia and to get the bobsled moving requires the strength of four strong people.*

FIND OUT BY DOING

Demonstrating Inertia

You can demonstrate that objects at rest tend to remain at rest by using a drinking glass, an index card, and a coin.

1. Place the glass on a table.

2. Lay a flat index card on top of the glass. Place the coin in the center of the card.

3. Using either a flicking motion or a pulling motion of your fingers, quickly remove the card so it flies out from under the coin. Can you remove the card fast enough so the coin lands in the glass? You might need to practice a few times.

How does this activity demonstrate inertia?

■ What happens to the coin if you remove the card slowly? How does removing the card slowly demonstrate inertia?

cart are at the top of the hill and begin to roll down. Again, you might know from experience that the full cart—the cart with more mass—will be more difficult to stop than the empty cart. In other words, it is more difficult to get the cart with more mass moving and it is more difficult to get it to stop.

The more mass an object has, the greater its inertia. So the force that must be used to overcome its inertia also has to be greater. That is why you must push or pull harder to speed up or slow down a loaded shopping cart than an empty one.

Mass is measured in units called grams (g) and kilograms (kg). One kilogram is equal to 1000 grams. The mass of small objects is usually measured in grams. The mass of large objects is usually measured in kilograms. For example, a nickel has a mass of about 5 grams. The mass of an average-sized textbook is about 1600 grams, or 1.6 kilograms. The mass of an elephant may be more than 3600 kilograms.

Weight: A Changeable Property of Matter

In addition to giving an object inertia, mass is also the reason an object has **weight.** Weight is another general property of matter. If a scientist is asked how much she weighs, she is correct in answering that it depends. This is because weight is not constant. Weight changes according to certain conditions. You probably know that your weight changes. It increases after you eat a large meal. It decreases after you spend time exercising. In these cases, your mass also changes. It increases when you  eat and decreases when you exercise and burn off Calories. (Remember, mass can only change if matter is added to an object or taken away from an object.) But weight can change even when an object's mass remains the same. An object's weight, unlike its mass,

Figure 1–6 *The mass of a harvest mouse balancing itself on some strands of wheat is so small that it is measured in grams. The polar bear is a different story. Its huge mass is measured in kilograms—and many of them. What is the metric unit used to measure weight?* ①

BACKGROUND INFORMATION

CALORIES AND WEIGHT

In the metric system of measurement, Calorie is the unit used to measure heat energy. A Calorie is the amount of energy needed to raise the temperature of 1 g of water 1°Celsius.

Our bodies use food as fuel to provide energy. By measuring the amount of heat given off by foods when they burn, scientists can tell how much energy a food provides when it is used by our bodies.

Calorie requirements vary, depending on a person's sex, age, height and weight, and activity level. Men have more muscle tissue than women, so they need more Calories. Children are still growing, so they need more Calories. Big people and very active people need more Calories. So do pregnant women and people out in cold weather.

The only way to lose weight—to make the body draw on the energy stored in its fat—is to take in fewer Calories and expend more energy: Eat less and exercise more.

REINFORCEMENT/RETEACHING

Encourage students to identify examples of inertia in everyday life.
• **What does a seat belt do for a passenger when a car stops suddenly?** (It prevents the passenger from moving forward.)
• **Why would the passenger move forward without the restraining force of the belt?** (The passenger's inertia causes the person to keep moving forward until acted on by a force.)

• **What would stop a passneger not wearing a seat belt?** (The windshield of the car.)

CONTENT DEVELOPMENT

● ● ● ● **Integration** ● ● ● ●

Use the discussion on Calories to integrate the topic of nutrition and weight control into your lesson.

INDEPENDENT PRACTICE

▶ *Activity Book*

Students who need practice with the concept of weight should complete the chapter activity Quick Weight Changes.

The force of attraction between two objects is described by the law of universal gravitation: $F = GM^1m^2/d_2$, where m^1 and m^2 are the masses of the objects in kilograms, d is the distance between the objects in meters, and G is the universal gravitational constant.

Figure 1–7 *It is the force of Earth's gravity that determines exactly what you weigh. The same person would weigh less on a mountaintop than in a mine deep within the Earth. Why would a person weigh more in a mine than on a mountaintop?* ❶

Figure 1–8 *It seems such a simple act: keeping three balls suspended in space at the same time. Remember, though, that the juggler is always acting against the force of gravity—which would surely cause the balls to fall to the ground at the first mistake.*

18 ■ N

is also dependent on its location (where it is). In order to understand what weight is and why it is not constant, you must know something about gravity.

Weight and Gravity

You have probably noticed that a ball tossed up in the air falls to the ground. This happens regardless of how hard the ball is thrown. You also know that an apple that drops from a tree falls down to the ground, not up in the air. Both the ball and the apple fall down because of the Earth's force of attraction for all objects. The force of attraction between objects is called **gravity.**

Gravitational force is not a property of the Earth alone. All objects exert a gravitational attraction on other objects. Indeed, your two hands attract each other, and you are attracted to books, papers, and chairs. Why then are you not pulled toward these objects as you are pulled toward the Earth? In fact, you are! But the attractions between you and the objects are too weak for you to notice them. The Earth's gravity, however, is great because the Earth is so massive. In fact, the greater the mass of an object, the greater its gravitational force. How do you think the gravity of Jupiter, many times more massive than Earth, compares with that of Earth? ❷

1–2 (continued)

GUIDED PRACTICE

Skills Development

Skill: Relating concepts

Have students consider the following question:
• **Why do we not feel the pull of gravity of Jupiter, when its mass is so great?** (It is too far away.)

REINFORCEMENT/RETEACHING

Some students may continue to confuse mass and weight. To help reinforce the distinction, challenge students to find the errors in sentences such as these:

This apple weighs 200 grams. (Grams are a measure of mass, not weight.)

Objects of equal mass always weigh the same. (Only if they are in the same location with respect to gravity.)

Gravity can increase a person's mass. (Mass is constant; gravity can increase weight.)

CONTENT DEVELOPMENT

Point out that gravity is a force of attraction between all objects in the universe. On Earth we might call the attraction between Earth and an object "Earth force" or "Earth pull." Earth force is the pull of Earth on objects. We normally call

The pull of gravity on an object determines the object's weight. On the Earth, your weight is a direct measure of the planet's force pulling you toward the center. The pull of gravity between objects weakens as the distance between the centers of the objects becomes greater. So at a high altitude—on top of a tall mountain, for example—you actually weigh less than you do on the surface of the Earth. This is because you are farther from the center of the Earth on top of a high mountain than you are at sea level. Remember this idea if you are ever on a diet. Bring a bathroom scale to the top of Mount Everest, the highest mountain on Earth, and weigh yourself there. There is no place on Earth where you will weigh less.

When an object is sent into space far from Earth, the object is said to become weightless. This is because the gravitational force of the Earth on the object decreases as the object moves away from the

FIND OUT BY CALCULATING

A Quick Weight Change

An inhabitant of Planet X weighs 243 eigers on her home planet. The gravity of Planet X is 2.7 times greater than that of Earth. How many eigers will she weigh on Earth?

Figure 1–9 *In the nineteenth century, weightlessness was only a dream in a writer's mind. The illustration is from a book written by the great French writer Jules Verne. Today, however, weightlessness is real—as this astronaut floating untethered high above the Earth's surface demonstrates. Even though this astronaut is weightless, has his mass changed?* ❸

N ■ 19

this force our "weight." Thus, our weight is the force of attraction between the mass of our body and the mass of Earth. Explain that unless an object has mass, it cannot have weight.

Point out that all objects attract one another. Explain that all objects have a gravitational attraction for one another.

● ● ● ● **Integration** ● ● ● ●

Use the discussion of Earth's gravity to integrate astronomy into your science lesson.

1-3 Volume and Density

MULTICULTURAL OPPORTUNITY 1-3

Some cultures rely on the idea of density for their survival and livelihood. The Eskimos may spend part of their time actually living and fishing on ice floes in the region of the Arctic Circle. This would not be possible if ice were not less dense than cold water. Ice fishing would not be possible either because the lake would freeze from top to bottom, and all life would be destroyed.

ESL STRATEGY 1-3

Have students measure and record the mass and liquid volume of at least three different-sized paper cups half full of water. Provide the cups (with half mark indicated), a triple-beam balance, a graduated cylinder, and water. Ask students to imagine where the cups would weigh more and where they would weigh less. Then have them write a short statement supporting the locations they would choose to illustrate the cups' weight gain and weight loss.

Ask students to explain orally what a raft is. Then ask them to explain in writing why a penny will not float and a raft will. Have students read aloud what they have written.

1-2 (continued)

GUIDED PRACTICE

Skills Development

Skills: Making calculations, making diagrams

In order to emphasize the difference between mass and weight, have each student calculate his or her mass in kilograms and weight in newtons (1 pound = 0.45 kg; weight in newtons = mass × 9.8). Then have students create diagrams to show how their weight would be less on the moon but that their mass would remain the same. For example, a student might draw one picture of herself on Earth and another on the moon, with mass and weight written under each picture.

CAREERS

Scuba Diver

At the beginning of this chapter you read about the divers who searched for the *Mary Rose*. Those divers were specially trained **scuba divers** who earn their living by completing underwater tasks with the use of scuba gear.

The tasks of scuba divers differ from job to job. Their work may include inspecting dams, pipelines, or cables. Or it may involve recovering valuable sunken objects or doing underwater repair and construction work.

If you are interested in scuba diving as a career, you can obtain more information by writing to NASDS Headquarters, PO Box 17067, Long Beach, CA 90807.

Guide for Reading

Focus on this question as you read.

▶ *How can you determine the density of an object?*

---

center of the Earth. An object in space is a great distance from the center of the Earth—in some instances, millions of kilometers. However, although the object is said to be weightless, it really is not. The gravitational force of the Earth is small, but it still exists.

Although an object in space is said to become weightless, it *does not* become massless. Mass, remember, does not change even though location changes. So no matter what happens to the force of gravity and the weight of an object, its mass stays the same. Only its weight can change.

The metric unit of weight is the newton (N). The newton is used because it is a unit of force, and weight is the amount of force the Earth's gravity exerts on an object. An object with a mass of 1 kilogram is pulled to the Earth with a force of 9.8 newtons. So the weight of this object is 9.8 N. An object with a mass of 50 kilograms is pulled toward the Earth with a force of 50 times 9.8, or 490 newtons. The object's weight is 490 N.

1-2 Section Review

1. What is mass? What is weight?
2. How are mass and inertia related?

Critical Thinking—*Applying Concepts*
3. The moon is smaller than the Earth. Where would you weigh less? Where would you have less matter?

1-3 Volume and Density

Let's use this textbook to help discover another general property of matter. Suppose you could wrap a piece of paper around this entire book and then remove the book inside. How would you describe what was left inside the paper? You would probably use the word space. For an important property of matter is that it takes up space. And when the book

---

CONTENT DEVELOPMENT

● ● ● ● **Integration** ● ● ● ●

Use the discussion on how to calculate newtons to integrate mathematics into your science lesson.

ENRICHMENT

As you just read, the metric unit of weight is the newton, which is a unit of force. If you have a typical scale at home, however, it provides your weight in pounds, not newtons. Your scale is not wrong: It

measures your weight using the English unit of force, which is called the pound.

INDEPENDENT PRACTICE

Section Review 1-2

1. Mass is the amount of matter in an object. Weight is the measure of the pull of gravity on an object.
2. The greater the mass, the greater the inertia.
3. You would weigh less on the moon, but you would have the same amount of matter in either place.

Figure 1–10 *The volume of solids is usually measured in cubic centimeters. This cube is 1 cm on each side. What is its volume?* ❶

CUBIC CENTIMETER
(cc or cm³)

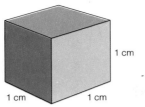

1 cm

1 cm

1 cm

is occupying its space, nothing else can be in that same space. You might prove this to yourself.

The amount of space an object takes up is called its **volume.** The metric units that are used to express volume are the liter (L), milliliter (mL), and cubic centimeter (cm³). In general, liters and milliliters are used to measure the volume of liquids, and cubic centimeters are used to measure the volume of solids. One milliliter is equal in volume to one cubic centimeter. One thousand milliliters is equal to one liter. How many milliliters are there in 2.5 liters? ❷

Volume is an important property of matter that you use every day. Many products you may buy at a store (milk and bottled water, for example) are sold in liter containers. Cough syrups and many prescription drugs are measured in milliliters. Although you may not see cubic centimeters as frequently, you would certainly need this unit of measurement to describe the volume of a set of wooden blocks you might want to purchase for a younger brother or sister.

You now know two important general properties of matter: Matter has mass and it occupies space. You can use these two properties to define matter in a more scientific way: **Matter is anything that has mass and volume.**

The properties of mass and volume can be used to describe another important general property of matter called **density.** Density is often used to describe things. A pine forest is often called a dense ❷ forest if the trees grow close together. You may have said your best friend was dense when he or she did not understand a joke you told. To a scientist, density has a specific meaning. **Density is the mass per unit volume of an object.**

Density is an important property because it allows you to compare different types of matter. Let's see how. Suppose you were asked to determine which is heavier, wood or steel. How would you go about doing it? Perhaps you would suggest comparing the masses of both on a balance. You are on the right track, but there is one problem with this solution. What size

FIND OUT BY DOING

Volume of a Solid

You can easily measure the volume of a liquid by using a graduated cylinder. Can this method be used to determine the volume of a solid?

Fill a graduated cylinder half full with water. Note the volume of the water. Now place a small solid object in the graduated cylinder. You might choose a rock, a block of wood, or a bar of soap. If the object floats, use a piece of wire to push it under the water's surface. Note the new volume of the water.

You now have two volumes for the liquid—the original volume and the new volume. Ask yourself these questions to find the volume of the solid:

What caused the change in volume?

Is the volume change different for different objects?

■ How is the change in liquid volume related to the volume of the solid object?

N ■ 21

FIND OUT BY DOING
VOLUME OF A SOLID

Discovery Learning
Skills: Making observations, making inferences, relating concepts
Materials: graduated cylinder, water, small object

Students should be able to determine the volume of the object by measuring the water. Point out that this is the quickest method for finding the volume of an irregular object. Students should quickly realize that the amount of displacement is directly proportional to the volume of the object.

CONTENT DEVELOPMENT

Show the class a box or a cube that measures 10 cm by 10 cm by 10 cm. Tell the class that this amount of space is called a liter (L). Point out that one thousandth of a liter is called a milliliter (mL). The volumes of liquids and gases are measured in liters and milliliters.

● ● ● ● **Integration** ● ● ● ●

Use the discussion of the word *density* to integrate language arts into your lesson.

ENRICHMENT
▶ *Activity Book*

Students will be challenged by the Chapter 1 activity called Volume—Taking Up Space, in which they explore the various aspects of the concept of volume.

REINFORCEMENT/RETEACHING

Review students' responses to the Section Review questions. Reteach any material that is still unclear, based on their responses.

CLOSURE

▶ *Review and Reinforcement Guide*
Students may now complete Section 1–2 in their *Review and Reinforcement Guide.*

TEACHING STRATEGY 1–3

FOCUS/MOTIVATION

Divide the class into teams of four to six students per team. Give each team a 100-mL graduated cylinder and three small cups or bottles. (These containers should have a volume less than 100 mL.) Have the teams label the containers A, B, and C. Teams can then use water and the graduated cylinder to measure the volume of each container.

MATHEMATICS

Formulas make it possible to calculate the volumes of regular solids when certain dimensions are known. Volume formulas for several common solids are given below.

Cube: V = (side)3

Rectangular prism (box): V = Length × Width × Height

Cylinder: V = Area of base × Height

Cone: V = 1/3 × Area of base × Height

Pyramid: V = 1/3 × Area of base × Height

Sphere: V = 4/3 Pi × (Radius)3

You may want to provide students with some common objects and let them find the volumes using these formulas.

COMMON ERRORS

When calculating density, many students divide volume by mass instead of mass by volume. Remind students that a fraction bar means divided by—thus the bottom number must be divided into the top number. Also, stress the meaning of density—that it is a measure of mass per unit volume, not volume per unit mass.

Some students may have difficulty dividing with decimals. A quick math review with some sample problems can be given before the formula for density is introduced. If some students continue to have problems, you might try pairing them with other students who can help them learn to divide correctly.

DENSITIES OF SOME COMMON SUBSTANCES

Substance	Density (g/cm³)
Air	0.0013
Gasoline	0.7
Wood (oak)	0.85
Water (ice)	0.92
Water (liquid)	1.0
Aluminum	2.7
Steel	7.8
Silver	10.5
Lead	11.3
Mercury	13.5
Gold	19.3

Figure 1–11 *This chart shows the densities of some common substances. Which substances would float on water? Which ones would sink?* 1

pieces of wood and steel would you use? After all, a small piece of steel might have the same mass as a large piece of wood.

You are probably beginning to realize that in order to compare the masses of two objects, you need to use an equal volume of each. When you do, you soon discover that a piece of steel has a greater mass than a piece of wood *of the same size.* And that is the important part of that statement—of the same size. So for our example we can say a cubic centimeter of steel is heavier than a cubic centimeter of wood. Or steel is denser than wood.

All matter has density. And the density of a specific kind of matter is a property that helps to identify it and distinguish it from other kinds of matter.

Since density is equal to mass per unit volume, we can write a formula for calculating the density of an object:

$$\text{Density} = \frac{\text{Mass}}{\text{Volume}}$$

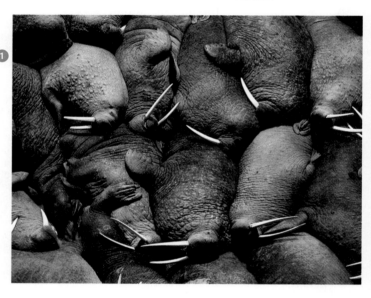

Figure 1–12 *Biologists use the term population density to refer to the number of individual organisms in a given area. The population density of these walruses on a crowded beach would prevent even one more walrus from squeezing in.*

22 ■ N

1–3 (continued)

GUIDED PRACTICE

▶ *Laboratory Manual*

Skills Development

Skill: Making calculations

At this point you may want to have students complete the Chapter 1 Laboratory Investigation, Determining Density, in their *Laboratory Manual.* Students will

learn how to determine the densities of various objects.

INDEPENDENT PRACTICE

▶ *Activity Book*

Students who need practice in calculating density should complete the Chapter 1 activity called Density Drill.

CONTENT DEVELOPMENT

Point out that all matter has volume and mass. Explain that when equal volumes of matter are compared to their mass, the density of the matter is determined.

Tell students that the density of a specific kind of matter is a property that helps to identify it and distinguish it from other kinds of matter. Explain that the density of an object is the amount of mass in a given amount of volume.

Point out that when things are com-

Density is often expressed in grams per milliliter (g/mL) or grams per cubic centimeter (g/cc³). The density of wood is about 0.8 g/cm³. This means that a piece of wood 1 cubic centimeter in volume has a mass of about 0.8 gram. The density of steel is 7.8 g/cm³. So a piece of steel has a mass about 9.75 times that of a piece of wood of the same size.

The density of fresh water is 1 g/mL. Objects with a density less than water float. Objects with a density greater than water sink. Thus wood floats in water because its density is less than the density of water. What happens to a piece of steel when it is put in water? ❷

If you have ever placed an ice cube in a glass of water, you know that ice floats. So frozen water (ice) must be less dense than liquid water. Actually, the density of ice is about 89 percent that of cold water. What this means is that only about 11 percent of a block of ice stays above the surface of the water. The rest is below the surface. This fact is what makes icebergs so dangerous. For it is only the "tip of the iceberg" that is visible.

Sample Problem	If 96.5 grams of gold has a volume of 5 cubic centimeters, what is the density of gold?
Solution	
Step 1 Write the formula.	$Density = \dfrac{Mass}{Volume}$
Step 2 Substitute given numbers and units.	$Density = \dfrac{96.5 \text{ grams}}{5 \text{ cubic centimeters}}$
Step 3 Solve for unknown variable.	$Density = \dfrac{19.3 \text{ grams}}{\text{cubic centimeter}}$
Practice Problems	1. If 96.5 g of aluminum has a volume of 35 cm³, what is the density of aluminum? How does its density compare with the density of gold? 2. If the density of a diamond is 3.5 g/cm³, what would be the mass of a diamond whose volume is 0.5 cm³?

N ■ 23

ANNOTATION KEY

Answers
❶ Ice, wood, gasoline, and air would float. All the other substances would sink. (Interpreting charts)
❷ It sinks. (Making observations)

Integration
❶ Life Science: Ecology. See *Ecology: Earth's Natural Resources,* Chapter 1.
❷ Mathematics

FACTS AND FIGURES

ICEBERGS

Icebergs are huge masses of ice that break away from glaciers and fall into the sea. Only about 7 to 10 percent of an iceberg's total mass is visible above the water. Also, the top is melted by the sun and wind. Consequently, the part that is showing is often completely out of proportion to what may be hidden below! The hidden parts of an iceberg pose a major danger to ships.

North Atlantic icebergs come from Greenland's ice sheet. Some drift as far south as Newfoundland before they melt. Sometimes they are hundreds of meters high and many kilometers long. Antarctic icebergs are even larger!

---

pared, it is important to compare similar volumes. Explain that the mass per unit volume of a substance is called density. Write

Density = Mass/Volume
Density = Grams/Milliliters
Density = g/mL

Show that if a substance has a mass of 220 g and a volume of 110 mL, its density would be

Density = Mass/Volume
Density = 220 g/110 mL
Density = 2 g/mL

Explain that 2 g/mL is read as "two grams per milliliter" and means that every 1 mL of the substance has a mass of 2 g.

● ● ● ● Integration ● ● ● ●

Use the photograph showing population density in walruses to integrate ecology into your lesson.

Use the formula to determine density to integrate mathematics into your lesson.

GUIDED PRACTICE
▶ *Laboratory Manual*
Skills Development
Skill: Applying concepts

Students can now complete the Chapter 1 Laboratory Investigation, Determining the Density of Liquids, in their *Laboratory Manual.* They will have the opportunity to determine the density of several liquids.

FIND OUT BY THINKING

Archimedes and the Crown

❶ The famous Greek mathematician and scientist Archimedes was once faced with a difficult task. He had to determine whether the new crown made by a goldsmith for King Hieron of Syracuse was pure gold or a mixture of gold and silver. And he had to accomplish this task without damaging the crown!

Pretend that you are Archimedes' assistant and describe an experiment that would help determine whether the crown is pure gold or a mixture of gold and silver. *Hint:* The concept of density is useful here.

You may have read or heard about the passenger ship *Titanic*, which sank in 1912 after it ran into an iceberg in the cold North Atlantic. The most advanced technology was used to build the *Titanic*. Special watertight doors were designed so that they could seal off a part of the ship that developed a leak. The ship was said to be unsinkable. However, its watertight doors were not able to keep the ocean waters from filling the *Titanic* when the iceberg ripped through the side of the ship. Once ocean water replaced the air in the *Titanic*, the density of the ship was no longer less than the density of water and the ship plunged to the ocean bottom on its maiden voyage!

Can you now solve the mystery posed at the beginning of this chapter? An object floats in water if its density is less than 1 g/mL. In order for the

Figure 1–13 *The "unsinkable"* Titanic *sank after striking an iceberg in the North Atlantic. As it filled with water—through the gaping hole in its hull caused by the iceberg—the density of this great ship became greater than the ocean water upon which it floated. And it sank under the waves.*

1–3 (continued)

CONTENT DEVELOPMENT

Have students observe Figure 1–13.

• **How can a ship of that size have a density less than 1 g/cm³?** (Some students might suggest that the ship has airtight compartments and that air is not very dense.)

Allow students time to discuss how a ship is built. Explain that although steel is used in shipbuilding, the hull of the ship contains many "air-locked" compartments. Point out that air has a density of 0.001 g/cm³. Explain that the air in the compartment allows the ship to float.

● ● ● ● **Integration** ● ● ● ●

Use the newspaper photographs and text copy on the *Titanic* to integrate social studies into your lesson.

INDEPENDENT PRACTICE

▶ *Activity Book*

Students who need practice with the concept of density should complete the activity called Does It Float?

REINFORCEMENT/RETEACHING

Obtain two objects of the same size and shape but with very different densities. A good choice would be a golf ball and a Ping-Pong ball. Display the objects.

ANNOTATION KEY

Answers
❶ The air in the life preserver helps to re-duce the density of the swimmer. (Draw-ing conclusions)

Integration
❶ Social Studies
❷ Social Studies
❸ Life Science: Fishes. See *Parade of Life: Animals,* Chapter 3.
❹ Earth Science: Astronomy. See *Exploring the Universe,* Chapter 2.

scuba diver searching for the *Mary Rose* to sink in the water, the diver's overall density has to be greater than 1 g/mL. So the diver wears a weighted belt to increase mass.

The density of water increases as the temperature of the water gets colder. Below the ocean's surface, the temperature of the water decreases. So the den-sity of deep cold water is greater than 1 g/mL. At a certain depth, the scuba diver's density is equal to the water's density. The diver will not be able to sink below this depth.

While the *Mary Rose* moved on the surface of the ocean, her hull was partly filled with air. The air helped make the ship's density less than 1 g/mL, and so it floated. The large volume of air balanced the added mass of the heavy bronze cannons. How-ever, when her hull partially filled with water, the *Mary Rose* and her heavy cannons became denser than the surrounding water at any depth. Down, down went the *Mary Rose!*

Figure 1–14 *Because of the air within it, a huge ocean liner can float on the surface of the ocean (left). By pumping water into and out of special tanks, submarines are able to sink or float at will (right). These fish can maintain their position in the water by emptying or filling an air bladder within their body (inset). How does a life preserver help a swimmer remain afloat?* ❶

Figure 1–15 *Unlike all the other planets in our solar system, magnificent Saturn has a density less than 1 g/mL. In fact, if you could find a large enough ocean, Saturn would float in it.*

HISTORICAL NOTE
ARCHIMEDES

The Greek mathematician, physicist, mechanical engineer, and inventor Archimedes discovered the concept of volume while taking a bath. He noticed that the water spilled out of the tub when he placed his body in the tub. He was so excited by this discovery that he ran out in the street shouting "Eureka!" ("I have found it!").

Archimedes must have shouted "Eure-ka!" a lot. He invented the lever, the screw, the compound pulley, and the catapult, and he discovered the formulas for find-ing the surface and volume of a sphere, among many other things.

N ■ 25

• **How are these objects alike?** (Same size, shape, and color.)
• **How are they different?** (One is much heavier.)

Point out that students are describing physical characteristics of the objects. Now display a container of water.

• **What do you think will happen if I place the golf ball in the water?** (It will sink.)

Place the golf ball in the water.

• **What do you think will happen if I place the Ping-Pong ball in the water?** (It will float.)

Place the Ping-Pong ball in the water.

• **Why do you think this happens?** (Possi-ble answers: The Ping-Pong ball is lighter; it is hollow; it is less dense; the air inside it makes it less dense; its density is less than that of water.)

Encourage students to apply the con-cepts they have learned in the chapter to explain the demonstration.

CONTENT DEVELOPMENT

● ● ● ● **Integration** ● ● ● ●

Use the photograph of the fish to in-tegrate the topic of fish behavior into your lesson.

Use the photograph of Saturn to inte-grate the concept of a planet's density into your lesson.

1–3 Section Review

1. What is density?

2. What determines whether an object floats or sinks in water?

Critical Thinking—*Making Comparisons*

3. Perhaps you have attended a party where balloons floated. A balloon filled with air does not rise above your head, but a balloon filled with helium gas rises in the air to the end of its string. What does this tell you about the density of helium?

PROBLEM Solving ? ? ?

A Density Disaster

Look closely at the accompanying photograph. It shows the densities of some common liquids and solids. As you can see, some objects float in water and others sink.

Now pretend that this photograph represents a small portion of the ocean. Floating on this ocean is a steel oil tanker filled with crude oil. (Remember that because much of its volume is filled with air, a large ship such as a tanker is less dense than water and thus will float.) Suddenly the tanker runs aground on a reef. A huge hole is torn in the ship's hull. Oil gushes out of the ship into the water. This could be a major environmental disaster!

Cause and Effect

Assume that the crude oil has the same density as corn oil.

1. Why does the oil pose a great danger?

2. Is the danger greater to birds and marine mammals than it is to fish and other organisms that live on the ocean bottom?

3. How is the density of oil an advantage in the cleanup?

4. Why would an oil spill be an even greater disaster if the density of oil were the same as that of corn syrup?

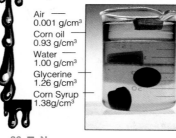

Air — 0.001 g/cm³
Corn oil 0.93 g/cm³
Water — 1.00 g/cm³
Glycerine 1.26 g/cm³
Corn Syrup 1.38g/cm³

Wood 0.85 g/cm³
Plastic 1.17 g/cm³
Rubber 1.34 g/cm³
Steel 7.81 g/cm³

26 ■ N

1–3 (continued)

CONTENT DEVELOPMENT

Point out that the density of the entire object (such as a ship) must be determined in order to know if the object is going to float or sink.

Point out that when water filled the air compartments of the *Mary Rose,* the total density of the ship increased, and the ship sank.

GUIDED PRACTICE

▶ *Laboratory Manual*

Skills Development

Skills: Making calculations, applying concepts

Students may now complete the Chapter 1 Laboratory Investigation, Determining Specific Gravity, in their *Laboratory Manual.* They will determine the specific gravity of several different objects.

CONNECTIONS

Up, Up, and Away

For many thousands of years, people have dreamed of flying through the air as gracefully as birds. According to Greek *mythology,* Daedalus and his son, Icarus, escaped from the labyrinth using wings made of feathers, wax, and thread. Icarus, however, flew too close to the sun and the wax melted, plunging this early aviator to his death in the sea.

In the eighteenth century, human flight became a reality, not just mythology. The Montgolfier brothers launched the first hot-air balloon in *history*—and in so doing, captured the imagination of the French people as well. Balloonamania swept France. The principles behind their hot-air ballooning are those you learned about in this chapter.

The balloon developed by the Montgolfiers was made of silk, carefully suspended over a fire. The flames of the fire heated the air in the balloon, causing the air

to expand. As the air expanded, it occupied more space and the balloon inflated. In other words, the volume of the air increased. As the volume of the heated air increased, the density of the hot-air balloon became less than the density of the cooler air that surrounded it. The balloon—now lighter than air—rose off the ground and began its historic voyage upward.

Unlike the balloon invented by the Montgolfier brothers, modern hot-air balloons rely on tanks of flammable gas to heat the air. The height of the balloon is controlled by heating the air within the balloon. Of course, even the most avid ballooners eventually want to come back to Earth. To do so, they allow the air in the balloon to cool. When this happens, an opposite reaction occurs. The air contracts and occupies less space. Its volume decreases and it becomes denser than the surrounding air. The balloon, no longer lighter than air, descends. If the pilot wants to descend rapidly, air can also be released from special flaps at the top of the balloon. By controlling the amount of heat as well as the amount of air released, the rate of ascent or descent of the balloon can be carefully regulated.

Today, many people fly hot-air balloons, but it was the pioneering work of the Montgolfier brothers that opened up the world of flight to humans—a world once limited only to birds and beasts.

Brave Icurus tried to fly and failed. However, the hot-air balloon took people to heights undreamed of.

Integration
❶ Life Science: Ecology. See *Ecology: Earth's Living Resources,* Chapter 4.
❷ Mythology
❸ Social Studies

CONNECTIONS
UP, UP, AND AWAY

Students will be intrigued by the discussion of the Montgolfier brothers and their hot-air balloon flights. Many students will not have previously connected the concept of density and hot-air balloons, and you may want to discuss the scientific concepts in the article carefully to ensure that all students comprehend and appreciate the "science" behind a hot-air balloon race. Interested students may want to construct a scale model of the early Montgolfier balloon.

If you are teaching thematically, you may want to use the Connections feature to reinforce the themes of energy or systems and interactions.

Integration: Use the Connections feature to integrate mythology and social studies into your lesson.

INDEPENDENT PRACTICE
Section Review 1–3
1. Density is defined as mass per unit volume of an object.
2. An object with a density greater than 1 g/mL (greater than water's density) will sink in water while an object with a density of less than 1 g/mL (less than water's density) will float.
3. The density of helium is less than that of air.

REINFORCEMENT/RETEACHING

Monitor students' responses to the Section Review questions. If students appear to have difficulty with any of the questions, review the appropriate material in the section.

CLOSURE

▶ *Review and Reinforcement Guide*
At this point have students complete Section 1–3 in their *Review and Reinforcement Guide.*

Laboratory Investigation

INERTIA

BEFORE THE LAB

1. Divide the class into groups of three to six students per group.
2. Gather all materials at least one day prior to the investigation. You should have enough supplies to meet your class needs, assuming three to six students per group.

PRE-LAB DISCUSSION

Have students read the complete laboratory procedure.
- **What is the purpose of the Laboratory Investigation?** (To define mass in terms of inertia.)
- **What is inertia?** (The resistance of a mass to changes in its motion.)
- **Why is it important to be sure that each push by the "broom spring" has the same amount of force?** (Accept all logical answers. If this force is not the same for each trial, the results will not be accurate.)

Laboratory Investigation

Inertia

Problem

How does an object's mass affect its inertia?

Materials *(per group)*

> several shoe boxes
> objects of various masses to fit in the shoe boxes
> smooth table top
> household broom
> meterstick or metric ruler

Procedure

1. Place an object in each shoe box and replace the lid on the shoe box. Number each box. (Your teacher may provide you with several shoe boxes that are already prepared.)
2. Position the box so that it hangs over the edge of the table by 8 cm.
3. Stand the broom directly behind the table. Put your foot on the straw part of the broom to hold it in place.
4. Slowly move the broom handle back away from the box.
5. When you release the handle, the broomstick should spring forward, striking the middle of the end of the box.
6. Measure how far the box moves across the table after it is struck by the broom.
7. Repeat this procedure with each of the boxes. Try to use the same force each time.

Observations

1. Enter the box number and the distance moved in a chart similar to the one shown here.

Box Number	Distance Traveled

2. Open the boxes and examine the contents. Record what object was in each box.

Analysis and Conclusions

1. What part of the definition of inertia applies to your observations about the movements of the boxes?
2. Why do you think some boxes moved farther than others?
3. What do you notice about the objects that moved farthest from the resting position? What do you notice about the objects that moved the shortest distance from the resting position?
4. Why was it important that you used the same force each time a box was struck?
5. **On Your Own** You can compare the masses of different objects by using a balance. Can you propose another way to determine the masses of different objects?

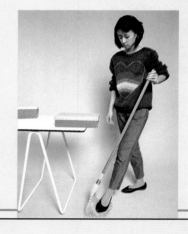

TEACHING STRATEGY

1. Have students practice manipulating the broom spring several times and check that the same amount of force is applied to each box.
2. Have teams follow the directions carefully as they work in the laboratory.

DISCOVERY STRATEGIES

Discuss how the investigation relates to the chapter ideas by asking open questions similar to the following:

- **What kinds of stationary objects have the least inertia?** (Objects with smaller mass—observing, measuring, relating.)
- **What kinds of stationary objects have the greatest inertia?** (Objects with larger mass—observing, measuring, relating.)
- **What do you predict about the inertia of an object on the moon as compared to its inertia on Earth?** (Even though the moon's gravity is less, the mass of the object stays the same. Therefore, its inertia stays the same, even though its weight would be less—predicting, comparing, analyzing.)

Study Guide

Summarizing Key Concepts

1–1 Matter

▲ All objects are made of matter.

▲ A property is a quality or characteristic that describes matter.

▲ General properties describe how all matter is the same. Specific properties describe the differences among forms of matter.

▲ All matter has the general properties of mass, weight, volume, and density.

1–2 Mass and Weight

▲ One property of matter is that it has mass. Mass is the amount of matter in an object.

▲ The property of matter that resists changes in motion is called inertia. Mass is a measure of the inertia of an object.

▲ Mass is commonly measured in grams or kilograms.

▲ The force of attraction between objects is called gravity.

▲ The gravitational attraction between objects is dependent on their masses.

▲ Gravitational attraction between objects becomes less as the distance between the objects increases.

▲ The pull of gravity on an object determines the object's weight.

▲ The weight of an object can vary with location, but its mass never changes unless matter is added to or taken from the object.

1–3 Volume and Density

▲ The amount of space an object takes up is called its volume.

▲ Volume is measured in liters, milliliters, and cubic centimeters. In general, liters and milliliters are used to measure liquid volumes and cubic centimeters are used to measure solid volumes.

▲ The density of an object is its mass per unit of volume. Density equals mass divided by volume.

▲ The density of a particular kind of matter is a specific property that helps identify it.

▲ The density of liquid water is 1 gram per milliliter (1 g/mL).

▲ Objects that float in water have a density less than 1 gram per milliliter. Objects with a density greater than 1 gram per milliliter sink in water.

Reviewing Key Terms

Define each term in a complete sentence.

1–1 Matter
matter
property

1–2 Mass and Weight
mass
inertia
weight
gravity

1–3 Volume and Density
volume
density

GOING FURTHER: ENRICHMENT

Part 1

Have students devise other ways to produce a constant force. They might use a pendulum, a ball rolling down a ramp, or some other method. Then have students repeat the activity using this different force. Students should then compare the data and conclusions.

Part 2

Students might explore the amount of mass needed to "just" stop a moving ball at different speeds. The speed of the ball could be varied by the height of a ramp. Students could then determine the inertia in terms of the amount of mass (in grams) required to stop the motion of the ball.

Part 3

Have students drop unequal (and non-buoyant) masses through the air to observe whether mass affects rate of fall. It turns out not to, as Galileo discovered. This actually indicates that the ratio of inertia to gravitational mass is equal for all objects.

OBSERVATIONS

1.–2. Students' chart entries should accurately reflect the data they collected during the investigation. Students should note that the stronger the initial force, the longer distance the box traveled

ANALYSIS AND CONCLUSIONS

1. An object's mass causes it to resist changes in motion, or to exhibit inertia.

2.–3. The boxes that contained more mass had greater inertia and were not set in as rapid a motion as were the lighter boxes.

4. If the force does not remain a constant, then there would be two different variables in the experiment, and it would not be clear if the results were due to inertia or to differing forces.

5. Students' suggestions should show that they understand the difference between mass and weight. One possibility is to use one object as a standard, then perform inertia tests on it and on other objects, and assign mass values on this basis.

Chapter Review

ALTERNATIVE ASSESSMENT

The *Prentice Hall Science* program includes a variety of testing components and methodologies. Aside from the Chapter Review questions, you may opt to use the Chapter Test or the Computer Test Bank Test in your *Test Book* for assessment of important facts and concepts. In addition, Performance-Based Tests are included in your *Test Book*. These Performance-Based Tests are designed to test science process skills, rather than factual content recall. Since they are not content dependent, Performance-Based Tests can be distributed after students complete a chapter or after they complete the entire textbook.

CONTENT REVIEW

Multiple Choice

1. d
2. b
3. c
4. c
5. b
6. a
7. b
8. d

True or False

1. T
2. F, Inertia
3. F, 1000
4. F, mass, weight, volume, and density
5. F, Volume
6. F, remains the same
7. T
8. F, less

Concept Mapping

Row 1: General properties
Row 2: Weight, Density

CONCEPT MASTERY

1. The fuel provides the force that propels the rocket upward. Because the gravitational pull of the moon is less than that of the Earth, the rocket will need less force to escape the moon's pull of gravity and hence less fuel.
2. Although the force of the Earth's gravity is reduced in space and the astronauts appear weightless, they are not because they are still being pulled toward the Earth by its gravity.

Chapter Review

Content Review

Multiple Choice

Choose the letter of the answer that best completes each statement.

1. Characteristics that describe how all matter is the same are called
   a. specific properties.
   b. universal differences.
   c. density numbers.
   d. general properties.
2. The amount of matter in an object is a measure of its
   a. volume.   c. density
   b. mass.   d. weight.
3. In describing the mass of an object, it is correct to say that
   a. mass changes with altitude.
   b. mass changes with location.
   c. mass remains unchanged.
   d. mass changes with weight.
4. The formula for finding density is
   a. volume/mass.   c. mass/volume.
   b. volume x mass. d. mass/weight.

5. As an object gets farther from Earth,
   a. its weight increases.
   b. its weight decreases.
   c. its mass decreases.
   d. its weight remains the same.
6. The amount of space an object takes up is called its
   a. volume.   c. weight
   b. density.   d. inertia.
7. An object's resistance to a change in motion is called its
   a. density.   c. mass.
   b. inertia.   d. volume.
8. The force of attraction between objects is
   a. inertia.   c. density.
   b. weight.   d. gravity.

True or False

If the statement is true, write "true." If it is false, change the underlined word or words to make the statement true.

1. All objects are made up of <u>matter</u>.
2. <u>Volume</u> is a measure of the resistance of an object to changes in its motion.
3. One liter is equal to <u>100</u> milliliters.
4. Some general properties of matter include <u>mass, weight, color, and volume</u>.
5. <u>Density</u> is the amount of space an object takes up.
6. As an object's weight increases, its mass <u>decreases</u>.
7. An object's mass per unit volume is called its <u>density</u>.
8. An object that floats in water has a density <u>greater</u> than 1 g/mL.

Concept Mapping

Complete the following concept map for Section 1–1. Refer to pages N6–N7 to construct a concept map for the entire chapter.

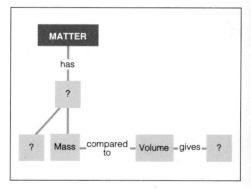

3. The density of salt water increases as the amount of salt increases.
4. The overall density of the boat must be less than 1 g/mL.
5. The fish can regulate the amount of air in its swim bladder and thus change its density so that it can remain at any given level in the water.
6. On the moon, the ballerina's weight would be less than it is on Earth because of the reduced pull of Earth's gravity.
7. When water freezes, its molecules become more compacted. Ice therefore is less dense than liquid water. Because ice is less dense, it floats.
8. Because oil is less dense than water, it floats on the surface instead of sinking. If you try to mix oil and water, they will separate into layers again as soon as you stop stirring or shaking them.

Concept Mastery

Discuss each of the following in a brief paragraph.

1. A rocket taking off from Earth needs much more fuel than the same rocket taking off from the moon. Explain why.
2. Why are astronauts floating above the Earth in a Space Shuttle really not weightless?
3. A person who cannot float in a freshwater lake can float easily in the Great Salt Lake in Utah. What does this tell you about the density of salt water?
4. Each year some college students have a contest to build and race concrete boats. What advice would you give the students to make sure their boats float?
5. Fish are able to remain at a specific depth in water without much trouble. Many fish have an organ called a swim bladder that they can fill with air and empty at will. How does a swim bladder help a fish stay at one level in the water?
6. On Earth, a ballet dancer has a great deal of trouble lifting a ballerina over his head. On the moon, however, he can lift her with ease. Explain this situation.
7. An ice cube is only frozen water. Why does an ice cube float on the surface of a glass of water and not sink to the bottom?
8. "Oil and water don't mix" is an old saying. Use what you have learned about density to explain the scientific reasons for this saying.

Critical Thinking and Problem Solving

Use the skills you have developed in this chapter to answer each of the following.

1. **Making comparisons** You are given two samples of pure copper, one with a mass of 20 grams and the other with a mass of 100 grams. Compare the two samples in terms of (a) volume, (b) weight, and (c) density.
2. **Applying concepts** Explain why selling cereal by mass rather than by volume would be more fair to consumers.
3. **Making calculations** If the density of a certain plastic used to make a bracelet is 0.78 g/cm³, what mass would a bracelet of 4 cm³ have? Would this bracelet float or sink in water?
4. **Designing an experiment** The common metal iron pyrite (bottom) is often called fool's gold because it can be mistaken for gold (top). Design an experiment to determine whether a particular sample is iron pyrite or real gold.
5. **Making inferences** Aluminum is used to make airplanes. Cast iron is used to make heavy machines. Based on this informa-

tion, compare the densities of aluminum and cast iron.
6. **Using the writing process** Write a short poem about matter. Use at least two general properties of matter in your work.

You might want to assign some of the Concept Mastery and Critical Thinking and Problem Solving questions as homework and have students include their responses to unassigned questions in their portfolios. Students should be encouraged to include both the question and the answer in their portfolios.

ISSUES IN SCIENCE

The following issues can be used as springboards for discussion or given as writing assignments:

1. The United States is the only major industrialized nation that does not use the metric system of measurement for common manufactured goods such as screws, nuts, bolts, and other machine parts. How might this difference in the size of "standard" objects affect United States export sales to other countries?
2. The United States still uses the inch-pound system of measurement mainly because of tradition and the fear of change. The rest of the world has changed to the metric system because of simplicity, logic, and ease of communication and selling/buying. Should the United States change to the metric system? Why or why not?

CRITICAL THINKING AND PROBLEM SOLVING

1. The volume and weight of the first sample is less than the second. Their densities, however, are equal.
2. Because the same amount of cereal can be placed in different-sized containers, consumers cannot really know how much they are purchasing by the size of the container. If consumers know the mass of the cereal, they can evaluate how much they are purchasing for a particular price.

3. 0.78 g/cm³ × 4.0 cm³ = 3.12 g. This object will float in water.
4. Students' experimental designs should be consistent with the scientific method. Most students will design a method to determine the density of the sample and then compare that to the density of gold.
5. Aluminum is less dense than cast iron.
6. Students' poems should be scientifically consistent with the chapter material. You may want to ask the language arts teacher to evaluate the poems.

CHAPTER OVERVIEW

Everything in the universe that has volume (occupies space) and mass is matter. Matter can exist as a solid, a liquid, a gas, or as plasma. These states are called *phases of matter.* Solids, liquids, and gases are familiar because they are the naturally occurring phases of matter on Earth. The fourth phase, plasma, exists mainly in stars. Plasma can be made on Earth, but only by using equipment that produces very high energy.

Solids, liquids, and gases can change from one phase to another. Energy must be added to or removed from a substance in order for a phase change to occur. During a phase change, the identity of the substance remains the same. Although most substances pass from a solid to a liquid to a gas phase, some substances pass directly from the solid phase to the gaseous phase. This process is known as sublimation.

All matter has chemical properties as well as physical properties. During a physical change, the substance may change form or phase, but the basic particles of which it is made remain unchanged. During a chemical change, a new substance with new physical and chemical properties is formed.

2–1 PHASES OF MATTER

THEMATIC FOCUS

The purpose of this section is to introduce students to the four phases of matter and to describe the movement of particles in each of the phases. Students will learn that on Earth matter exists in solid, liquid, and gaseous phases, and they will investigate the movement of particles in each phase. They will also learn of another phase of matter called plasma that exists in stars. The main thrust of the section, however, is to note the differences among the phases that occur naturally on Earth. When studying the gaseous phase, students will be introduced to Boyle's and Charles's laws and will use them to predict the effects of temperature and pressure on the volume of a gas.

The themes that can be focused on in this section are energy, patterns of change, and scale and structure. All these themes, as they relate to phases of matter, are interconnected by the commonality of the structure and motion of particles in each phase.

Energy: Tell students that the amount of energy that the particles of a substance possess is what determines what phase the substance is in. Particles in the solid have less energy than the particles of the liquid. Particles of the gas have more energy than the particles in the liquid phase.

*Patterns of change: Point out that matter can exist in four phases: solid, liquid, gas, and plasma. Although the physical properties of a substance change as it passes through the various phases, the particles themselves do not change. The substance remains the same substance. No new substances are produced.

*Scale and structure: Stress that the properties of solids, liquids, and gases are related to the arrangement of particles that make up the substance. You may wish to point out that the particles in a solid are so tightly packed that they are only able to vibrate. In a liquid, they can slide over one another, and in a gas they are spread even farther apart.

PERFORMANCE OBJECTIVES 2–1

1. Identify a physical change as an important physical property of matter.
2. Describe the four phases of matter.
3. State the gas laws.

SCIENCE TERMS 2–1

physical property p. N34
phase p. N34
solid p. N34
crystal p. N35
liquid p. N36
gas p. N37
plasma p. N40

2–2 PHASE CHANGES

THEMATIC FOCUS

In this section students learn about the five phase changes of matter: melting, freezing, vaporization, condensation, and sublimation. These phase changes are physical changes, and the identity of the substance involved remains the same. Students discover that phase changes are produced when energy is added to or taken away from the substance. When heat is added to or removed from a substance between phase changes, the temperature of the substance increases or decreases respectively.

The themes that can be focused on in this section are energy, diversity and unity, and stability.

Energy: Point out that the only difference between water in the solid phase and water in the liquid phase is the amount of energy possessed by the particles of water. Explain that the addition of heat energy to a substance will raise its temperature while it is in that particular phase, but that the addition of heat energy to a substance at its melting point or boiling point is used to overcome the forces that hold the particles together and thus produces a change in phase.

Unity and diversity: Explain that the basic properties of matter, such as weight, volume, and density, are physical properties. A substance may change from a liquid to a gas. It may expand because of a temperature change. It may appear to be quite different, but the basic particles remained unchanged. The substance you started with is still the same substance.

*Stability: Stress that when a substance undergoes a physical change, its physical properties are altered, but the substance remains the same kind of matter. You may be able to pick up an ice cube and transport it across a room with no spillage. You could not do that with water in the liquid stage unless it was in a container. And you'd be hard pressed to see water in its gaseous phase. Nevertheless, the particles of which all three phases are composed remain the same.

PERFORMANCE OBJECTIVES 2–2
1. Identify the phase changes in matter.
2. Explain how adding or taking away energy will produce a phase change.
3. Discuss the relationship between heat, energy, and phase change.

SCIENCE TERMS 2–2
melting p. N42
melting point p. N42
freezing p. N43
freezing point p. N43
vaporization p. N44
evaporation p. N44
boiling p. N44
boiling point p. N44
condensation p. N45
sublimation p. N46

2–3 CHEMICAL PROPERTIES AND CHANGES
THEMATIC FOCUS
In this section students will learn that the physical and chemical properties of a substance are useful in determining the identity of a substance. The properties that distinguish one substance from another without changing the substance are called physical properties. The properties that describe how a substance changes into another new substance are called chemical properties.

Students will investigate flammability, or the ability of a substance to burn, as a chemical property. They will discover that the substance produced by the burning is a new substance that has been altered by the chemical change. Thus flammability is a chemical property, and burning is a chem-ical change. They will note that another name for a chemical change is a chemical reaction.

The themes that can be focused on in this section are energy, patterns of change, and systems and interactions.

Energy: Point out that substances can be made to change phase by adding or taking away energy but that in a chemical change energy is released or added to the particles making up the old substances to create the particles making up the new substances. Sometimes energy must be added to produce a chemical change, and sometimes a chemical change releases energy. Breaking up water into hydrogen and oxygen is an example of the first. The burning of hydrocarbons is an example of the second.

*Patterns of change: Explain that a chemical change effects a change in the particles of a substance. Point out that the particles of a substance are indeed made of smaller particles that do not undergo a change when they are rearranged to form the new substances. Things change, but things do stay the same.

*Systems and interactions: Note that during a chemical reaction, new substances with different physical and chemical properties are produced. Two or more substances, each with its own physical and chemical properties, interact under certain conditions to produce one or more new substances, each with its own physical and chemical properties.

PERFORMANCE OBJECTIVES 2–3
1. Distinguish between physical and chemical properties of matter.
2. Explain how chemical properties are useful in identifying substances.
3. Define and discuss the chemical property of flammability.
4. Discuss the chemical property of the ability to support combustion.
5. Distinguish between a chemical property and a chemical change.

SCIENCE TERMS 2–3
chemical property p. N48
flammability p. N48
chemical change p. N49
chemical reaction p. N49

Discovery *Learning*

TEACHER DEMONSTRATIONS MODELING
Acids and Bases
Show the class a beaker of vinegar and a box of baking soda. Point out that the vinegar and baking soda are specific substances. Pour 50 mL of vinegar into a 1-L beaker. Add a spoonful of baking soda. Display the beaker.
• **What happened when the baking soda was added to the vinegar?** (Fizz and bubbles appeared.)
• **What was formed?** (Gas bubbles.)
• **Where did the gas bubbles come from?** (Answers will vary. Students might suggest a wide variety of explanations. At this time accept their answers. Later in the chapter they will learn that the bubbles are a new substance that formed from the chemical reaction of vinegar and baking soda.)

Separating Substances
Evaporation can be used to separate dissolved solids from the liquid solvent. As a class demonstration, leave a solution of salt and water exposed to the air until the water evaporates. (This may take several days.) You may want to use ocean water if it is available in your area. Have students develop logical hypotheses regarding their observations of this demonstration.

CHAPTER 2
Physical and Chemical Changes

INTEGRATING SCIENCE

This physical science chapter provides you with numerous opportunities to integrate other areas of science, as well as other disciplines, into your curriculum. Blue numbered annotations on the student page and integration notes on the teacher wraparound pages alert you to areas of possible integration.

In this chapter you can integrate earth science and geology (pp. 34, 41, 43), earth science and rocks and minerals (p. 35), earth science and meteorology (pp. 35, 45), auto mechanics (p. 36), earth science and astronomy (pp. 37, 40), mathematics (pp. 39, 46), physical education (p. 44), language arts (p. 45), life science and plants (p. 50), social studies (p. 51), and life science and ecology (p. 51).

SCIENCE, TECHNOLOGY, AND SOCIETY/COOPERATIVE LEARNING

Skiers and ski resort personnel anxiously watch the weather during late fall and throughout the winter to see what kind of natural snowfall they can expect. Skiers migrate to the ski resorts in parts of the country with the "best snow." Nature makes snow when water vapor in the air condenses onto molecules of dust called ice nuclei to form crystals of snow.

Nature will not always guarantee snow, so technology was developed to solve this problem—snowmaking. The original synthetic snow differed from natural snow in

INTRODUCING CHAPTER 2

DISCOVERY LEARNING

▶ *Activity Book*

Begin your teaching of the chapter by using the Chapter 2 Discovery Activity from your *Activity Book*. Using this activity, students will discover the difference between physical and chemical changes.

USING THE TEXTBOOK

Have students observe the photograph on page N32.
- **What has happened to the oranges?** (Students might suggest that rain covered the oranges with water, which then froze when the temperature dropped.)
- **What do you predict will happen to the oranges?** (Most students will say that the oranges will freeze and be ruined.)

Have students read the chapter introduction.

- **Why do you think the workers sprayed the oranges with water to save them?** (To protect them from the cold.)
- **What would you think if someone suggested that you keep yourself warm with a covering of ice.** (Answers will vary. Most students will probably say that the idea sounds crazy.)
- **How does freezing protect fruit from the cold?** (Students probably will not know the answer at this time, but someone may suggest "by releasing heat energy.")

Physical and Chemical Changes

At dawn's first light the weather forecast indicated the day would be sunny and bright. But throughout the day the temperature at the orange grove dropped. By afternoon it was so cold that the workers became concerned about the orange trees whose branches were heavy with fruit not yet ripe enough to be picked. Such low temperatures could wipe out the entire crop.

The workers knew that something had to be done quickly. Some workers lighted small fires in smokepots scattered throughout the groves. But they soon realized that the heat produced in this way would not save the fruit. Suddenly other workers raced into the grove hauling long water hoses! These workers began to spray the trees with water. As the temperature continued to drop, the water would freeze into ice. The ice would keep the oranges warm!

Does it seem strange to you that oranges can be protected from cold by ice? Was this some sort of magic? In a sense, yes. But it was magic that anyone who knows science can do. And as you read further, you will learn how freezing water can sometimes work better than a fire to keep things warm.

Journal *Activity*

You and Your World You know that water is a liquid. You also know that when it is frozen, water can also be a solid. Make a list of the kinds of things that you can do with liquid water. Make a second list of things you can do with solid water. Enter your lists in your journal.

To keep oranges from being destroyed by freezing temperatures, the oranges are sprayed with water that quickly freezes into ice. How does ice protect the oranges? The answer to this question lies within the pages of this chapter.

the way it was made. Cold air and water were put under tremendous pressure to form pellets of snow that were blown out onto ski slopes. Today, new methods of snowmaking produce snow more closely related to natural snow.

Using the steps found in nature, newer technology enhances the crystallization of the freezing water by providing a particle, a type of ice nucleus, on which the water can crystallize and form snowflakes, not just pellets. First, a bacterium is fermented, filtered, and frozen in liquid nitrogen. This frozen concentrate is then killed and pelletized to produce a protein pellet that can be used for ice nuclei. The pellet with the addition of air and water produces larger quantities of more natural snow than the older techniques of snowmaking do.

Cooperative learning: Using preassigned groups or randomly selected teams, have groups complete one of the following assignments:

• Conduct tests to determine if the new technology for making snow really produces high-quality snow that even the most demanding skiers will like and if this new snow melts more slowly or rapidly than natural snow does. Each group should design an experiment to compare snow with artificial snow. Groups should be reminded that their experiments must follow the experimental method and contain both an experimental and control setup.

• Draw a cartoon illustrating the economic impact of snowmaking in an area with two main ski resorts—one ski resort has technology that produces high-quality artificial snow, and the other has no artificial-snowmaking capabilities.

See Cooperative Learning in the *Teacher's Desk Reference.*

JOURNAL ACTIVITY

You may wish to use the Journal Activity as the basis of a class discussion. As students share their list of things they can do with solid and liquid water, lead them to a discussion of some properties of liquids and solids. Point out that they will understand more about the different phases of matter after they have completed this chapter. Students should be instructed to keep their journal activity in their portfolio.

Refer to the chapter introduction again and help students recognize that a rather obvious solution to the problem of protecting the fruit by heating did not work.

• **Why do you think the small fires did not work?** (The heat they provided was not very great, and what heat they did produce was soon dissipated in the atmosphere.)

• **If you had been standing in the orange grove, what would you have thought of the idea of spraying the fruit with water?** (Answers will vary. Many students may say that they would have doubted that this procedure could save the fruit.)

• **Have you ever had a problem to solve in which an unusual and unexpected solution turned out to be better than an obvious solution?** (Encourage students to share experiences involving this type of situation.)

2-1 Phases of Matter

Have students do a home inventory and list five examples each of a solid, a liquid, and a gas that they have around their home.

ESL STRATEGY 2-1

Remind students that Boyle's law and Charles's law both refer to a fixed amount of gas and its volumes. Have them demonstrate their understanding of these laws by completing the blanks in the following sentences. You may want to write the sentences on the board and ask for volunteers to complete them. Have students read and complete sentences aloud.

Boyle's Law

With a fixed amount of gas, when the _____ is increased, the volume _____. When the _____ is decreased, the volume _____. (Pressure, decreases, pressure, increases.)

Charles's Law

With a fixed amount of gas, when the _____ is increased, the volume _____. When the _____ is decreased, the volume _____. (Temperature, increases, temperature, decreases.)

TEACHING STRATEGY 2-1

FOCUS/MOTIVATION

Have students look up the word *phase* in the dictionary and read some of the definitions aloud. Discuss the definitions with the following questions in mind:
• **What are the key words in each definition?** (Part, change, cycle, and so on.)
• **What do you predict a phase of something is?** (A change of appearance or behavior.)

Point out that the word *phase* is used in science to describe changed forms or states. Tell students that there are phases of the moon, phases in electrical current, and many other phases in the universe.

CONTENT DEVELOPMENT

Tell students that matter is classified by the phase in which it exists. Point out that matter can exist in any of four phas-

---

Guide for Reading

Focus on this question as you read.

▶ What are the four phases of matter?

1

Figure 2–1 *Living up to its name, Old Faithful geyser in Yellowstone National Park erupts on schedule. What phases of water can you observe in this photograph?* **1**

Figure 2–2 *Sodium chloride, or table salt, and potassium chloride, which is sometimes used to season foods by people who must limit the amount of sodium they eat, are two common crystalline solids. The illustration shows how atoms are arranged in a sodium chloride crystal.*

34 ■ N

2-1 Phases of Matter

The general properties of matter that you learned about in Chapter 1—mass, weight, volume, and density—are examples of **physical properties.** Color, shape, hardness, and texture are also physical properties. Physical properties are characteristics of a substance that can be observed without changing the identity of the substance. Wood is still wood whether it is carved into a baseball bat or used to build the walls of a house.

Ice, liquid water, and water vapor may seem different to you. Certainly they differ in appearance and use. But ice, liquid water, and water vapor are all made of exactly the same substance in different states. These states are called **phases.** Phase is an important physical property of matter. Scientists use the phases of matter to classify the various kinds of matter in the world. **Matter can exist in four phases: solid, liquid, gas, and plasma.**

Solids

A pencil, a cube of sugar, a metal coin, and an ice cream cone are examples of **solids.** All solids share two important characteristics: Solids have a definite shape and a definite volume. Let's see why. The tiny particles that make up a solid are packed very close together. Because of this arrangement, the particles cannot move far out of their places, nor can they flow over or around one another. In a solid, the tightly packed particles are able only to vibrate. Little other motion occurs. Thus a solid is able to keep its definite shape.

---

es. Explain that matter is found naturally occurring on Earth as either a solid, a liquid, or a gas. Point out that the fourth phase of matter, plasma, does not occur naturally on Earth.

Explain that matter in the solid phase has less energy than matter in the liquid phase. Matter in the gas phase has more energy than matter in the liquid phase.

Point out that phase changes are physical changes. One phase can change into another phase provided that the necessary amount of energy is gained or lost.

● ● ● ● **Integration** ● ● ● ●

Use Figure 2–1 to integrate the concept of phase change with geology.

CONTENT DEVELOPMENT

Point out that when solids form, the particles may arrange themselves in two different ways, depending on the conditions. Sometimes the particles are arranged in regular repeating patterns called crystals. Have students observe Figure 2–2.

Figure 2–3 *Crystals can vary in color and shape. Valuable ruby crystals are used to make jewelry (left). Gypsum crystals are valuable in their own right (center). Gypsum is used to make wallboard and other construction materials. Fluorite crystals (right), which can be clear or colored, are used as a source of fluorine and in glassmaking.*

If you could examine the internal structure of many solids, you would see that the particles making up the solids are arranged in a regular, repeating pattern called a **crystal.** Solids made up of crystals are called crystalline solids. A good example of a crystalline solid is common table salt. Figure 2–3 shows several other, more colorful examples of crystalline solids.

Crystals often have beautiful shapes that result from the arrangement of the particles within them. Snowflakes are crystals of water in the solid phase. If you look at them closely, you will see that all snowflakes have six sides. However, what is so amazing is that no two snowflakes in the world are ever exactly alike.

There are some solids, however, in which the particles are not arranged in a regular, repeating pattern. These solids do not keep their definite shapes permanently. Because the particles in these solids are not arranged in a rigid way, they can slowly flow around one another. Solids that lose their shape under certain conditions are called amorphous (uh-MOR-fuhs) solids. Have you ever worked with sealing wax or silicone rubber? If so, you have worked with an amorphous solid.

Actually, an amorphous solid can also be thought of as a slow-moving liquid. Candle wax, window glass, and the tar used to repair roads are amorphous solids that behave like slow-moving liquids. You were

Figure 2–4 *The computer-generated drawing of a portion of a snowflake shows the repeating pattern of the particles of ice that make up the crystal.*

N ■ 35

solids are not arranged in a rigid way. These particles are held together loosely in an irregular arrangement. When the particles are held together loosely, the substance does not keep the same shape. Solids that have an irregular arrangement of particles are called amorphous solids. Amorphous solids do not keep their shape permanently.

● ● ● ● Integration ● ● ● ●

Use Figure 2–3 to integrate the concept of crystal formation into your lesson.

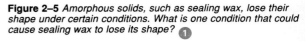

Figure 2–5 *Amorphous solids, such as sealing wax, lose their shape under certain conditions. What is one condition that could cause sealing wax to lose its shape?* **1**

probably surprised to learn that glass is a slow-moving liquid. Although it moves too slowly to actually observe, you can see the results of its movement under certain conditions. If you look at the windowpanes in a very old house, you will notice that they are thicker at the bottom than at the top. Over time, the glass has flowed slowly downward, just like a liquid. In fact, glass is sometimes described as a super-cooled liquid. Glass forms when sand and other materials in the liquid phase are cooled to a rigid condition without the formation of crystals.

Liquids

Although the particles in a **liquid** are close together, they are not held as tightly together as are the particles in a solid. So the particles in a liquid are free to move. Thus a liquid has no definite shape. It takes the shape of its container. A liquid in a square container is square. The same liquid in a round container is round.

Although liquids do not have a definite shape, they do have a definite volume. One liter of water is still one liter of water whether it is in a round container or a square one. And if that one liter of water is poured into a two-liter bottle, it will occupy only half the bottle's volume. It will not fill the bottle. One liter of water does not spread out to fill a two-liter bottle. What do you think would happen if you tried to pour that one liter of water into a half-liter bottle? **2**

Remember that the particles in a liquid are free to move. This movement is basically a flowing around one another. Some liquids flow more easily than others, however. The resistance of a liquid to flow is called viscosity (vihs-KAHS-uh-tee). Honey has a high viscosity compared to water. This means that honey flows more slowly than water. If you have ever poured honey from a jar, you are probably familiar with this fact. The oil you put in an automobile also has a high viscosity. This is important because the oil coats the moving parts in the motor and prevents **1** them from rubbing together and wearing out.

Observing Viscosity

Remember that some liquids flow more easily than others. Viscosity is the resistance of a liquid to flow.

1. Obtain samples of the following: catsup, corn syrup, milk, honey, maple syrup.

2. Cover a piece of cardboard with aluminum foil.

3. Place the cardboard on a plate or baking pan at about a 45- to 50-degree angle with the bottom of the plate or pan.

4. With four classmates helping you, pour a measured amount of each liquid from the top of the cardboard at the same time.

5. Determine the order in which the liquids reach the bottom of the cardboard.

Which liquid is the most viscous? The least viscous?

■ How does the viscosity of foods influence how certain foods are used?

FIND OUT BY DOING

OBSERVING VISCOSITY

Discovery Learning

Skills: Making observations, making comparisons

Materials: ketchup, corn syrup, milk, honey, maple syrup, cardboard, aluminum foil, baking pan

In this activity students will observe the viscosity of various substances. Students should infer that the substance that flows the quickest is the least viscous. That substance will be the milk. The most viscous substance will flow the slowest. The most viscous substance will depend on the substances students use.

Substances of low viscosity are usually served in glasses or cups. Those of high viscosity can be poured over other substances served on a plate.

ECOLOGY NOTE

OIL SPILLS

The high viscosity of oil as well as its toxicity makes oil spills particularly destructive. Oil slicks are deadly to marine animals that swallow the toxic material, but the high viscosity of the substance enables it to coat the feathers, scales, or fur of the wildlife, causing equally disastrous results.

2–1 (continued)

CONTENT DEVELOPMENT

Emphasize the definition of a liquid as a type of matter having definite volume but not definite shape.

Fill a beaker or cylindrical container with water. As students watch, pour the water into a rectangular container or fish tank.

• **How do you know that this substance is a liquid?** (It pours; it changes shape; it stays together as it flows.)

• **Could I pour this water into any size container?** (No.) **Why not?** (It would overflow a container that was too small.)

• **Would this water fit any shape container provided it was large enough?** (Yes.)

• **How would you predict how the particles**

of a liquid are arranged? (They are free to flow and move, but they stick together.)

Remind students of the meaning of viscosity.

• **If I had used motor oil instead of water in this experiment, would the results have been the same or different?** (The results would have been the same, but the motor oil would have poured slower, and more would have clung to the sides of the beaker.)

● ● ● ● Integration ● ● ● ●

Use the discussion of the viscosity of

motor oil to integrate auto mechanics into your lesson.

INDEPENDENT PRACTICE

▶ *Product Testing Activity*

Have students perform the product test on yogurt from the Product Testing Activity worksheets. Ask students to test the viscosity of the yogurt.

FOCUS/MOTIVATION

Have students imagine that they are standing in a crowded car of a train. Sud-

Figure 2–6 *A gas has no definite volume and will expand to fill its container. If allowed to, it will expand without limit. That is what happened to this balloon. A hole in Donald's arm allowed the helium gas within the balloon to escape into the atmosphere. Without gas, the arm hangs limply downward.*

Gases

Another phase of matter—the **gas** phase—does not have a definite shape or a definite volume. A gas fills all of the available space in a container, regardless of the size or shape of the container.

Although the particles of a gas tend to spread far out from one another, they can be pushed close together. When you pump air into a bicycle tire or blow up a party balloon, you squeeze a large amount of gas into a small volume. Fortunately, you can do this to the particles in a gas.

Just the opposite can also happen. The particles of a small amount of gas can spread out to fill a large volume. The smell of an apple pie baking in the oven in the kitchen will reach you in another room of your house because gases given off by the pie spread out to fill the whole house. In fact, if they are allowed to, gases will expand without limit. If not for the pull of gravity, the gases that make up the atmosphere of the Earth would expand into deep space. Can you explain then why a small planet like Mercury has little or no atmosphere? ❸

Like liquids, gases have no definite shape. The particles that make up a gas are not arranged in any set pattern. So it is easy for gas particles to move around, either spreading apart or moving close together.

Figure 2–7 *Mercury, the closest planet to the sun, is a small planet. Because of its relatively small size, it does not have a great deal of gravity. What can you predict about Mercury's atmosphere?* ❹ ❷

HISTORICAL NOTE
ROBERT BOYLE

Robert Boyle (1627–1691), an English scientist, was the first person to investigate what he called the "spring of the air." His experiments show that air has elasticity, and they explained the behavior of gases. He was a contemporary of Isaac Newton.

CONTENT DEVELOPMENT

Point out that air is one example of a gas phase of matter. Matter in the gas phase has neither a definite shape nor a definite volume. Air is composed of a mixture of nitrogen, oxygen, carbon dioxide, and other gases. Gas molecules move rapidly. Although there are some small solid particles in our atmosphere—soot and the like—Earth's atmosphere is made up primarily of gas.

● ● ● ● **Integration** ● ● ● ●

Use the text material on Mercury and Figure 2–7 to integrate astronomy into your lesson.

ENRICHMENT

▶ *Activity Book*

Students will be challenged by the Chapter 2 activity in the *Activity Book* called Pouring a Gas, in which they discover an unexpected property of gases.

---

denly someone starts pushing and shoving.
• **What do you predict will happen?** (Someone may start pushing back; people will bump into one another; someone may fall down; some people will bang into the walls of the car, etc.)

Explain that the force of pushing people in a train car is similar to the pressure created within a closed container when gas particles collide with one another and with the container. Then show students an air-filled balloon.
• **What is inside this balloon?** (Air.)

• **What phase of matter is air?** (Gas.)
• **What shape is the air?** (The shape of the balloon.)
• **What is the volume of the air?** (The same as the volume of the balloon.)
Let the air out of the balloon.
• **What is the shape of the air now?** (It has combined with the air in the room and therefore has taken on the shape of the room.)
• **What does this tell you about the particles of a gas?** (They spread apart easily and do not seem to hold together.)

Because the particles of a gas are in constant motion, they have kinetic energy. Increasing the temperature of a gas makes the particles move faster, thus increasing their kinetic energy. Collisions also increase kinetic energy as faster-moving, high-energy particles transfer energy to slower-moving particles.

FIND OUT BY
DOING
DETERMINING PARTICLE SPACE

Discovery Learning

Skills: Making observations, manipulative

Materials: 250-mL beaker, marbles, sand, water

In this activity students will notice that there is space between the particles in a solid and in a liquid. Students will observe that the marbles do not fill all the available space in the beaker. Sand can be added, which will fill the spaces between the marbles. The amount of water that can be added will vary, but students should note that the water can also fill some of the space between the particles of sand and the marbles.

Rain disappears into the spaces between the particles of dirt in the lawn.

Figure 2–8 *A liquid has a definite volume but not a definite shape. It takes the shape of its container. An identical volume of liquid in three differently shaped glass vessels has three different shapes. A gas has neither a definite volume nor a definite shape. How would you describe the volume of a gas?*

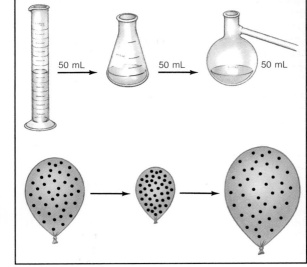

FIND OUT BY
DOING

Determining Particle Space

1. Fill one 250-mL beaker with marbles, another with sand, and a third with water.

2. Describe the appearance of the beaker filled with marbles. Do the marbles occupy all the space in the beaker? Can you fit more marbles in the beaker?

3. Carefully pour some sand from its beaker into the beaker of marbles. How much sand are you able to pour? Is all the space in the beaker now occupied by marbles and sand?

4. Carefully add some water from its beaker to the beaker of marbles and sand. How much water can you add?

Is there space between the particles of a solid or a liquid?

■ How does what you observed partially explain the disappearance of rain on a lawn?

The behavior of gases can be explained in terms of the arrangement and movement of their particles. The world inside a container of gas particles is not as quiet as it may seem. Although you cannot see the particles of gas, they are in constant motion—moving about freely at speeds of nearly 500 meters per second. Whizzing around at such great speeds, the particles are constantly hitting one another. In fact, a single particle undergoes about 10 billion collisions per second! The particles are also colliding with the walls of the container. The effect of all these collisions is an outward pressure, or push, exerted by the gas. This pressure is what makes the gas expand to fill its container. What do you think would happen if the pressure in the container became too great?

BOYLE'S LAW Imagine you are holding an inflated balloon. If you press lightly on the outside of the balloon, you can feel the air inside pushing back. Now if you squeeze part of the balloon, what do you feel? You probably feel the air pressing against the wall of the balloon with even greater force.

This increase in pressure is due to a decrease in volume. By squeezing the balloon, you reduce the

2–1 (continued)

CONTENT DEVELOPMENT

Point out that when the particles of a gas collide, the pressure increases. Explain that as the pressure increases, the gas particles move faster and faster, causing more and more collisions. Point out that anything that increases the number of particle collisions within a gas will increase the pressure.

Tell students to imagine two streets: One street is crowded with many cars; the other street has only two cars.

• **On which street do you predict it is more likely to have a collision? Why?** (The street crowded with cars. The cars have less room to move.)

• **Now picture a container full of gas particles. What will happen to the number of collisions if the container becomes smaller? Why?** (It will increase. Each particle has less space in which to move because the particles are closer to one another and to the sides of the container.)

• **Suppose the container becomes much larger. What will happen to the number of collisions? Why?** (It will decrease. Each particle has more space in which to move.)

Write the following on the chalkboard: Volume up ↑, pressure down ↓. Volume down ↓, pressure up ↑.

Point out that this relationship between volume and pressure is called Boyle's law. Explain that Boyle's law states that the volume of a fixed amount of gas varies inversely with the pressure exerted on it, provided the temperature remains constant.

Then tell students that when pressure is held constant, the volume of a gas increases as temperature increases and de-space the gas particles can occupy. As the particles are pushed a bit closer together, they collide with one another and with the walls of the balloon even more. So the pressure from the moving gas particles increases. The relationship between volume and pressure is explained by Boyle's law. According to ❶ Boyle's law, the volume of a fixed amount of gas varies inversely with the pressure of the gas. In other words, as one increases, the other decreases. If the volume of a gas decreases, its pressure increases. If the volume increases, its pressure decreases.

CHARLES'S LAW Imagine that you still have that inflated balloon. This time you heat it very gently. What do you think happens to the volume of gas inside the balloon? As the temperature increases, the gas particles absorb more heat energy. They speed up and move farther away from one another. So the increase in temperature causes an increase in volume. If the temperature had decreased, the volume would have decreased. This relationship between temperature and volume is explained by Charles's law. According to Charles's law, the volume of a

Figure 2–9 *In a solid, such as these crystals of iron pyrite, or fool's gold (top left), the particles are packed closely together and connot move far out of place. In a liquid, such as molten iron (top center), the particles are close together but are free to move about or flow. In a gas, such as iodine, bromine, and chlorine (top right), the particles are free to spread out and fill the available volume.*

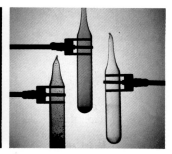

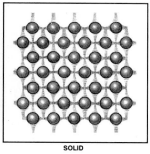
SOLID

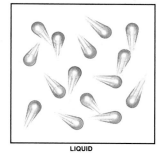
LIQUID

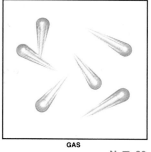
GAS

INTEGRATION
MATHEMATICS

Boyle's law and Charles's law can be represented by proportions. Boyle's law, which is an example of an inverse proportion, can be stated as follows:
$$P_1V_1 = P_2V_2$$
or
$$P_1/P_2 = V_2/V_1$$
Charles's law, which is an example of a direct proportion, can be stated as follows:
$$T_1V_2 = T_2V_1$$
or
$$T_1/T_2 = V_1/V_2$$

creases as temperature decreases. This is Charles's law. Stress that this temperature-volume relationship presumes that the pressure remains constant.

Have students observe Figure 2–8. Read the caption. Read the explanations accompanying the illustrations of Boyle's law and Charles's law.

• **What is the constant in Boyle's law?** (Temperature.)

• **How does Charles's law differ from Boyle's law?** (Heat is added to the gas, and pressure is kept constant.)

● ● ● ● **Integration** ● ● ● ●

Use the discussion of Boyle's law and Charles's law to integrate mathematics into your lesson.

GUIDED PRACTICE

Skills Development
Skill: Relating concepts

Have students determine which of the following statements represent an inverse relationship and which represent a direct relationship:

The greater the number of hours worked, the more money earned. (Direct.)

The greater a car's speed, the farther it travels in one hour. (Direct.)

The more hours you sleep in a day, the fewer hours you are awake. (Inverse.)

The greater the number of cars on the road, the greater the chances of an accident. (Direct.)

The more people who enter a contest, the less chance I have of winning. (Inverse.)

ENRICHMENT

▶ *Activity Book*

Students will be challenged by the Chapter 2 activity in the *Activity Book* called Behavior of Gases.

FIND OUT BY DOING

DEMONSTRATING CHARLES'S LAW

Skills: Relating concepts, relating cause and effect, manipulative

Materials: balloon, string, metric ruler, oven, freezer unit

In this activity students obtain a better understanding of Charles's law by observing the effects of heat and cold on the circumference of a balloon. Students should note that the circumference of the balloon increases when heated and decreases when cooled. You may want to work with students when placing the balloon in the heated oven. Instruct students to use heat-resistant gloves.

ANNOTATION KEY

Answers

❶ The volume decreases. (Making inferences)

❷ When the pressure is halved, the volume doubles. When the temperature is halved, the pressure is halved. (Applying relationships)

❸ Energy is being added to the ice cube. (Applying concepts)

Integration

❶ Earth Science: Astronomy

❷ Earth Science: Geology. See *Exploring Planet Earth,* Chapter 1.

Demonstrating Charles's Law

1. Inflate a balloon. Make sure that it is not so large that it will break easily. Make a knot in the end of the balloon so that the air cannot escape.

2. Measure and record the circumference of the balloon. You can measure the circumference by placing a string around the fattest part of the balloon. Place your finger at the spot where one end of the string touches another part of the string. Now use a ruler to measure the distance between the two spots.

3. Place the balloon in an oven set at a low temperature—not more than 65°C (150°F). Leave the balloon in the oven for about 5 minutes.

4. Remove the balloon and quickly use the piece of string to measure its circumference. Record this measurement.

5. Now place the balloon in a refrigerator for 15 minutes.

6. Remove the balloon and immediately measure and record its circumference.

What happens to the size of the balloon at the higher temperature? At the lower temperature? Do the results of your investigation support Charles's law?

---

fixed amount of gas varies directly with the temperature of the gas. If the temperature of a gas increases, its volume increases. What do you think happens if the temperature decreases? ❶

Boyle's law and Charles's law together are called the gas laws. The gas laws describe the behavior of gases with changes in pressure, temperature, and volume.

Plasma

The fourth phase of matter is called **plasma.** Plasma is quite rare on Earth. But the plasma phase is actually one of the most common phases in which matter is found in the universe. For example, stars ❶ such as the sun contain matter in the plasma phase.

Matter in the plasma phase is extremely high in energy and therefore dangerous to living things. Plasma can be made on the Earth only by using equipment that produces very high energy. But plasma cannot be contained by the walls of a container

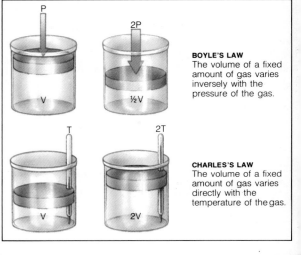

Figure 2–10 *The illustration at top shows the effect of increasing the pressure on a fixed amount of gas. If the pressure is doubled, the volume is halved. The illustration at bottom shows the effect of increasing the temperature on the volume of a fixed amount of gas. If the temperature is doubled, the volume also doubles. What do you think happens to the volume of a fixed amount of gas when the pressure is halved? When the temperature decreases by half?* ❷

BOYLE'S LAW
The volume of a fixed amount of gas varies inversely with the pressure of the gas.

CHARLES'S LAW
The volume of a fixed amount of gas varies directly with the temperature of the gas.

2–1 (continued)

CONTENT DEVELOPMENT

● ● ● ● **Integration** ● ● ● ●

Use the text material on plasma to integrate astronomy into your lesson.

ENRICHMENT

▶ *Activity Book*

Students will be challenged by the Chapter 2 activity in the *Activity Book* called

The Ideal Gas Law.

INDEPENDENT PRACTICE

Section Review 2–1

1. Solid, liquid, gas, plasma.
2. Crystalline: regular arrangement of particles, keep its shape; amorphous: no rigid arrangement of particles, can flow.
3a. Volume decreases to 1/3.
   b. Volume is halved.
   c. Volume increases by a factor of 5.
   d. Volume increases by a factor of 4.

REINFORCEMENT/RETEACHING

Review students' responses to the Section Review questions. Reteach any material that is still unclear, based on their responses.

CLOSURE

▶ *Review and Reinforcement Guide*

Students may now complete Section 2–1 in their *Review and Reinforcement Guide.*

made of ordinary matter, which it would immediately destroy. Instead, magnetic fields produced by powerful magnets are needed to keep the high-energy plasma from escaping. One day, producing plasmas on the Earth may meet most of our energy needs.

2–1 Section Review

1. What are the four phases of matter?
2. How is a crystalline solid different from an amorphous solid?

Critical Thinking—*Making Predictions*

3. Using the gas laws, predict what will happen to the volume of a gas if (a) the pressure triples, (b) the temperature is halved, (c) the pressure is decreased by a factor of five, (d) the pressure is halved and the temperature is doubled.

Figure 2–11 *Because the sun is a ball of matter with tremendous energy, matter exists there in the plasma phase. This photograph shows a huge solar flare erupting from the sun's surface.*

2–2 Phase Changes

Earth has been called the "water" planet. It is because of this abundant water that life can exist on Earth. But did you know that the water that makes up almost three fourths of the Earth's surface and about 1 percent of its atmosphere exists in three different phases? Ice, liquid water, and water vapor are all the same substance. What, then, causes the particles of a substance to be in one particular phase rather than another? The answer has to do with energy—energy that can cause the particles in a substance to move faster and farther apart.

A solid substance tends to have less energy than that same substance in the liquid phase. A gas usually has more energy than the liquid phase of the same substance. So ice has less energy than liquid

Figure 2–12 *Matter can change phase when energy is added or taken away. Is energy being added to or taken away from this ice cube?* ❸

Guide for Reading

Focus on this question as you read.

▶ What is the relationship between energy and phase changes?

N ■ 41

How would life be different if you lived in a climate where water was frozen almost the entire year? This might sound like science fiction, but the people who live in the Arctic Circle face this reality. Encourage students to research these cultures, and then project how their life would be different if they lived in this region of the world.

ESL STRATEGY 2–2

Ask students to determine which of the following descriptions represent physical changes: a pencil after it has been sharpened, a flower whose petals have been plucked, a match that has been burned, an aluminum can that has been crushed. Have students write short sentences to support their answers. Proceed by having them give their own examples of physical change.

ing process. Tell students that the human body maintains a constant temperature because of evaporation.
- **What do you predict would happen to body temperature if body perspiration did not evaporate?** (Body temperature would rise.)
- **Could the liquid phase change into a gas phase through a physical change? How?** (Yes. The liquid will eventually evaporate into the gas phase.)

Point out that the ice could easily go through three phases by starting out as a solid, then melting into a liquid, and then evaporating into a gas.
- **Describe a realistic situation in which the gaseous phase naturally passes through the liquid phase to end up as a solid.** (Answers may vary. One possible answer would be that water vapor in the air condenses on windowpanes and then, because of low external temperatures, freezes to form ice.

CONTENT DEVELOPMENT

● ● ● ● **Integration** ● ● ● ●

Use the textbook discussion to integrate geology into your lesson.

TEACHING STRATEGY 2–2

FOCUS/MOTIVATION

Show students a block of ice or some ice cubes.
- **What phase of matter is the ice?** (Solid.)
- **What will happen if the ice sits at room temperature for a long time?** (It will melt.)
- **What phase of matter is melted ice?** (Liquid.)

CONTENT DEVELOPMENT

Tell students that a change of phase from liquid to a gas is called vaporization.
- **What must happen to the particles of a liquid in order for them to change into a gas?** (They must gain energy.)
- **What kind of energy?** (Heat energy.)

CONTENT DEVELOPMENT

Point out that if vaporization takes place on the surface of a liquid, it is called evaporation. Explain that evaporation is a cool-

Figure 2–13 *If the children had eaten their ice cream cones quickly, the ice cream would have remained a solid until it was eaten. But because they took their time, heat energy caused the solid ice cream to become a liquid.*

water, and steam has more energy than ice or liquid water. The greater energy content of steam is what makes a burn caused by steam more serious than a burn caused by hot water!

Because energy content is responsible for the different phases of matter, substances can be made to change phase by adding or taking away energy. The easiest way to do this is to heat or cool the substance. This allows heat energy to flow into or out of the substance. This idea should sound familiar to you since you frequently increase or decrease heat energy to produce phase changes in water. For example, you put liquid water into the freezer to remove heat and make ice. And on a stove you add heat to make liquid water turn to steam.

The phase changes in matter are melting, freezing, vaporization, condensation, and sublimation. Changes of phase are examples of physical changes. In a physical change, a substance changes from one form to another, but it remains the same kind of substance. No new or different kinds of matter are formed, even though physical properties may change.

Solid-Liquid Phase Changes

What happens to ice cream on a hot day if you do not eat it quickly enough? It begins to melt. **Melting** is the change of a solid to a liquid. Melting occurs when a substance absorbs heat energy. The rigid crystal structure of the particles breaks down, and the particles are free to flow around one another.

The temperature at which a solid changes to a liquid is called the **melting point.** Most substances have a characteristic melting point. It is a physical

Figure 2–14 *Energy from within the Earth is great enough to melt rocks. Now in the liquid phase, the melted rocks flow from a volcano as a stream of lava.*

property that helps to identify the substance. For example, the melting point of ice is 0°C. The melting point of table salt is 801°C, whereas the melting point of a diamond is 3700°C.

The opposite phase change—that of a liquid changing to a solid—is called **freezing.** Freezing occurs when a substance loses heat energy. The temperature at which a substance changes from a liquid to a solid is called the **freezing point.** Strangely enough, the freezing point of a substance is equal to its melting point. So ice melts at 0°C and water freezes at 0°C.

Substances called alcohols have freezing points much lower than 0°C. Because of this property, these substances have an important use: They are used in automobile antifreeze. When alcohols are added to the water in an automobile's radiator, they lower the freezing point of the mixture. So even the coldest winter temperatures will not cause the water in the radiator to freeze. One such alcohol, ethylene glycol, when mixed with water can lower the freezing point of the mixture to –49°C.

The fact that freezing involves a loss of heat energy explains the "magic" worked by the orange growers you read about at the beginning of this chapter. The liquid water sprayed onto the trees released heat energy as it froze. Some of this heat energy was released into the oranges, keeping them from freezing.

Figure 2–15 *Would you believe that freezing water can produce a violent explosion? A cast-iron ball filled with water is placed in a beaker of dry ice and alcohol. As the water freezes and expands, a huge amount of force is exerted against the walls of the cast-iron ball, causing it to eventually explode.*

N ■ 43

ANNOTATION KEY

Integration
❶ Earth Science, Geology. See *Dynamic Earth,* Chapter 2.

FACTS AND FIGURES

HEAT OF FUSION AND VAPORIZATION

The heat released by a substance as it freezes (or absorbed as it melts) is called the heat of fusion. The heat of fusion for water is 80 Calories per gram.

Heat absorbed by a substance as it changes from a liquid into a gas (or released as it condenses) is called the heat of vaporization. The heat of vaporization for water is 540 Calories per gram.

diator? (The radiator can crack as the water freezes and expands.)
• **Why do many potholes appear in roadways during the winter?** (Water gets into cracks in the pavement, then expands as it freezes, breaking up the pavement.)

INDEPENDENT PRACTICE

▶ *Product Testing Activity*
Have students perform the product test on disposable cups from the Product Testing Activity worksheets. Ask students to compare the cups tested for the rate of cooling of hot liquids and melting of ice cubes.

GUIDED PRACTICE

▶ *Laboratory Manual*
Skills Development
Skills: *Observing, recording observations, manipulative*

At this point you may wish to have students complete the Chapter 2 Laboratory Investigation in the *Laboratory Manual* called Investigating Phase Changes. Students will graph the temperatures that occur when a substance changes phase.

phase of the substance changes into the solid phase, or its freezing point. Emphasize that the melting point of a substance is equal to its freezing point. Note that although the melting point of ice is only 0°C, the melting point of some substances is extremely high.

● ● ● ● Integration ● ● ● ●
Use Figure 2–14 to integrate the concepts of melting point and liquid phase with geology.

GUIDED PRACTICE

Skills Development
Skill: *Applying concepts*

Have students observe Figure 2–15 and read the caption. Have them discuss the following questions:
• **Why is it not a good idea to leave bottled beverages outside in cold weather?** (If the beverage freezes, the bottle may explode and shatter.)
• **What damage can be done to a car if antifreeze is not added to the water in the ra-**

BACKGROUND INFORMATION

PHASE-CHANGE DIAGRAMS

Heat plays an important role in phase changes. Heat is energy that causes the particles of matter to move faster and farther apart. As the particles move faster, they leave one phase and pass into another.

The addition of heat to a substance is usually accompanied by a rise in temperature. But if a record were kept of the temperature and heat energy involved in changing ice into steam, several interesting things would be observed. These observations can best be explained by constructing a phase-change diagram, which shows the relationship between heat energy and temperature during phase changes. This diagram clearly shows that phase changes are accompanied by increases in heat energy but not by increases in temperature. The heat energy that is absorbed is used to overcome forces that hold the particles of the substance together. Once the forces have been overcome and the substance has changed phase, added energy causes a rise in temperature.

It is important to remember that the gas phase consists of exactly the same particles of matter as the liquid phase and the solid phase. Phase changes produce changes in the physical properties of matter only. Regardless of its phase, it is still the same kind of matter.

Liquid-Gas Phase Changes

Have you ever left a glass of water standing on the kitchen counter overnight? If so, did you notice that the water level was lower the next morning? Some of the liquid in the glass changed phase and became a gas. The gas then escaped into the air.

The change of a substance from a liquid to a gas is called **vaporization** (vay-puhr-ih-ZAY-shuhn). During this process, particles in a liquid absorb enough heat energy to escape from the liquid phase. If vaporization takes place at the surface of the liquid, the process is called **evaporation** (ee-vap-uh-RAY-shuhn). So some of the water you left in the glass overnight evaporated.

Evaporation is often thought of as a cooling process. Does this sound strange to you? Think for a moment about perspiration on the surface of your skin. As the water in perspiration evaporates, it absorbs and carries away heat energy from your body. In this way, your body is cooled. Can you explain **(1)** why it is important for you to sweat on a hot day or after you perform strenuous exercise? **(1)**

Vaporization does not occur only at the surface of a liquid. If enough heat energy is supplied, particles inside the liquid can change to gas. These particles travel to the surface of the liquid and then into the air. This process is called **boiling.** The temperature at which a liquid boils is called its **boiling point.** The boiling point of water under normal conditions at sea level is 100°C. The boiling point of table salt is 1413°C, and that of a diamond is 4200°C!

The boiling point of a liquid is related to the pressure of the air above it. Since the gas particles must escape from the surface of the liquid, they

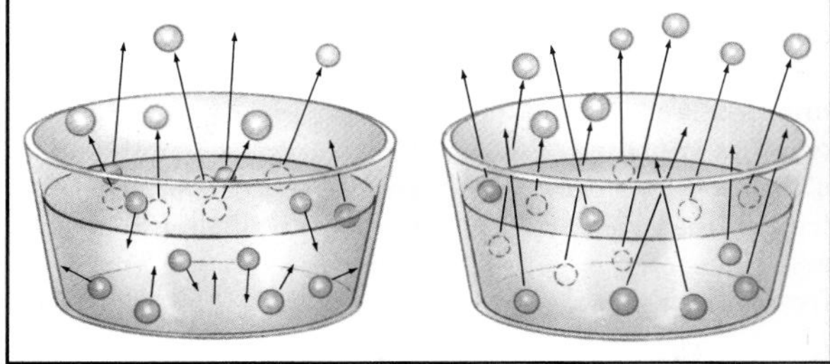

Figure 2–16 *During both evaporation (left) and boiling (right), particles of a liquid absorb heat energy and change from the liquid phase to the gas phase. Based on this illustration, what is the difference between evaporation and boiling?* **(2)**

2–2 (continued)

CONTENT DEVELOPMENT

Tell students that a change of phase from liquid to a gas is called vaporization.
• **What must happen to the particles of a liquid in order for them to change into a gas?** (They must gain energy.)
• **What kind of energy?** (Heat energy.)

CONTENT DEVELOPMENT

Point out that if vaporization takes place on the surface of the liquid, it is called evaporation. Explain that evaporation is a cooling process. Tell students that the human body maintains a constant temperature because of evaporation.
• **What do you predict would happen to body temperature if body perspiration did not evaporate?** (Body temperature would rise.)

Point out that vaporization does not only occur at the surface of a liquid. Explain that if enough heat energy is supplied to the substance, the particles of the substance will travel to the surface of the liquid and then into the air as a gas. This is called boiling. Tell students that the temperature at which a substance boils is called its boiling point.

Figure 2–17 *The phase change from gas to liquid is called condensation. Water vapor in the air can condense and form rain. With the aid of cool night temperatures, water vapor in the air can also condense to form drops of dew.*

need to have enough "push" to equal the "push" of the air pressing down. So the lower the air pressure (the less the "push" of the air pressing down), the more easily the bubbles of gas can form within the liquid and then escape. Thus, lowering the air pressure lowers the boiling point.

At high altitudes, air pressure is much lower, and so the boiling point is reduced. If you could go many kilometers above the Earth's surface, the pressure of the air would be so low that you could boil water at ordinary room temperature! However, this boiling water would be cool. You would not be able to cook anything in this water. For it is the heat in boiling water that cooks food, not simply the boiling process.

Gases can change phase too. If a substance in the gas phase loses heat energy, it changes into a liquid. Scientists call this change in phase **condensation** (kahn-duhn-SAY-shuhn). You have probably noticed that cold objects, such as glasses of iced drinks, tend to become wet on the outside. Water vapor present in the surrounding air loses heat energy when it comes in contact with the cold glass. The water vapor condenses and becomes liquid drops on the glass. Can you think of another example of condensation? ③

FIND OUT BY

WRITING

Some Fuelish Thoughts

Almost everyone in the United States depends upon the flammability of fuels to produce the energy needed to warm their homes and light their way. For the average user, these fuels are available in three phases: solids, liquids, and gases. Compile a list of several commonly used fuels and the phase in which they are used to produce energy. Then write a story that describes what would happen if all the fuels in one of the phases disappeared overnight. ③

N ■ 45

● ● ● ● **Integration** ● ● ● ●

Use the discussion on perspiration to integrate the concept of evaporation with physical education.

INDEPENDENT PRACTICE

▶ *Product Testing Activity*

Have students perform the product test on bottled water from the Product Testing Activity worksheets. Have students test phases of matter due to reactions among solids, liquids, and gases.

CONTENT DEVELOPMENT

Point out that gases also change into liquids.

• **What are some examples of a gas changing into a liquid?** (Steam on the windows during cool weather; dewdrops on the grass; steam condensing as it gives off heat in a steam engine or steam heating system.)

• **What happens to the particles of a gas as they change into the liquid phase?** (They lose energy.)

• **How is this energy loss accomplished?** (By removing heat.)

Point out that when a substance in the gas phase loses energy, it changes into a liquid. Tell students that this process is called condensation.

● ● ● ● **Integration** ● ● ● ●

Use Figure 2–17 to integrate the concept of phase changes with meteorology.

This feature should help students understand the function of heat energy during and between phase changes. The sloping segments of the graph indicate that between phase changes, the addition of heat energy causes an increase in temperature and the removal of heat energy causes a decrease in temperature. This is true for all three phases: solid, liquid, and gas. During phase changes the heat energy functions differently. The addition of energy to the individual particles enables them to move faster, thus converting a solid structure into a liquid structure or a liquid into a gas. Conversely, the removal of energy from the individual particles slows them up, converting a gaseous structure into a liquid structure or a liquid into a solid. There is no change of temperature during the phase change.

Integration: Use the Problem Solving feature to integrate mathematics concepts into your lesson.

ANNOTATION KEY

Answers
1 Sublimation. (Identifying concepts)

Integration
1 Mathematics

2–2 (continued)

CONTENT DEVELOPMENT

Tell students that some solids do not pass through the liquid phase and then into the gas phase. Certain solids pass directly from a solid into a gas phase by a process called sublimation.

INDEPENDENT PRACTICE

▶ *Activity Book*

Students who need practice on changes of phase should complete the chapter activity Phase Changes.

PROBLEM Solving

It's Only a Passing Phase

Heat plays an important role in phase changes. Heat is energy that causes particles of matter to move faster and farther apart. As particles move faster, they leave one phase and enter another. Phase changes produce changes in only the physical properties of matter. They do not produce changes in the chemical properties. A substance is still the same kind of matter regardless of its phase.

The accompanying diagram is called a phase-change diagram. It shows the heat energy-temperature relationships as an ice cube becomes steam. Study the diagram and then answer the following questions.

Interpreting Diagrams

1. At which points does the addition of heat energy cause an increase in temperature?

2. At which points is there no temperature change despite the addition of heat energy?

3. What is happening at these points?

4. What is happening to the heat energy at the points where there is no temperature drop?

5. How can you apply this information to activities and/or occurrences in your daily life?

Solid-Gas Phase Changes

If you live in an area where winters are cold, you may have noticed something unusual about fallen snow. Even when the temperature stays below the melting point of the water that makes up the snow, the fallen snow slowly disappears. What happens to it? The snow undergoes **sublimation** (suhb-luh-MAY-shuhn). When a solid sublimes, its surface particles escape directly into the gas phase. They do not pass through the liquid phase.

INDEPENDENT PRACTICE

Section Review 2–2

1. By adding or removing heat energy.

2. Melting point: temperature at which a solid changes into a liquid; freezing point: temperature at which a liquid changes into a solid.

3. Evaporation: liquid-to-gas change at surface of liquid; condensation: gas-to-liquid change.

4. As dry ice sublimes, it absorbs heat energy, and its surface particles escape directly into the gas phase.

5. Over time, the ice cubes melt, the temperature of the water in the glass decreases, and the level of the water in the glass goes up.

REINFORCEMENT/RETEACHING

Review students' responses to the Section Review questions. Reteach any material that is still unclear, based on their responses.

A substance called dry ice is often used to keep other substances, such as ice cream, cold. Dry ice is solid carbon dioxide. At ordinary pressures, dry ice cannot exist in the liquid phase. So as it absorbs heat energy, it sublimes, or goes from the solid phase directly to the gas phase. By absorbing and carrying off heat energy as it sublimes, dry ice keeps materials that are near it cold and dry. Just think what would happen to an ice cream cake if it was packed with regular ice—ice that becomes liquid water before entering the gas phase—rather than with dry ice.

2–2 Section Review

1. How can substances be made to change phase?
2. What is a melting point? A freezing point?
3. What is the difference between evaporation and condensation?
4. Describe the changes in heat energy and particle arrangement as dry ice sublimes.

Critical Thinking—*Applying Concepts*
5. Suppose you place several ice cubes in a glass of water that is at room temperature. What happens to the ice cubes over time? What happens to the temperature of the water in the glass? What happens to the level of water in the glass? (Assume that you do not drink any of the liquid and that evaporation does not occur to any great extent.)

Figure 2–18 *Certain substances can go from the solid phase directly to the gas phase. Here you see dry ice becoming gaseous carbon dioxide (top) and iodine crystals becoming gaseous iodine (bottom). What is this process called?* ❶

2–3 Chemical Properties and Changes

At the beginning of this chapter, you learned that you could identify different substances by comparing their physical properties. It was easy to see differences in color, shape, hardness, and volume in solid objects. But now suppose you have to distinguish between two gases: oxygen and hydrogen. Both are colorless, odorless, and tasteless. Since they are

Guide for Reading

Focus on this question as you read.

▶ *What is the difference between a chemical property and a chemical change?*

2-3 Chemical Properties and Changes

MULTICULTURAL OPPORTUNITY 2–3

Introduce this activity with an inquiry demonstration. Show students examples of chemical and physical changes. Tell students that you are going to show them examples of two different things and they are to determine how all the things in one group are alike and how all the things in the other group are alike. Examples of physical changes might include writing on paper, tearing or cutting paper, melting an ice cube, and dissolving salt in water. Examples of chemical changes might include mixing baking soda and water, lighting a match or a Bunsen burner, and changing red litmus paper to blue. It is not important that students know the terms of physical and chemical change. What is important is that they identify the critical attributes of each: For a physical change, the substance may appear different, but no new substance is formed; for a chemical change, a new substance is produced.

ESL STRATEGY 2–3

Ask students to provide an illustration of the four phase changes in matter. Students may choose to make a poster or a montage, or to use any other method that demonstrates their knowledge of each phase and its meaning. Ask them to refer to their illustrations as they explain orally what causes phase changes.

To reinforce what students have learned, have them complete the blanks in the sentences.

1. A _____ _____ describes a property of a substance. (Physical property.)
2. A _____ _____ in matter is an example of a _____ change. (Phase change, physical.)
3. A _____ _____ describes a substance's ability to _____ into a _____ substance. (Chemical property, change, new.)
4. A chemical reaction is another name for a _____ _____. (Chemical change.)
5. When _____ changes occur, the _____ is altered but still remains the same basic _____. When _____ changes occur, _____ substances are formed. (Physical, phase [form], substance, chemical, new.)

CLOSURE

▶ *Review and Reinforcement Guide*
Students may now complete Section 2–2 in their *Review and Reinforcement Guide.*

TEACHING STRATEGY 2–3

FOCUS/MOTIVATION

Show students a wooden splint.
• **What is this object made of?** (Wood.)
Light a match and set the splint on fire.

Let it burn until at least half of it has become charred or has fallen off as ash.
• **What changes do you see in the part of the splint that burned?** (The color changed to black; the burned part became brittle and easily crumbled; much of the wood seemed to disappear.)
• **Do you think the identity of the original substance has changed?** (Answers may vary; the correct answer is yes.)

The ability of hydrocarbons to burn is what makes these substances so useful as fuels. The burning of hydrocarbons, which is often called combustion, results in the production of carbon dioxide and water plus energy. Some examples of hydrocarbon fuels include gasoline, home heating oil, natural gas, and diesel fuel.

FIND OUT BY DOING

LET'S GET PHYSICAL AND CHEMICAL

Discovery Learning

Skills: Making observations, making inferences

Materials: two 500-mL beakers, citric acid crystals, teaspoon, tablespoon, baking soda, water

In this activity students will observe a physical change and a chemical change. Combining citric acid and baking soda creates a physical change; the two substances merely mix without reacting. When water is added, a chemical change occurs. Evidence is the carbon dioxide bubbles that result. The water plays a vital role: It allows the two substances to dissolve and react chemically.

Substances that may react with water are labeled "Store in a dry place only."

Figure 2–19 *Flammability is an important chemical property that may affect your life directly—as it does this firefighter, who watches helplessly as a home is totally destroyed by flames.*

FIND OUT BY DOING

Let's Get Physical and Chemical

1. In a dry 500-mL beaker, mix 1 teaspoon of citric acid crystals with 1 tablespoon of baking soda. Observe what happens.

2. Fill another beaker halfway with water. Pour the citric acid-baking soda mixture into the water. Observe what happens.

What type of change took place in the first step of the procedure? In the second step?

Did the water have an important role in the procedure? If so, what do you think was its purpose?

■ Why are some substances marked "Store in a dry place only"?

gases, they have no definite shape or volume. And although each has a specific density, you cannot determine that density by dropping the gases into water to see what happens. In this particular case, physical properties are not very helpful in identifying the gases.

Fortunately, physical properties are not the only way to identify a substance. Both oxygen and hydrogen can turn into other substances and take on new identities. And the way in which they do this can be useful in identifying these two gases. The properties that describe how a substance changes into other new substances are called **chemical properties.**

In this case, if you collected some hydrogen in a test tube and put a glowing wooden stick in it, you would hear a loud pop. The pop occurs when hydrogen combines with oxygen in the air. What is actually happening is that the hydrogen is burning. The ability to burn is called **flammability** (flam-uh-BIHL-uh-tee). It is a chemical property. A new kind of matter forms as the hydrogen burns. Do you know what this new substance is? This substance—a combination of oxygen and hydrogen—is water.

Oxygen is not a flammable gas. It does not burn. But oxygen does support the burning of other substances. A glowing wooden splint placed in a test

---

2–3 (continued)

CONTENT DEVELOPMENT

Point out that chemical properties describe ways in which substances change into other substances.
• **What chemical property of wood did you observe in the demonstration with a wooden splint?** (The ability to burn.)
• **What is another name for this property?** (Flammability.)
• **What other substances have this chemical property?** (Possible answers: cloth,

leaves, hydrogen gas, oil, and other hydrocarbons.)

Explain to students that chemical changes are often called chemical reactions. Point out that chemical reactions can involve the combining of substances to form new substances or the breaking down of a substance into simpler substances.

Tell students that oxygen alone will not burn, nor rust items, nor produce fireworks. Explain that oxygen combined with other substances produces all these processes, plus many others.

Emphasize that the ability to support burning or other chemical changes is a distinguishing property of a substance.

GUIDED PRACTICE

Skills Development
Skill: Applying concepts

Divide the class into teams of four to six students. Distribute a small candle (birthday type), jar lid, and matches to each team. Have teams light the candle, set it on the lid to protect the desk, and then

tube of oxygen will continue to burn until the oxygen is used up. This ability to support burning is another example of a chemical property. By using the chemical properties of flammability and supporting burning, you can distinguish between the two gases hydrogen and oxygen.

The changes that substances undergo when they turn into other substances are called **chemical changes.** Chemical changes are closely related to chemical properties, but they are not the same. **A chemical property describes a substance's ability to change into a different substance; a chemical change is the process by which the substance changes.** For example, the ability of a substance to burn is a chemical property. However, the process of burning is a chemical change. Figures 2–20 and 2–21 show several chemical changes.

Another name for a chemical change is a **chemical reaction.** Chemical reactions often involve chemically combining different substances. For example, during the burning of coal, oxygen combines chemically with carbon—the substance that makes up most of the coal. This combining reaction produces a new substance—carbon dioxide. The carbon and oxygen have changed chemically. They no longer exist in their original forms.

The ability to use and control chemical reactions is an important skill. For chemical reactions produce a range of products, from glass to pottery glazes to medicines. Your life is made easier and more enjoyable because of the products of chemical reactions.

CAREERS

Firefighter

Flammability—the ability to burn—is a chemical property of some kinds of matter. **Firefighters** deal with this chemical property daily. Often these brave men and women risk their lives to protect people and property from the many thousands of fires that occur every year. The duties of firefighters include driving emergency vehicles, hooking up hoses and pumps, setting up ladders, and rescuing people.

Some firefighters are trained to conduct fire safety checks in office buildings and homes. Others are trained to investigate false alarms and suspicious fires. If you are interested in this career, write to the Department of Fire Protection and Safety Technology, Oklahoma State University, 303 Campus Fire Station, Stillwater, OK 74078.

Figure 2–20 *Nylon was one of the first synthetic fibers. Here you can see threads of nylon forming as chemicals squirted from barely visible holes undergo changes.*

N ■ 49

GUIDED PRACTICE

Skills Development

Skills: Making observations, comparing properties, drawing conclusions

At this point have students complete the in-text Chapter 2 Laboratory Investigation: Observing a Candle. Students practice distinguishing physical and chemical properties.

REINFORCEMENT/RETEACHING

▶ *Activity Book*

Students who need further work with properties should complete the chapter activity Properties of Matter.

blow it out.
• **Why did the candle burn?** (It was lit with a match.)
• **What did the match do?** (Heated the wick until it was hot enough to burn.)
• **What combined with the wick and wax to cause combustion?** (Oxygen.)
• **Where did the oxygen come from?** (The air.)

Distribute a 500-mL beaker to each team. Have teams light the candle again and then cover the candle with the inverted beaker.

• **What happened?** (The flame went out.)
• **Why did the flame go out?** (The burning used up all the oxygen that was inside the beaker. Without oxygen, things will not burn.)

INDEPENDENT PRACTICE

▶ *Activity Book*

Students who need practice observing and reporting properties should complete the chapter activity General and Specific Properties.

WHY SILVER TARNISHES

A familiar chemical change that may be of interest to students is the tarnishing of silver. Tarnish is the result of silver reacting with sulfur to form silver sulfide. Silver can be made to tarnish by wrapping a rubber band around it. The sulfur in vulcanized rubber will react with the silver. In everyday use, silver usually comes into contact with sulfur in the form of hydrogen sulfide. Hydrogen sulfide is present in egg yolks. It is also present in small concentrations in the atmosphere.

Figure 2–21 *Many chemical changes occur in the world around you. Rust formed on the ship when iron combined with oxygen in the air. The copper in this statue reacted with sulfur in the air to form the soft green substance called verdigris. Fireworks produce beautiful colors and forms as a result of chemical changes. Chemical changes also occur in a leaf with the approach of cold winter weather.*

Synthetic fibers such as nylon and rayon, plastics, soaps, building materials, and even some of the foods you eat are the products of chemical reactions. The next time you eat a piece of cheese or a slice of bread, remember that you are eating the product of a chemical reaction.

2–3 Section Review

1. Give two examples of chemical properties.
2. What is chemical change? Give an example.

Connection—*Astronomy*

3. Suppose you visited another planet and wanted to test a sample of the planet's air. What kinds of tests would you perform to determine some physical properties of your sample? What kinds of tests would you perform to determine some chemical properties?

50 ■ N

2–3 (continued)

GUIDED PRACTICE

Skills Development

Skill: Applying concepts

Have each student bring one or two pebbles or small rocks to class. Divide the class into teams of four to six students. Distribute a medicine dropper, a beaker of vinegar, and a paper towel to each team. Have teams place several drops of vinegar onto each pebble.

• **What rocks produced a chemical reaction with the vinegar?** (The rocks that fizzed.)

• **How do you know a chemical reaction occurred?** (A new substance and gas bubbles were formed.)

• **Which rocks did not produce a chemical reaction with the vinegar?** (The ones that did not fizz.)

INDEPENDENT PRACTICE

▶ *Activity Book*

Students who need more practice distinguishing between physical and chemical changes should complete the chapter activity Identifying Physical and Chemical Changes.

GUIDED PRACTICE

▶ *Laboratory Manual*

Skills Development

Skills: Making observations, drawing conclusions

Students may now complete the Chapter 2 Laboratory Investigation in the *Laboratory Manual* called Investigating Physical and Chemical Changes. They will observe physical and chemical changes and learn to recognize each type of change.

CONNECTIONS

The Mess We Make

Throughout history, people have lived in groups: small family groups and larger groups such as those found in towns and cities. All people, in groups large and small, produce wastes. The amount of wastes each person produces is astounding—and, unfortunately, increasing! It has been estimated that in 1900 each person living in New York City produced 538 kilograms of waste. In 1989, the amount of waste produced by each person jumped to more than 825 kilograms. In a city of 8 million people, such amounts stagger the imagination and tax the ability of a city to deal with them.

Some of the waste materials—food scraps, paper, and other natural materials—are *biodegradable.* Biodegradable materials are capable of undergoing chemical changes that cause them to break down over time. Tiny animals, plants, and microscopic organisms such as bacteria that live in the soil are responsible for these changes. The result is that biodegradable materials are broken down into simpler chemical substances.

Some of these chemical substances can be used by organisms for growth and repair. Others can be used as a source of energy. Biodegradable materials also undergo physical changes.

Certain waste materials, however, such as some plastics, are not biodegradable. These materials do not break down. They remain intact in the environment for many hundreds of years. Scientists are now working to replace many of the non-biodegradable materials we use with those that are biodegradable. This would drastically reduce the amount of nonbiodegradable wastes we produce.

The problem of *waste disposal* is sure to loom ever greater in our future. The areas where we can safely dump wastes are rapidly filling up. Other methods to deal with waste materials will have to be developed soon in order to prevent the Earth from becoming a tremendous garbage dump tomorrow. You can help even now. You can use materials that are biodegradable. For example, you can use products wrapped in biodegradable materials. You can consume less. The less wastes you produce, the smaller the problem of waste disposal becomes. We must all assume responsibility for our actions—every little bit helps.

New York City, one of the world's largest cities, has the world's largest solid-waste dump site. In but a few more years, this site will be full—unable to accept another scrap of paper. It is imperative that we limit the amount of wastes we add to the environment.

CONNECTIONS
THE MESS WE MAKE

Students should be interested in the topic of waste disposal. It is fascinating to note the amount of waste one individual produces in a year. Students might be encouraged to investigate the waste-disposal practices in their community. Have them find out whether their family uses biodegradable products or products that are not biodegradable.

If you are teaching thematically, you may want to use the Connections feature to reinforce the themes of energy or systems and interactions.

Integration: Use the Connections feature to integrate social studies and ecology into your science lesson.

ENRICHMENT

Have each student choose one of the following topics to research. Then have them prepare an oral or written report in which they discuss the chemical changes involved in each process.
1. rusting of iron
2. bread dough rising
3. leaves changing color in the fall
4. chemical weathering of rock
5. milk turning sour
6. combustion of gasoline in a car engine

INDEPENDENT PRACTICE
Section Review 2–3
1. Flammability, ability to support combustion.
2. A chemical change is the process by which a substance changes into a different substance; an example is burning.
3. Physical properties that students might suggest are making observations about the color or density of the air. Checking whether substances would burn in the air would be a test for chemical properties.

REINFORCEMENT/RETEACHING

Review students' responses to the Section Review questions. Reteach any material that is still unclear, based on their responses.

CLOSURE

▶ *Review and Reinforcement Guide*
Students may now complete Section 2–3 in their *Review and Reinforcement Guide.*

Laboratory Investigation

OBSERVING A CANDLE

BEFORE THE LAB

1. Gather all materials at least one day before the investigation. If students are to work in groups, each student should have his or her own candle, but one package or box of matches per group should be sufficient.

2. Check the wicks of the candles to make sure they light easily. Have a few extra candles on hand in case some candles prove hard to light or get broken.

3. Check fire extinguishers to make sure they are in working order and are easily accessible to students.

PRE-LAB DISCUSSION

Review the definitions of physical and chemical properties. Also review the idea that the process by which a chemical substance changes is called chemical change or chemical reaction.

This investigation, although relatively simple in appearance, challenges students to "see and do" science in their daily lives. You may want to offer incentives for the most complete list of properties obtained by a lab group. The objective of this investigation is to differentiate between physical and chemical properties of matter. Students should develop a hypothesis that stresses that objective.

Laboratory Investigation

Observing a Candle

Problem

How can physical and chemical properties be distinguished?

Materials *(per group)*

small candle
matches
metric ruler
candle holder or small empty food can
sand

Procedure 🧪 🔥 👉 👁

1. On a separate sheet of paper, prepare a data table similar to the one shown here.

2. Observe the unlighted candle. List as many physical and chemical properties as you can.

3. Place the candle in the candle holder. If you are not using a candle holder, fill the small food can with sand and place the candle in the center of the sand. Make sure that the candle is placed securely.

4. Under your teacher's supervision, carefully light the candle.

5. Observe the lighted candle. Continue to list as many physical and chemical properties as you can. Record your observations in the correct columns in your data table.

	Physical properties	Chemical properties
Unlighted candle		
Lighted candle		

Observations

1. What physical properties of the unlit candle did you observe?

2. What senses did you use when you made these observations?

3. What physical changes did you observe after you lit the candle?

4. What did you have to do to observe a chemical property of the candle?

5. What evidence of chemical change did you observe?

Analysis and Conclusions

1. What do you think is the basic difference between a physical property and a chemical property?

2. Can a physical property be observed without changing the substance?

3. What name is given to a process such as burning a candle? What is the result of such a process?

4. Which type of property—physical or chemical—is easier to determine? Why?

5. On Your Own Obtain a recipe for making bread. List the chemical and physical properties of the ingredients. How do the properties of the ingredients result in a loaf of bread?

TEACHING STRATEGY

1. Have students prepare the data table they will need to collect the data from the experiment.

2. If candle holders are not available, have students practice securing the candle in the sand. Make sure all the candles are securely in place before allowing students to light them.

3. Have teams follow the directions carefully as they work in the laboratory.

DISCOVERY STRATEGIES

Discuss how the investigation relates to the chapter ideas by asking open questions similar to the following:

• **What are some physical properties of a substance?** (Mass, color, volume, shape, density, texture, hardness, odor.)

• **What are some examples of physical change that we discussed?** (Temperature change and phase change of substances.)

• **What is the difference between chemical properties and chemical reactions?** (Chemical properties describe how a sub-

Study Guide

Summarizing Key Concepts

2–1 Phases of Matter

▲ Physical properties of matter include color, shape, hardness, and density.

▲ A physical change occurs when the physical properties of a substance are altered. However, the substance remains the same kind of matter.

▲ Matter can exist in any of four phases: solid, liquid, gas, and plasma.

▲ A solid has a definite shape and volume.

▲ A crystal is the regular, repeating pattern in which the particles of some solids are arranged.

▲ Amorphous solids do not form crystals and thus do not keep a definite shape.

▲ A liquid has a definite volume but not a definite shape. A liquid takes the shape of its container.

▲ A gas has no definite shape or volume.

▲ Boyle's law states that the volume of a fixed amount of gas varies inversely with the pressure. Charles's law states that the volume of a fixed amount of gas varies directly with the temperature.

▲ Matter in the plasma state is very high in energy.

2–2 Phase Changes

▲ Phase changes are accompanied by either a loss or a gain of heat energy.

▲ Melting is the change of a solid to a liquid at a temperature called the melting point. Freezing is the change of a liquid to a solid at the freezing point.

▲ Vaporization is the change of a liquid to a gas. Vaporization at the surface of a liquid is called evaporation. Vaporization throughout a liquid is called boiling.

▲ The boiling point of a liquid is related to the air pressure above the liquid.

▲ The change of a gas to a liquid is called condensation.

▲ The change of a solid directly to a gas without going through the liquid phase is called sublimation.

2–3 Chemical Properties and Changes

▲ Chemical properties describe how a substance changes into a new substance.

▲ Flammability, the ability to burn, is a chemical property.

▲ When a substance undergoes a chemical change, or a chemical reaction, it turns into a new and different substance.

Reviewing Key Terms

Define each term in a complete sentence.

2–1 Phases of Matter
physical property
phase
solid
crystal
liquid
gas
plasma

2–2 Phase Changes
melting
melting point
freezing
freezing point
vaporization
evaporation
boiling
boiling point
condensation
sublimation

2–3 Chemical Properties and Changes
chemical property
flammability
chemical change
chemical reaction

ANALYSIS AND CONCLUSIONS

1. Chemical properties can be detected only through interaction with other materials.
2. Yes.
3. Chemical change or chemical reaction. A new substance with new and different physical and chemical properties is formed.
4. Physical, because observing physical properties of an object requires no other materials.
5. Answers will vary depending on the recipe. In general, the mixing of the ingredients involves physical changes, and the baking of the bread involves chemical changes as well. If yeast is used as an ingredient, some chemical changes take place as the yeast rises before baking.

GOING FURTHER: ENRICHMENT
Part 1

To continue the study of physical and chemical properties, have students investigate the properties of sugar. In addition to observing the physical properties, they can observe a physical change by dissolving the sugar in water. Some chemical properties of sugar can be determined by burning a small amount in a flameproof dish.

Part 2

Ask students the following questions:
• **Based on your observation of the candle, what are some signs that indicate that a chemical change is taking place?** (Flame, heat and light given off, smoke, burning smell.)
• **Can any of these signs indicate a physical change?** (Yes. Heat given off can be a sign of a phase change.)
• **Based on your own experience and what you have read, what are some other signs that indicate chemical change?** (Substance changing color or texture; electric current generated; gas given off; new substance such as water appears.)

stance changes into other new substances; chemical reactions produce new substances with new and different physical and chemical properties.)

OBSERVATIONS

1. Mass, color, volume, shape, texture, hardness, odor.
2. Touch, smell, sight, hearing.
3. Wax became hotter and melted.
4. Ignite the candle wick.
5. New material (smoke) was produced.

Chapter Review

ALTERNATIVE ASSESSMENT

The *Prentice Hall Science* program includes a variety of testing components and methodologies. Aside from the Chapter Review questions, you may opt to use the Chapter Test or the Computer Test Bank Test in your *Test Book* for assessment of important facts and concepts. In addition, Performance-Based Tests are included in your *Test Book*. These Performance-Based Tests are designed to test science process skills, rather than factual content recall. Since they are not content dependent, Performance-Based Tests can be distributed after students complete a chapter or after they complete the entire textbook.

CONTENT REVIEW

Multiple Choice
1. c
2. b
3. c
4. d
5. d
6. b
7. c
8. b

True or False
1. T
2. F, gas
3. F, Charles's law
4. F, loses
5. T
6. F, condensed
7. F, chemical

Concept Mapping
Row 1: No definite volume; always fills the container regardless of size or shape; takes the shape of the container.
Row 2: Solid, Liquid, Plasma

CONCEPT MASTERY

1. (a) Physical, (b) Chemical, (c) Physical, (d) Physical, (e) Physical, (f) Chemical. The two properties identified as chemical, (b) and (f), describe how a substance changes into other new substances. All the others are physical because the basic particles remain unchanged.
2. (a) Chemical, (b) Chemical, (c) Chemical, (d) Physical, (e) Physical, (f) Chemical, (g) Chemical. The two changes iden-

tified as physical, (d) and (e), describe changes in which the basic particles remain unchanged. All the other changes are chemical because new substances are formed that have new physical and chemical properties.
3. When ice reaches a temperature of 0°C and more heat is added, that heat is used to overcome the forces that hold the ice together. The ice melts, but the temperature remains at 0°C until it is all liquid. Only then will additional heat raise the temperature of the water. The reverse is

true when water reaches a temperature of 0°C and more heat is removed. Hence the melting point and freezing point are both 0°C.
4. Solid: definite volume and shape; particles packed closely together; motion of particles is relatively slow. Liquid: definite volume; assumes the shape of its container; particles close but able to slide over one another; motion of particles is faster than in the solid, but slower than in the gas. Gas: assumes the shape and volume of its container; motion of particles

---

Content Review

Multiple Choice

Choose the letter of the answer that best completes each statement.

1. Color, odor, and density are
   a. chemical properties.
   b. chemical changes.
   c. physical properties.
   d. solid properties.
2. A regular pattern of particles is found in
   a. molecules.   c. compressions.
   b. crystals.   d. plasmas.
3. The phase of matter that is made up of very high-energy particles is
   a. liquid.   c. gas.
   b. plasma.   d. solid.
4. As the volume of a fixed amount of gas decreases, the pressure of the gas
   a. decreases.
   b. remains the same.
   c. first increases then decreases.
   d. increases.

5. As the temperature of a fixed amount of gas increases, the volume
   a. decreases.
   b. remains the same.
   c. increases then decreases.
   d. increases.
6. All liquids have
   a. definite shape and definite volume.
   b. no definite shape but definite volume.
   c. no definite shape and no definite volume.
   d. definite shape but no definite volume.
7. A solid changes to a liquid by
   a. evaporation.   c. melting.
   b. freezing.   d. sublimation.
8. Vaporization that takes place at the surface of a liquid is called
   a. boiling.   c. sublimation.
   b. evaporation.   d. condensation.

True or False

If the statement is true, write "true." If it is false, change the underlined word or words to make the statement true.

1. Particles that make up a <u>solid</u> are packed very close together.
2. The particles of matter are spread farthest apart in a <u>liquid</u>.
3. The relationship between the temperature of a gas and the volume it occupies is described by <u>Boyle's law</u>.
4. A liquid will freeze when it <u>absorbs</u> heat energy.
5. The process by which a liquid changes to a gas is called <u>vaporization</u>.
6. Drops of water on the outside of a cold glass are water vapor that has <u>sublimed</u> into a liquid.
7. New substances that have different properties are formed as a result of <u>physical</u> changes.

Concept Mapping

Complete the following concept map for Section 2–1. Refer to pages N6–N7 to construct a concept map for the entire chapter.

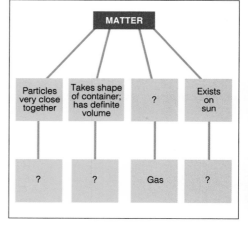

Concept Mastery

Discuss each of the following in a brief paragraph.

1. Identify the following properties as either physical or chemical. Explain your answers. (a) taste, (b) flammability, (c) color, (d) odor, (e) ability to dissolve, (f) tendency to rust
2. Identify the following changes as either physical or chemical. Explain your answers. (a) burning coal, (b) baking brownies, (c) digesting food, (d) dissolving sugar in hot water, (e) melting butter, (f) exploding fireworks, (g) rusting iron

3. Explain why both the melting point and the freezing point of water are 0°C.
4. Compare the solid, liquid, and gas phases of matter in terms of shape, volume, and arrangement and movement of molecules.
5. Explain how evaporation and boiling are similar. How are they different?

Critical Thinking and Problem Solving

Use the skills you have developed in this chapter to answer each of the following.

1. **Applying concepts** I am one of the most common substances on Earth. I am easily seen in the liquid phase and the solid phase. I am hard to observe as a gas. Identify me and explain the clues.
2. **Applying concepts** You are coming home from school one cold winter's day when you observe a neighbor filling the radiator of his car with plain tap water. What advice would you give this person? Why?
3. **Making inferences** Several campers who have set up camp on a high mountain peak decide they would like to enjoy a cup of coffee. They notice that although the water they use to make the coffee has boiled, the coffee does not seem as hot as the coffee they drink while camping out at sea level. Use your knowledge of the effects of altitude on boiling to explain their observation.
4. **Relating cause and effect** Rubbing alcohol, or isopropyl alcohol, evaporates quickly at room temperature. Explain why people with a high fever are often given rubdowns with isopropyl alcohol as a means of reducing their fevers.

5. **Applying concepts** An automobile mechanic may suggest that you test the pressure of the air in a car's tires after the car has been moving for a while and the tires have heated up. Why do you think this is good advice?

6. **Developing a hypothesis** Solid room air fresheners "disappear" over a period of time and must be replaced. What do you think happens to the solid? How is this related to the way in which the freshener releases its pleasant odor?
7. **Using the writing process** Write a 250-word story to describe the day on which your birthday party was almost a disaster. Use the following words in your story: boiling, freezing, crystal, evaporation, liquid, melting, phase, physical change, solid, sublimation.

---

fee the campers drink at sea level.

4. As the alcohol evaporates, it removes heat from the body of the person with a high fever.

5. When the tires are cool, the air in the tire is at a lower pressure than when the tires are warm. As you drive, the air in the tire tends to warm up and exerts more pressure. If you fill the tire when it is cool, you might overinflate it. Then, once the air heats up and exerts more pressure, the tire could explode.

6. The solid sublimates, changing from a solid into a gas directly without passing through a liquid stage. The pleasant odor is the aroma of the freshener in the gaseous phase.

7. Stories will vary. Check to see that the required words are used and that they are used correctly.

KEEPING A PORTFOLIO

You might want to assign some of the Concept Mastery and Critical Thinking and Problem Solving questions as homework and have students include their responses to unassigned questions in their portfolio. Students should be encouraged to include both the question and the answer in their portfolio.

ISSUES IN SCIENCE

The following issues can be used as a springboard for class debate or given as writing assignments:

1. Many chemical changes in our environment are caused by the presence of sulfur in the atmosphere. A major source of excess sulfur in the air is pollutants from factories that burn sulfur-containing fuels. Have students research sulfur pollution and the various chemical changes caused by sulfur. Encourage students to express an opinion as to whether the chemical changes caused by sulfur are harmful, helpful, or of no consequences to living things.

2. There is great concern about the destruction of tropical forests in Central and South America, Africa, and Asia. The loss of these forests not only jeopardizes many species of plant and animal life but also threatens to cause a change in the amount of carbon dioxide in the atmosphere. Have students research the problem. Encourage them to express an opinion about what should be done about the problem.

---

extremely fast and random.

5. Both are phase changes from the liquid phase into the gaseous phase. Evaporation takes place only at the surface of the liquid. The liquid itself can be below the boiling point. Boiling takes place only when the liquid is at the boiling point. It occurs throughout the liquid. The gas particles then move to the surface and escape into the air.

CRITICAL THINKING AND PROBLEM SOLVING

1. Water, because it is common, easily seen in the liquid and solid states, and difficult to observe as a gas. Steam is invisible.

2. Add antifreeze. Without antifreeze in the radiator, the water could freeze, expand, and rupture the radiator.

3. At high altitudes, the air pressure is lower than the air pressure at sea level. As a result, liquids boil at a lower temperature. The temperature of the coffee is lower than the temperature of the cof-

Chapter 3   MIXTURES, ELEMENTS, AND COMPOUNDS

SECTION	LABORATORY INVESTIGATIONS AND DEMONSTRATIONS
3–1 Classes of Matter pages N58–N59	**Teacher Edition** Classifying Objects, p. N56d
3–2 Mixtures pages N60–N68	**Laboratory Manual** Determining Solubility **Teacher Edition** Creating a Mixture, p. N56d
3–3 Elements pages N68–N71	
3–4 Compounds pages N71–N77	**Student Edition** Making Models of Chemical Reactions, p. N78 **Laboratory Manual** Elements, Mixtures, and Compounds
Chapter Review pages N78–N81	

*All materials in the Chapter Planning Guide Grid are available as part of the Prentice Hall Science Learning System.

OUTSIDE TEACHER RESOURCES

Books

Stone, A. H. *The Chemistry of a Lemon,* Prentice-Hall.

Stone, A. H., and D. Ingmanson. *Crystals From the Sea: A Look at Salt,* Prentice-Hall.

Zubrowski, B. *Messing Around With Baking Chemistry: A Children's Museum Activity Book,* Little, Brown

Audiovisuals

Matter and Molecules: Clue-Compounds and Changes, filmstrip, Singer Educational Division

OTHER ACTIVITIES	MULTIMEDIA

Activity Book
    Chapter Discovery: Types of Mixtures
    ACTIVITY: Classifying Matter
    ACTIVITY: A Classification Scheme
    ACTIVITY: Classifying Common Objects
Student Edition
    Find Out by Doing: Classifying Common Objects, p. N59
Review and Reinforcement Guide
    Section 3–1
	English/Spanish Audiotapes
	    Section 3–1

Activity Book
    ACTIVITY: Separating Substances
Student Edition
    Find Out by Reading: Danger in the Air, p. N63
    Find Out by Doing: Is It a Solution? p. N66
    Find Out by Doing: Where's the Fizz? p. N67
Review and Reinforcement Guide
    Section 3–2
	English/Spanish Audiotapes
	    Section 3–2

Student Edition
    Find Out by Doing: Name That Element, p. N69
Review and Reinforcement Guide
    Section 3–3
	English/Spanish Audiotapes
	    Section 3–3

Activity Book
    ACTIVITY: Counting Atoms
    ACTIVITY: Elements, Compounds, and Mixtures
Student Edition
    Find Out by Calculating: Count the Atoms, p. N74
Review and Reinforcement Guide
    Section 3– 4
	Transparency Binder
	    Molecules
	Video/Videodisc
	    Elements, Compounds, and Mixtures
	English/Spanish Audiotapes
	    Section 3– 4

Test Book
    Chapter Test
    Performance-Based Tests
	Test Book
	    Computer Test Bank Test

Naming Chemical Substances, Parts 1 and 2,
  filmstrip, PH Media
Solutions, filmstrip, Encyclopaedia
  Britannica

CHAPTER OVERVIEW

Matter is all around us. It makes up every living and nonliving thing. Because of the varieties of matter, scientists devised classification systems so that matter can be studied in an organized manner. One of the classification systems is based on the makeup of matter. Scientists studying the makeup of matter are concerned with mixtures, solutions, elements, and compounds.

Mixtures are composed of two or more pure substances that are mixed but not chemically combined. They can be in any of the four phases—solid, liquid, gas, or plasma—or they can be combinations of different phases. Mixtures are classified by the size of the particles in them and by how well mixed they are. There are two general types of mixtures: heterogeneous and homogeneous. Solutions are important types of homogeneous mixtures that are formed when one substance dissolves in another.

Elements are the simplest type of pure substances. A pure substance is made of only one kind of matter with a definite chemical composition. A pure substance is the same throughout. An element is composed of building blocks called atoms. An atom is the smallest particle of an element that has the properties of that element. All atoms of a particular element are alike. An element cannot be changed into simpler substances by heating or by any chemical process. Elements are represented by chemical symbols.

Compounds are pure substances that contain two or more elements chemically combined in a definite composition. A molecule is the smallest particle of a compound that has the properties of that compound.

Compounds are represented by chemical formulas, which are combinations of chemical symbols showing the kind of elements and number of atoms of each element in the compound. A description of a chemical reaction using symbols and formulas is called a chemical equation.

3–1 CLASSES OF MATTER
THEMATIC FOCUS

The purpose of this section is to introduce students to the classification systems. The section begins with an explanation of why classification systems are necessary and how they organize matter in various ways. Students learn that classification systems are used by collectors, stores, and libraries or by anyone who needs to group objects based on a particular property. Scientists use a classification system that makes the study of matter easier; the system is based on the makeup of matter. The study of the matter involves the study of mixtures, solutions, elements, and compounds. This section serves as an introduction to this chapter.

The theme that can be focused on in this section is unity and diversity.

Unity and diversity: As you discuss the variety of matter in this universe, make sure students understand that despite the diversity, all the matter has common characteristics. Matter can be organized according to elements, compounds, mixtures, and solutions.

PERFORMANCE OBJECTIVES 3–1

1. Identify the four makeup classes of matter.

2. Explain why it is more useful to classify matter according to makeup than according to phase.

3–2 MIXTURES
THEMATIC FOCUS

The purpose of this section is to introduce students to mixtures and to the properties of mixtures. Mixtures are composed of two or more pure substances. They can vary in amount but not in chemical composition. Students should understand that mixtures can change their appearance but not their properties. Mixtures can be combinations of elements or compounds. They can be in any of the four phases—solid, liquid, gas, or plasma—or they can be combinations of different phases. A mixture that does not appear to be the same throughout is said to be heterogeneous. One that appears to be the same throughout is said to be homogeneous. A solution is a type of homogeneous mixture.

The themes that can be focused on in this section are patterns of change and scale and structure.

*Patterns of change: Stress that the substances in a mixture can vary in amounts and can change in physical appearance. They do not, however, change in chemical composition or in their original properties when combined.

*Scale and structure: Make students aware that the particles in a heterogeneous mixture are large enough to be seen and to separate from the mixture. The particles in a homogeneous mixture are too small to be seen and cannot easily be separated from the mixture.

PERFORMANCE OBJECTIVES 3–2

1. Describe the three important properties of a mixture.

2. Compare a heterogeneous mixture with a homogeneous mixture.

3. Explain what a solution is and what its properties are.

SCIENCE TERMS 3–2
mixture p. N60
heterogeneous mixture p. N63
homogeneous mixture p. N63
colloid p. N63
solution p. N64
solute p. N64
solvent p. N64
soluble p. N66
insoluble p. N66
solubility p. N66
alloy p. N66

3–3 ELEMENTS
THEMATIC FOCUS

The purpose of this section is to introduce students to the concept of elements, atoms, and molecules. Students will learn what a pure substance is and that elements are the simplest pure substances. An element cannot be changed into simpler substances by heating or by any physical process such as burning. Students will be introduced to chemical symbols in this section, and they will learn that the symbols are a shorthand way of representing elements. Make sure students understand that the smallest particle of an element is an atom.

The themes that can be focused on in this section are patterns of change, scale and structure, and stability.

*Patterns of change: Make sure students understand that there is no change involved in elements. The particles in an element are in their simplest form. What may change, however, is the phase. A substance may change from a liquid into a solid, for example.

*Scale and structure: Tie the concept of an atom being the smallest particle of an element that has the properties of that element to scale and structure. Students should be aware that atoms of the same element are alike and that atoms of different elements are different.

*Stability: Students should be aware that elements, the simplest pure substances, cannot be broken down any further without losing their identity.

PERFORMANCE OBJECTIVES 3–3

1. Describe a pure substance.
2. Explain the relation between atoms and an element.
3. Identify the chemical symbols for some common elements.

SCIENCE TERMS

pure substance p. N68
element p. N69
atom p. N69
chemical symbol p. N70

3–4 COMPOUNDS
THEMATIC FOCUS

The purpose of this section is to introduce students to compounds. Most compounds are made of molecules, and a molecule is made of two or more atoms that are chemically combined. A molecule can be a combination of atoms of different elements or the same element.

Students will learn that names of compounds are represented by a combination of chemical symbols that show the number of each kind of atom in the compound. They will also learn that the combinations of chemical symbols are called chemical formulas. Lastly, students will come to understand that chemical equations represent chemical reactions.

The themes that can be focused on in this section are energy and systems and interactions.

Energy: Make students aware that energy can be used to separate some compounds into their elements. Point out that copper sulfide, for example, can be separated into the elements copper and sulfur by heating it to high temperatures.

*Systems and interactions: Tie in the fact that atoms of different elements can be chemically combined to form compounds. The compounds have different properties from the elements that formed them.

PERFORMANCE OBJECTIVES 3–4

1. **Describe how a compound differs from an element.**
2. **Explain how a molecule is represented.**
3. **Explain why a chemical equation must be balanced.**

SCIENCE TERMS 3–4

compound p. N72
molecule p. N73
chemical formula p. N73
subscript p. N74
chemical equation p. N75
coefficient p. N76

Discovery *Learning*

TEACHER DEMONSTRATIONS MODELING
Classifying Objects

Place a rock, a glass of water, a hard rubber ball, and an air-filled balloon on a desk in front of the room. Have students observe the objects.

• **How are these objects related?** (Accept all logical answers. Students should suggest that they are all objects and have physical properties.

• **How could they be classified into groups?** (Students should compare the shapes and sizes. Some students may suggest that the glass is filled with water and the balloon is filled with air. Therefore they could be classified as "filled things." The rock and the ball are both "hard things.")

• **What is classifying?** (Accept all logical answers. Students should describe classifying as putting like things together.)

• **Why is classifying important in a grocery store?** (If like things were not put in the same area, people could not find what they were looking for.)

• **Why do you think scientists classify things?** (Students may be reluctant to predict why scientists classify; accept all logical answers.)

Creating a Mixture

Show students 2 cups of cornflakes in a wide-mouthed jar. Hold up a box or bag of raisins. Discuss the following questions:

• **What kind of substances are cornflakes and raisins?** (Cornflakes and raisins are both solids.)

Point out that a mixture is a combination of substances. Pour 1/4 cup of raisins onto the cornflakes. Cover the jar. Shake and turn the jar to mix the raisins and cornflakes. Hold the jar up for the class to observe.

• **What kind of matter do we have now?** (The students should respond by saying that is is a mixture.)

Explain that a mixture is a combination of two or more substances *not* chemically combined. Pour the cornflake-and-raisin mixture onto a sheet of paper.

• **How could we separate the cornflakes from the raisins?** (Students may say that the raisins can be picked out of the mixture.)

CHAPTER 3

Mixtures, Elements, and Compounds

INTEGRATING SCIENCE

This physical science chapter provides you with numerous opportunities to integrate other areas of science, as well as other disciplines, into your curriculum. Blue numbered annotations on the student page and integration notes on the teacher wraparound pages alert you to areas of possible integration.

In this chapter you can integrate earth science and geology (pp. 60, 62), food science (pp. 63, 66), language arts (pp. 63, 71), earth science and oceanography (p. 64), mathematics (p. 74), and life science and plants (p. 77).

SCIENCE, TECHNOLOGY, AND SOCIETY/COOPERATIVE LEARNING

Element number 86, radon, is a radioactive gas lacking color, odor, and taste. It is a natural product of decaying uranium found in the Earth's crust and escapes into the atmosphere through fissures. Radon itself is not harmful, but the "radon daughters" (polonium, lead, and bismuth) produced by the radioactive decay of radon are solid particles that stick to the lining of the lungs. As these radon daughters decay and emit radiation, there is an increased risk of developing lung cancer.

Radon becomes a problem only when it accumulates in buildings and contaminates the environment. It can enter

INTRODUCING CHAPTER 3

DISCOVERY LEARNING

▶ *Activity Book*

Begin your teaching of the chapter by using the Chapter 3 Discovery Activity from your *Activity Book*. Using this activity, students will discover that all mixtures can be described through certain general properties.

USING THE TEXTBOOK

Have students study the photograph on page 56 and read the caption on page 57.
• **What is detective Sherlock Holmes doing?** (Gathering clues.)

Have students read the chapter introduction. Point out that Holmes's success had a simple, solid basis: logical thinking combined with a knowledge of chemistry.
• **How might knowledge of chemistry help a detective?** (Students should suggest that by knowing chemistry, the detective can

analyze blood samples, liquids, or other forms of evidence found at the scene of the crime.)
• **How does it help the detective to know what a substance contains?** (The detective would know if the substance could have been used in the crime.)

Point out that all substances contain combinations of atoms or molecules.
• **Could the way certain atoms or molecules combine make a difference in the substance formed?** (Yes.)

Explain that author Sir Arthur Conan

Mixtures, Elements, and Compounds

Guide for Reading

After you read the following sections, you will be able to

3–1 Classes of Matter
- Describe how matter is classified according to its makeup.

3–2 Mixtures
- List the different kinds of mixtures.
- Compare the properties of solutions with the properties of other mixtures.

3–3 Elements
- Explain why elements are considered pure substances.

3–4 Compounds
- Explain why compounds are considered pure substances.
- Describe how chemical symbols, formulas, and balanced equations are used to describe a chemical reaction.

A reddish stain on a scrap of fabric . . . some bits of dust gathered in the creases of a man's clothing . . . a seemingly unimportant clump of mud in the corner of a room . . . a few pieces of pipe tobacco found at the murder scene . . . What could all these details mean? To detective Sherlock Holmes, the creation of British author Arthur Conan Doyle, they were clues to the most mysterious crimes imaginable. By paying close attention to the evidence, Holmes was able to solve many perplexing crimes. And in so doing, he amazed not only the London police but also his own assistant, Dr. Watson.

Holmes's success had a simple, solid basis: logical thinking combined with a knowledge of chemistry. Using this knowledge, he was able to classify and analyze various substances that were clues to the mysteries. Holmes was a master at using scientific principles to solve crimes.

The whole world is a place of mystery, filled with puzzles and wonders that await the investigation of detectives like you. But before you set out on your adventure, you will need to know how chemical substances are classified. And soon you will share the delight of Holmes, who exclaimed at moments of discovery, "By Jove, Watson, I've got it!"

Journal *Activity*

You and Your World   Detectives often use the scientific method to solve crimes. Pretend that you are a detective who has been asked to solve the theft of cookies from a jar in the student cafeteria. There are many suspects. Write down the method you would use to solve this "terrible" crime.

Basil Rathbone played Sherlock Holmes in a series of movies that detailed the exploits of the great fictional detective.

Doyle practiced medicine when he first started writing, but he abandoned his practice after his books became successful.
- **How might Doyle's medical knowledge have helped him successfully write detective stories?** (He could use his knowledge to create medical-related clues.)

Doyle wrote 68 stories featuring Sherlock Holmes. The series of Sherlock Holmes movies were based on these stories. Doyle also wrote books on spiritualism, poems, plays, and an autobiography. Tiring of writing stories about Holmes,

Doyle tries killing him off in an 1893 story. Popular demand led to the reincarnation of Holmes in the 1904 story "The Return of Sherlock Holmes."

---

through cracks in a basement wall or foundation, water supplies, or the materials the building itself is composed of.

Because the risk of radon contamination exists everywhere, many homeowners are testing their homes. The charcoal canister test exposes activated carbon for three to seven days to the test area. The radon daughters collected are then analyzed and measured. The alpha-track detector test exposes plastic film sensitive to alpha radiation (a product of radioactive decay) for one to three months in the test area. The film is then analyzed, and the radiation present is measured. A third option is to have professional computer-based testing done. When high levels of radon are present, homeowners can reduce or eliminate the contamination by improving ventilation, reducing dust and smoke to which radon daughters attach themselves, and sealing leaks and cracks in basements.

Cooperative learning: Using preassigned lab groups or randomly selected teams, have groups complete one of the following assignments:
• Write a soap-opera script for a series of five episodes on the experiences of a family exposed to radon. Have each group present one or more episodes.
• Prepare a public-service campaign that provides information on all aspects of radon. The following media can be used: radio or TV, newspapers or magazines, billboard, or pamphlet.

See Cooperative Learning in the *Teacher's Desk Reference.*

JOURNAL ACTIVITY

Before students begin the Journal Activity, initiate a discussion on what the scientific method is. Then lead students to understand what the basic steps of the scientific method are. After students have completed the Journal Activity, have them give examples from their writing of each of the basic steps. Stress the importance of knowing science as an aid in solving crimes. Students should be instructed to place their Journal Activity in their portfolio.

3-1 Classes of Matter

Have students brainstorm examples of things that they organize or classify in their lives. They may have their record albums classified by type of music. Most likely their clothing is classified and put away in different places by type and function. What are some other examples?

ESL STRATEGY 3-1

To help students compare the four phases of matter and the four classes of matter (according to makeup), ask them to make a chart using the headings Phases and Classes. Dictate the following terms and ask students to write them under the proper heading:

solid solutions elements liquid
gas plasma mixtures compounds

Have students give two reasons why classifying matter according to phase can be confusing.

Guide for Reading

Focus on this question as you read.

▶ How is matter classified according to makeup?

Figure 3-1 *It is much easier to select exactly what you want to purchase if articles are grouped together. The vegetables are classified by type; the wool, by color.*

58 ■ N

3-1 Classes of Matter

Have you ever collected rocks, stamps, or marbles? If so, you probably know how important it is to classify, or group, the objects in a collection. To do this, you might use characteristics such as color, shape, or texture. Or maybe you would classify the objects in a collection according to their uses. In any case, you would be using a classification system based on a particular property to group the objects.

Classification systems are used all the time to organize objects. Books in a library are arranged in an organized manner. So too are the clothes in a department store and the food in a supermarket. Next time you are in a record store, notice how the records and tapes have been organized.

You can see how classifying objects—whether they be collections, books, foods, or tapes—makes it easier for you to organize them (and to locate a particular item). In order to make the study of matter easier to understand, scientists have developed different ways to classify matter. In Chapter 2, you learned that matter exists in four phases: solid, liquid, gas, and plasma. Phases are one way to classify matter.

But classifying matter by phase is not specific enough and can lead to confusion. One kind of substance can exist in more than one phase. Water is a good example. Water can be a solid in the form of ice, a liquid, or a gas in the form of water vapor. How, then, would you classify water? ❶

TEACHING STRATEGY 3-1

FOCUS/MOTIVATION

Before class begins, collect a group of easily available objects such as various types of pens, pencils, color markers, pieces of chalk, erasers, paper clips, tapes, clips, small pieces of wood, books, notebooks, and marbles. Spread them out in a random manner on a flat surface. Discuss the characteristics of the objects, such as color, shape, and function, and so on. Then ask a volunteer to come to the front of the class and show one way of how these objects might be classified. You

might want to point out that to classify objects one has to organize them according to one or more characteristics the objects have in common. Encourage other volunteers to suggest alternative ways of classifying the objects.

CONTENT DEVELOPMENT

Point out to students that everything in the universe is composed of matter and that scientists use classification systems to create order so that they can study the matter.

• **What are some examples of how a chemist might want to classify matter?** (Answers will vary. According to gases, solids, liquids, plasma; according to types of gases, solids, and so on.)

ENRICHMENT

▶ *Activity Book*

Students can gain additional experience in classifying common objects by completing the Chapter 3 activity called Classifying Common Elements.

Classifying matter according to phase often groups very different substances together. Table salt, gold, steel, and sand are all solids. Although they are all solids, they differ from each other in many important ways. Should they be grouped together? What about water and gasoline, which are both clear liquids? In what ways do these two liquids differ?

In order to make the study of matter easier, scientists have used a classification system based on the makeup of matter. **According to makeup, matter exists as mixtures, solutions, elements, or compounds.**

Figure 3–2 *Although they are both clear liquids, gasoline and water differ from each other in important ways. Would this truck run well if water was put into the tank instead of gasoline or diesel fuel?* ②

3–1 Section Review

1. According to makeup, what are the four classes of matter?
2. Why is it more useful to classify matter according to makeup rather than according to phase?

Critical Thinking—*Applying Concepts*
3. A librarian wanted to save space, so he decided to classify books according to size. By putting all the small books together and all the large books together, he was able to fit more shelves in a bookcase. Soon, the number of readers using the library decreased dramatically. Why was this method of classification not appreciated by the readers?

FIND OUT BY
DOING

Classifying Common Objects

1. Obtain samples of the following materials: sugar, salt water, copper wire, taco shell, pencil eraser.
2. Observe each material. Describe its appearance in a few sentences.
3. Use simple physical tests to determine which of your samples are mixtures, solutions, elements, or compounds.
4. Present your observations in a chart.

FIND OUT BY DOING
CLASSIFYING COMMON OBJECTS

Skills: Gathering information, experimenting, stating a conclusion
Materials: sugar, salt, water, copper wire, taco shell, pencil eraser

After students have gathered the information, they should be able to think up simple physical tests they could conduct to determine which of the materials are mixtures, solutions, elements, or compounds.

INDEPENDENT PRACTICE

▶ *Activity Book*
Students who need practice in classifying should be provided with the Chapter 3 activity called A Classification Scheme.

REINFORCEMENT/RETEACHING

▶ *Activity Book*
Students who need additional practice in classifying matter should be given the Chapter 3 activity, Classifying Matter.

INDEPENDENT PRACTICE
Section Review 3–1
1. Mixtures, solutions, elements, and compounds.
2. Classifying matter according to phase often groups very different substances together; classifying matter according to makeup makes the study of matter easier.
3. It was not helpful in finding books by subject matter or author.

REINFORCEMENT/RETEACHING
Review students' responses to the Section Review questions. Reteach any material that is still unclear, based on their reponses.

CLOSURE
▶ *Review and Reinforcement Guide*
Students may now complete Section 3–1 in their *Review and Reinforcement Guide.*

3–2 Mixtures

MULTICULTURAL OPPORTUNITY 3–2

This section has many vocabulary words that might pose problems for students new to the language or with varying cultural backgrounds. Help students distinguish the scientific and common uses of such terms as heterogeneous, homogeneous, matter, mixture, and solution.

ESL STRATEGY 3–2

Have students use complete sentences to compare a heterogeneous mixture and a solution.

Verify that students understand the meaning of the verb *to dissolve*. Have them copy and match the words in Column A with the definitions in Column B.

A	B
Solutions	Substance that is dissolved
Solute	Substance that does the dissolving
Soluble	"Best mixed" of mixtures, that can exist as liquids, gases, or solids
Solvent	Substance that does not dissolve in water
Insoluble	Substance that dissolves in water

Figure 3–3 *Granite rock is made of the minerals quartz, feldspar, and mica. It is not a pure substance. Is granite a mixture? Why?* ❶

3–2 Mixtures

Look at the photograph of a piece of granite in Figure 3–3. Granite, which is a type of rock, is made of different minerals mixed together. You can see some of these minerals—quartz, mica, and feldspar—when you look at the granite. Sand is also ❶ made of different minerals mixed together. When you pick up a handful of sand, you see dark and light grains mixed together. Granite, sand, soil, concrete, and salad dressing are examples of matter that consists of several substances mixed together.

Matter that consists of two or more substances mixed together but not chemically combined is called a mixture. A **mixture** is a combination of substances. Each substance that makes up a mixture has its own specific properties and is the same throughout. But the mixture as a whole is not the same throughout. Let's go back to our example of granite. As you just read, granite is a mixture of minerals. The individual minerals in granite share the same properties. Every piece of quartz has the same properties as every other piece of quartz. This is true of mica and feldspar also.

Properties of Mixtures

The substances in a mixture are not chemically combined. The substances keep their separate identities and most of their own properties. This is an important property of mixtures. Think for a moment of a mixture of sugar and water. When sugar and water are mixed, the water is still a colorless liquid. The sugar still keeps its property of sweetness even though it is dissolved in the water. Although they may look identical, you can easily taste the difference between plain water and a sugar-water mixture.

Substances in a mixture may change in physical appearance, as when they dissolve. Some physical properties of the mixture, such as its melting point and boiling point, may also change. But the substances do not change in chemical composition. In the sugar-water mixture, the same particles of water and sugar are present after the mixing as before it. No new chemical substances have been formed.

TEACHING STRATEGY 3–2

FOCUS/MOTIVATION

Obtain several pieces of granite ahead of class time. Pass them around the classroom for students to observe.

• **What do you see in the granite?** (Small pieces of different-colored rock.)

Point out that the lighter parts in the rocks are probably quartz; the orange-colored parts, feldspar; and the darker parts, mica.

Point out that all these different-colored parts are minerals and that if they were separated, each would retain its individual properties.

CONTENT DEVELOPMENT

Ask students to study the photograph of the superburger on page 61.

• **Could you separate the superburger into substances as you could a complex cereal mixture?** (Yes, because it is made up of a mixture of substances.)

Point out that many of the substances that they see in the photograph are themselves combinations of substances.

• **What substance is itself a combination of substances?** (Most students will identify the meat as a combination of beef and spices; pickle relish as a combination of cucumbers, peppers, and spices; ketchup as a combination of tomatoes, water, and spices.)

Explain that mixtures are made of materials that are combined physically. A mixture consists of two or more substances that are mixed but not chemically com-

If you eat cereal for breakfast, you are probably making a mixture. That is what you produce when you pour milk over the cereal. And if you put berries, banana slices, or raisins into your cereal, you make an even more complex mixture. But you do not use exactly the same amounts of cereal, milk, and fruit each time. This illustrates another property of mixtures.

The substances that make up a mixture can be present in any amount. The amounts are not fixed. A salt-and-pepper mixture, for example, may be one-third salt and two-thirds pepper, or one-half salt and one-half pepper. You can mix lots of sugar or only a little in a glass of iced tea. But in both cases, the mixture is still iced tea.

Because the substances in a mixture retain their original properties, they can be separated out by simple physical means. Look at Figure 3–4. A mixture of powdered iron and powdered sulfur has been made. The particles of iron are black, and the particles of sulfur are yellow. The mixture of the two has a grayish color. If you look closely at the mixture, however, you will see that particles of iron and particles of sulfur are clearly visible. You can separate the particles that make up this mixture in a rather simple way. Because iron is attracted to a magnet and sulfur is not, iron can be separated from the sulfur by holding a strong magnet near the mixture. The particles of iron can be removed from the mixture by simple

Figure 3–4 By combining powdered iron (top) with powdered sulfur (center), an iron-sulfur mixture is formed. What physical property of iron is being used to separate the mixture (bottom)? ❷

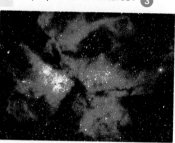

Figure 3–5 Black sand on a Hawaiian beach, a superburger, and a nebula far from Earth are all mixtures. What are some properties of mixtures? ❸

N ■ 61

bined. Each substance in a mixture has its own specific properties. No new substance is formed when a mixture is made.

The amounts of the substances that make a mixture are not fixed; any amount of one substance can be added to any amount of another substance.

● ● ● ● **Integration** ● ● ● ●

Use the text discussion on granite to integrate earth science topics into your lesson.

GUIDED PRACTICE
Skills Development
Skill: Relating facts

Relate this activity to the textbook discussion on the mixture of sugar and water.

Divide the class into groups of four to six students. Give each group a beaker of water and some sugar. Have students dissolve 5 mL of sugar in the water at a time. Have them taste the liquid after each addition.

• **What did you observe?** (The mixtures were sweet and wet. They became sweeter as more sugar was added. Different amounts of sugar can be mixed with the water to form mixtures.)

ANNOTATION KEY

Answers

❶ Yes. It is a combination of minerals. (Relating facts)

❷ Magnetic attraction. (Inferring)

❸ Substances in a mixture keep their own properties, but they may change in physical appearance. (Relating facts)

Integration

❶ Earth Science: Geology. See *Dynamic Earth,* Chapter 4.

HISTORICAL NOTE
ARE THE PYRAMIDS A MIXTURE?

For many years, anthropologists and historians believed that the Egyptian pyramids were build by thousands of slaves. Supposedly, they cut each stone miles away at a quarry and dragged it somehow to the building site. There they pulled up each stone on large ramps to its intended place in the pyramid.

Joseph Davidovits, a chemist at Barry University, believes the blocks from which the pyramids are built were cast rather than cut. According to his theory, workers ground up stone at a faraway quarry, brought the ground-up limestone to the building site, mixed the limestone with water, and poured the mixture into molds with a chemical hardener.

Paint is a familiar fluid used by artists. Paint is usually a mixture of a liquid and a finely powdered pigment.

Sometimes the liquid in paint is only a wetting agent (such as water or thinner) used to make the pigment brushable. The liquid evaporates, and the dried pigment remains as a pure substance on the painted surface. Watercolors and tempera are usually mixed only with a wetting agent. Although this kind of paint sometimes looks homogeneous, it is really a heterogeneous mixture.

Sometimes the liquid in paint is a wetting agent plus other liquid chemicals that cause the dry paint to have a hard, shiny surface. The liquid part of the paint is usually a homogeneous solution. When the pigment is added, the paint becomes a heterogeneous mixture that can look as if it were homogeneous. An example of this kind of paint is artists' oil paints, a combination of linseed oil and solvent in solution added to a powdered pigment. When the wetting agent evaporates, the surface contains a heterogeneous mixture of pigment and a dull or shiny hardening substance.

physical means—in this case, a magnet can be used to separate the iron from the sulfur.

The methods used to separate substances in a mixture are based on the physical properties of the substances that make up the mixture. No chemical reactions are involved. What physical property of iron made it possible to separate it from sulfur in the sulfur-iron mixture? What are some other physical properties that can be used to separate the substances that make up a mixture? For example, how could you separate a mixture of sugar and water? ❶

Types of Mixtures

You now know that granite is a mixture. Other mixtures include concrete and stainless steel. Concrete is a mixture of pieces of rock, sand, and cement. Stainless steel is a mixture of chromium and iron. (You might be interested to learn that stainless steel does "stain," or rust. However, it "stains less" than regular steel—hence, its name.) From your experience, you would probably say that stainless steel seems "better mixed" than concrete. You cannot see individual particles of chromium and iron in stainless steel, but particles of rock, sand, and cement are visible in concrete. Mixtures are classified according to how "well mixed" they are.

Figure 3–6 *This gold miner in Finland is separating heavy pieces of gold from lighter pieces of rock, sand, and soil by swirling the mixture in a shallow pan of water. The gold will settle to the bottom of the pan. Salt water is a mixture of salts and water. When the water evaporates, deposits of salt, such as these in Mono Lake, California, are left behind.*

62 ■ N

3–2 (continued)

CONTENT DEVELOPMENT

Point out that all mixtures can be separated because they are two or more substances that are physically, not chemically, combined. Mixtures can be in any of the four phases. When a mixture is separated, each substance in the mixture retains its own properties.

Tell students that the methods most commonly used for separation of mixtures are filtration and evaporation. Point out that if metallic iron is involved, separation can be done with a magnet.

● ● ● ● **Integration** ● ● ● ●

Use the discussion on gold and salt water to integrate the concept of mixtures with Earth science.

GUIDED PRACTICE

Skills Development
Skill: Applying concepts

Divide the class into groups of four to six students. Give each group three small beakers, a magnifying glass, filters, a magnet, water, and small amounts of sand,

salt, and metal filings. Tell the groups to make the following mixtures: sand and water; salt and water; and sand, salt, and metal filings. Have them determine how to separate the mixtures. Discuss the findings.

● **What was the best method to separate the sand from the water?** (Filtration.)

● **How was the salt separated from the water?** (Evaporation.)

● **How were the sand, salt, and metal filings separated?** (A magnet was used to remove the filings; water was added to al-

HETEROGENEOUS MIXTURE A mixture that does not appear to be the same throughout is said to be heterogeneous. A **heterogeneous** (heht-er-oh-JEE-nee-uhs) **mixture** is the "least mixed" of mixtures. The particles in a heterogeneous mixture are large enough to be seen and to separate from the mixture. Concrete is an example of a heterogeneous mixture. Can you think of some other examples? ②

Not all heterogeneous mixtures contain only solid particles (as does concrete). Shake up some pebbles or sand in water to make a liquid-solid mixture. This mixture is easily separated just by letting it stand. The pebbles and sand will settle to the bottom of the jar. Oil and vinegar, often used as a salad dressing, make up a liquid-liquid heterogeneous mixture. When the mixture has been shaken well, drops of oil are spread throughout the vinegar. This mixture, too, will separate when allowed to stand. Now you know why you have to shake a bottle of salad dressing that has not been used for a while.

HOMOGENEOUS MIXTURE A mixture that appears to be the same throughout is said to be homogeneous (hoh-moh-JEE-nee-uhs). A **homogeneous mixture** is "well mixed." The particles that make up the mixture are very small and not easily recognizable. These particles do not settle when the mixture is allowed to stand. Stainless steel is a homogeneous mixture.

Although you may not be aware of it, many of the materials you use and eat every day are homogeneous mixtures. Milk, whipped cream, toothpaste, and suntan lotion are just a few examples. In these homogeneous mixtures, the particles are mixed together but not dissolved. As a group, these mixtures are called **colloids** (KAHL-oidz).

The particles in a colloid are relatively large in size and are kept permanently suspended. They are also continuously bombarded by other particles. This bombardment accounts for two important properties of a colloid. One property is that a colloid will not separate upon standing (as do many heterogeneous mixtures). Because the particles are constantly bombarded, they do not have a chance to settle out. Another property is that a colloid often appears cloudy. This is because the constant bombardment of particles

Figure 3–7 *Tacos are heterogeneous mixtures in which the parts are easy to recognize and to separate from the mixture.*

FIND OUT BY
READING

Danger in the Air

Fog, a colloid you are probably familiar with, forms when tiny droplets of water become suspended in air. Drive along a fog-shrouded road and you will soon realize how dangerous fog can be. On a clear day, you can see forever; on a foggy day, however, your car's headlights offer scant help in piercing the gloom. ③

You might like to find out about the poet Carl Sandburg's impressions of this common colloid by reading his poem "Fog."

FIND OUT BY DOING

DANGER IN THE AIR

Skill: Reading comprehension

You might check students' understanding of the poem and discuss Sandburg's perception of fog versus a scientist's perception. You may want to alert the language arts teacher of this assignment and have the teacher discuss some of Sandburg's other poems.

Integration: Use the Find Out by Reading feature to integrate language arts skills into your science lesson.

---

low the salt to mix with the water; the sand was filtered out; the salt was separated from the water by allowing the water to evaporate.)

CONTENT DEVELOPMENT

Explain that mixtures are classified into two types: those that separate easily and those that do not separate easily. Point out that mixtures separate differently because of the size of their particles. Tell students that the two types of mixtures are heterogeneous and homogeneous.

Have students study Figure 3–6 and Figure 3–7.

• **What are the differences between the tacos as a heterogeneous mixture and the soil–water mixture?** (Most of the ingredients can easily be taken off the tacos, whereas some of the soil seems to be well mixed with the water.)

Explain that when soil is mixed with water, the particles of soil slowly settle to the bottom. The particles of soil are made of groups of molecules.

A mixture in which the substances will settle out is known as a suspension.

● ● ● ● **Integration** ● ● ● ●

Discuss oil and vinegar in salad dressing as a liquid-liquid heterogeneous mixture to integrate food science into the discussion.

TYNDALL EFFECT

In 1869, John Tyndall, an Irish physicist, noted that molecules of colloids scatter light. He also noted that light of short-wave length is more efficiently scattered than light of long-wave length. This "Tyndall effect" helps explain that the sky is blue because of the scattering effect of dust particles in the atmosphere on the short-wave sunlight. At sunset, when light passes through a greater thickness of atmosphere that is dusty from the day's activity, light is scattered, and only the red and orange are left. As a result of this effect, we have beautiful sunsets on Earth.

Figure 3–8 *A gelatin desert is a colloid that contains liquid particles mixed with a solid. Whipped cream is a colloid that contains gas particles in a liquid. The smoke from a campfire is a colloid that contains solid particles mixed in a gas.*

enables a colloid to scatter light. So if a beam of light is passed through a colloid, the beam becomes visible. The white cloudy appearance of milk is due to the scattering of light by the bombarding particles in this familiar colloid. If you have ever seen a searchlight sweep through the air at night, you have observed another example of this property of colloids. Figure 3–9 is a table of several different types of colloids. Which ones are you familiar with? ❶

Solutions

A solution (suh-LOO-shuhn) is a type of homogeneous mixture formed when one substance dissolves in another. You might say that a **solution** is the "best mixed" of all mixtures. You are probably familiar with many different solutions. Ocean water is one example. In this solution, different salts are dissolved in water. Another example of a solution is antifreeze. Lemonade and tea are also solutions. One important solution helps keep you alive. Do you know what it is? Air is a solution of oxygen and other gases dissolved in nitrogen.

All solutions have several important properties. Picture a glass of lemonade as you read about them. How do you think the lemonade was made? Lemon juice and sugar were probably added to water. They dissolved in the water. A solution always has a substance that is dissolved and a substance that does the dissolving. The substance that is dissolved is called the **solute** (SAHL-yoot). The substance that does the dissolving is called the **solvent** (SAHL-vuhnt). In the case of the lemonade, there are two solutes: lemon juice and sugar. The solvent is water.

Figure 3–9 *You might be surprised to learn how many commonly used materials are colloids. What type of colloid is mayonnaise? Butter?* ❷

TYPES OF COLLOIDS

Name	Example
Fog (liquid in gas)	Clouds
Smoke (solid in gas)	Smoke
Foam (gas in liquid)	Whipped cream
Emulsion (liquid in liquid)	Mayonnaise
Sol (solid in liquid)	Paint
Gel (liquid in solid)	Butter

64 ■ N

3–2 (continued)

CONTENT DEVELOPMENT

Initiate a discussion on colloids.
• **What are two important properties of colloids?** (Colloids will not separate when standing. They are cloudy.)
• **Is chocolate milk a colloid?** (Yes.)
• **What type of colloid is air polluted by gasoline emissions?** (Solid in gas.)
• **What types of colloids are mustard and ketchup?** (Solid in liquid.)

● ● ● ● **Integration** ● ● ● ●
Use the discussion on colloids to integrate the importance of the study of mixtures with food science.

CONTENT DEVELOPMENT

Emphasize that a solution is the best mixed of all mixtures. One of the substances in a solution is dissolved in another substance. Point out that a solution can be a solid, such as sugar dissolved in a liquid such as water. It can be a gas dis-

solved in a liquid, a liquid dissolved in a liquid, or a gas dissolved in a gas.

Refer to the textbook discussion to point out that the substance that is dissolved is called the solute and the substance that is dissolving is called the solvent.
• **Which do you think contains more solute, a glass of very sweet lemonade or a glass of barely sweet lemonade? Why?** (A glass of very sweet lemonade. The sweeter lemonade contains more sugar, which is one of the solutes.)

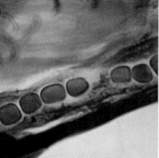

Looking at the glass of lemonade, you will notice that the particles are not large enough to be seen. Because the particles in a solution are so small, most solutions cannot easily be separated by simple physical means. Unlike many colloids, liquid solutions appear clear and transparent. The particles in a liquid solution are too small to scatter light.

Tasting the lemonade illustrates another property of a solution. Every part of the solution tastes the same. This might lead you to believe that one property of a solution is that its particles are evenly spread out. And you would be right!

There are nine possible types of solutions, as you can see from Figure 3–12 on page 66. Many liquid solutions contain water as the solvent. Ocean water is basically a water solution that contains many salts. Body fluids are also water solutions. Because water can dissolve many substances, it is called the "universal solvent."

Figure 3–10 *Solutions are the "best mixed" of all mixtures. Seawater, blood, and lava from an erupting volcano are all solutions. What other common solutions can you name?* ③

Figure 3–11 *You can form three kinds of solutions using a liquid solvent. Name a common solution that is a solid dissolved in a liquid. A liquid dissolved in a liquid. A gas dissolved in a liquid.*

Solid solute

Liquid solute

Gas solute

Liquid solvent (water)

Liquid solvent (water)

Liquid solvent (water)

ECOLOGY NOTE
WATER TREATMENT

Most of the water that people use in their homes for drinking, cooking, and washing comes from lakes and rivers. This water is treated before and after it is used in most of the wealthy, industrialized countries of the world.

In some areas where there is a shortage of potable water, seawater is being desalinized. Desalination is a simple but expensive process. It takes place in huge plants, where seawater is heated until it evaporates. The vapor formed through evaporation is condensed back into liquid water by passing it over pipes that hold cold water.

• **Ketchup is prepared by crushing tomatoes, spices, and sugar and suspending them in water and vinegar. Based on what you know about solutes and solvents, why is ketchup not a solution?** (It does not have a solute. The ground-up tomatoes and spices do not dissolve.)

● ● ● ● **Integration** ● ● ● ●

Use the discussion of ocean water mixtures to integrate oceanography into your lesson.

GUIDED PRACTICE

Skills Development
Skill: Classifying matter

Have students look around the classroom and list the different mixtures they observe. (Additional mixtures might be observed at home.) Each material should be discussed and analyzed carefully to determine whether it is homogeneous, heterogeneous, a pure substance, a mixture, and/or a solution. Many substances may be listed, but the following will be helpful:

Plaster: homogeneous solid mixture
Tap water: homogeneous liquid mixture (contains some dirt particles)
Distilled water: homogeneous pure substance
Wood: heterogeneous solid mixture
Metal: homogeneous pure substance or homogeneous solution if an alloy
Glass: homogeneous solid mixture
Pure air: homogeneous gas solution of nitrogen, oxygen, water vapor, and the like
Regular air (with dust): homogeneous mixture

OIL POLLUTION

Water and oil do not mix. When an oil carrier breaks apart and spills its cargo into the ocean, the ecosystem along nearby coastlines is seriously damaged. Because oil rises to the surface of water, it has an effect on animal and plant life in the ocean that are dependent on it. The oil clings to animals such as birds and seals, and because it does not dissolve in water, it eventually leads to their deaths. Spilled oil has dirtied many beaches and is a serious long-term threat along all coastlines in the world.

FIND OUT BY DOING

IS IT A SOLUTION?

Discovery Learning

Skills: Making observations, making comparisons, forming conclusions, applying concepts

Materials: 8 glasses of water, sugar, flour, powdered drink, cornstarch, instant coffee, talcum powder, soap powder, gelatin

Students could do this simple activity at home or in the classroom. They will learn that some household substances, such as sugar and instant coffee, are very soluble in water, whereas others, such as flour and powdered milk, have low solubility. With water, the sugar, powdered drink, instant coffee, and gelatin form true solutions.

Figure 3–12 *Nine different types of solutions can be made from three phases of matter. Can most solutions be separated by simple physical means? Explain.* ❶

TYPES OF SOLUTIONS

Solute	Solvent	Example
Gas	Gas	Air (oxygen in nitrogen)
Gas	Liquid	Soda water (carbon dioxide in water)
Gas	Solid	Charcoal gas mask (poisonous gases on carbon)
Liquid	Gas	Humid air (water in air)
Liquid	Liquid	Antifreeze (ethylene glycol in water)
Liquid	Solid	Dental filling (mercury in silver)
Solid	Gas	Soot in air (carbon in air)
Solid	Liquid	Ocean water (salt in water)
Solid	Solid	Gold jewelry (copper in gold)

FIND OUT BY DOING

Is It a Solution?

1. Obtain samples of the following substances: sugar, flour, powdered drink, cornstarch, instant coffee, talcum powder, soap powder, gelatin.

2. Crush each substance into pieces of equal size. Make sure you keep the substances separate.

3. Determine how much of each substance you can dissolve in samples of the same amount of water at the same temperature. Determine how quickly each substance dissolves.

4. Determine which substances dissolved fastest and to the greatest extent. Record your findings in a data table.

■ Use your knowledge of the properties of solutions to determine which substances formed true solutions.

SOLUBILITY A substance that dissolves in water is said to be **soluble** (SAHL-yoo-buhl). Salt and sugar are soluble substances. Mercury and oil do not dissolve in water. They are **insoluble.**

The amount of a solute that can be completely dissolved in a given amount of solvent at a specific temperature is called its **solubility.** What is the relationship between temperature and the solubility of solid solutes? In general, as the temperature of a solvent increases, the solubility of the solute increases. What about gaseous solutes? An increase in the temperature of the solvent usually decreases the solubility of a gaseous solute. This explains why soda that warms up goes flat. The "fizz" of soda is due to bubbles of carbon dioxide dissolved in the solution. As soda warms, the dissolved CO_2 comes out of solution. It is less soluble. Without the CO_2, the soda tastes flat.

Some substances are not very soluble in water. But they dissolve easily in other solvents. For example, one of the reasons you use soap to wash dirt and grease from your skin or clothing is that soap dissolves these substances, whereas water alone does not. The soap dissolves the grease and then, along with the grease, it is washed away by the water.

ALLOYS Not all solutions are liquids. Solutions can exist in any of the three phases—solid, liquid, or gas—as the table in Figure 3–12 indicates. Metal solutions called **alloys** are examples of solids dissolved in solids. Gold jewelry is actually a solid solution of gold and copper. Brass is an alloy of copper and zinc.

3–2 (continued)

CONTENT DEVELOPMENT

Tell students that a substance that dissolves in another substance is said to be soluble. If a substance does not dissolve in another substance, it is said to be insoluble. Point out that water is the most commonly used solvent and is thought of as the "universal solvent."

• **What solvents can you think of besides water that are used around the home?**

(Answers will vary but may include the following examples: paint thinner, nail polish remover.)

Point out to students that the amount of solute that will completely dissolve in a given amount of solvent at a specific temperature is called solubility. Explain that as the temperature of a solvent increases, the solubility of the solute increases.

● ● ● ● **Integration** ● ● ● ●

Use the discussion on soda fizz to integrate food science into your discussion.

GUIDED PRACTICE

▶ *Laboratory Manual*
Skills Development
Skill: Applying concepts

To reinforce concepts of solubility, students may now complete the Chapter 3 Laboratory Investigation called Determining Solubility in the *Laboratory Manual.*

REINFORCEMENT/RETEACHING

▶ *Activity Book*
For additional experience in separating

Figure 3–13 *The important alloy stainless steel is a mixture of iron and chromium. Here it is being poured as a white-hot liquid from a vat. What type of mixture is stainless steel?* ❷

Sterling silver contains small amounts of copper in solution with silver. And stainless steel, which you read about before, is an alloy of chromium and iron. You may find it interesting to learn about the make-up of other alloys, such as pewter, bronze, and solder. How do you think alloys are made? ❸

3–2 Section Review

1. What is a mixture? What are three properties of a mixture?
2. How does a heterogeneous mixture differ from a homogeneous mixture?
3. What is a colloid?
4. What is a solution? What are the two parts of a solution? What are two properties of a solution?

Connection—*Making Predictions*

5. Trout are fish that need to live in water that has a great deal of oxygen dissolved in it. What can you predict about the temperature of the water in a trout stream? Explain your answer. The correct answer may improve your luck the next time you go fishing!

FIND OUT BY
DOING

Where's the Fizz?

You can determine what conditions affect the solubility of a gas in a liquid.

1. Remove the cap from a bottle of soda.

2. Immediately fit the opening of a balloon over the top of the bottle. Shake the bottle several times. Note any changes in the balloon.

3. Heat the bottle of soda very gently by placing it in a pan of hot water. Note any further changes in the balloon.

What two conditions of solubility are being tested here?

■ What general statement about the solubility of a gas in a liquid can you now make?

FIND OUT BY
DOING

WHERE IS THE FIZZ?

Discovery Learning

Skills: Making observations, comparing occurrences, relating concepts, hypothesizing, drawing conclusions

Materials: bottle of soda, balloon, pan, hot plate or Bunsen burner

In this activity students investigate the properties of gas in a liquid. Students should find that the balloon inflates when the liquid is heated. The two conditions being tested are pressure and temperature. Students should conclude that the solubility of a gas in a liquid decreases with a decrease in pressure and with an increase in temperature.

mixtures, have students complete the chapter activity called Separating Substances in the *Activity Book.*

INDEPENDENT PRACTICE
Section Review 3–2

1. A combination of two or more substances that are mixed together but not chemically combined.

2. A heterogeneous mixture has large particles and does not appear to be the same throughout. A homogeneous mixture has small particles that are well blended and is said to be the same throughout.

3. A homogeneous mixture that is often cloudy in which the particles are mixed together but not dissolved and are permanently suspended.

4. A type of homogeneous mixture formed when one substance dissolves in another. Two parts of a solution are the solute and the solvent. Two properties of a solution are that its particles are so small they cannot be seen and that most particles in it are not easily separated by simple physical means.

5. To have a lot of oxygen, the trout stream should be cold.

REINFORCEMENT/RETEACHING

Review students' responses to the Section Review questions. Reteach any material that is still unclear.

CLOSURE

▶ *Review and Reinforcement Guide*
Students may now complete Section 3–2 in their *Review and Reinforcement Guide.*

3-3 Elements

Have students research the history of the discovery of some of the elements. Which cultures played an important role in the discovery of the elements? Students may find the work of Andres Manuel del Rio (1764–1849) to be of interest. Del Rio, Spanish by birth, spent most of his life working in Mexico City. In 1801, he discovered what was thought to be a new element, which he named erythonium. Most scientists, however, felt that the new element was really chromium, so Del Rio abandoned his claim to the discovery. Several years later, N. G. Sefström discovered an element, which he named vanadium. This was shown to be identical to Del Rio's erythonium.

Ask students to compare in writing a pure substance with a mixture. Suggest that they use the following words as they write their comparisons: material(s), properties, elements, atom, substances, identities, amount, and physical means. Ask for volunteers to write these words on the board. Suggest that students read aloud their comparisons and discuss them in class.

In the Earth's crust, oceans, and atmosphere are found 92 elements. These elements are known as the "natural" elements. Only 8 of these are found in the Earth's crust. Oxygen makes up nearly 50 percent and silicon about 25 percent. Aluminum, iron, calcium, magnesium, sodium, potassium, and titanium together make up 24 percent. Carbon, which is fundamental to all living things, is present in amounts less than 0.1 percent.

PROBLEM Solving

What's the Solution?

Look closely at the four photographs below. Each shows a familiar solution. For each photograph, tell what solute is dissolved in what solvent. List other solutions that are similar to the solutions shown. Use Figure 3–12 to help you. Solve this problem and you are part of the solution!

Guide for Reading

Focus on this question as you read.

▶ *What are the simplest pure substances?*

3-3 Elements

Scientists often examine, in great detail, the particles that make up a substance. Close observation shows that in some cases all the particles that make up a substance are alike; in other cases, all the particles are not alike. When all the particles are alike, the substance is called a **pure substance.** A pure substance is made of only one kind of material and has definite properties. A pure substance is the same throughout. All the particles in a pure substance are exactly the same. Iron, aluminum, water, sugar, and table salt are examples of pure substances. So is the oxygen your body uses from the air you breathe. A sample taken from any of these substances is identical to any other sample taken from that substance. For instance, a drop of pure water taken from a well in Arizona, a river in Australia, or the hard-packed snow and ice of Antarctica is the same.

Elements are the simplest pure substance. An **element** cannot be changed into a simpler substance by heating or by any chemical process. The particles that make up an element are in their simplest form. (You will learn just what these particles are in the next paragraph.) Suppose you melt a piece of iron by adding heat energy to it. You may think that you have changed the iron into a simpler substance. But the liquid iron you now have still contains only iron particles. True, the heat has changed the iron's phase—from a solid to a liquid. But it is still iron. No new or simpler substance has been formed.

Elements and Atoms

The smallest particle of an element that has the properties of that element is called an **atom.** An atom is the basic building block of matter. All elements are made of atoms. Atoms of the same element are alike. Atoms of different elements are different.

Scientists now know that an atom is made of even smaller particles. These particles, however, do not have the properties of the elements they make up. You will learn more about the particles that make up atoms in Chapter 4.

Chemical Symbols

For many years, scientists had to spell out the full names of elements when writing about them. As you can imagine, this practice was time consuming. Then in 1813, a system of representing the elements with symbols was introduced. After all, why couldn't chemists do what mathematicians and musicians had been doing for years?

Figure 3–14 *This miner examines a rock specimen closely because if he is lucky, the rocks he mines will contain the element gold.*

Ask students to study Figure 3–14.
• **Is the gold in this rock and the bullion an example of a pure substance? Why?** (Yes. It is the same throughout.)

Point out some of the items in your collection or elsewhere in the classroom that are pure substances.

Tell students that elements are the simplest type of pure substances.
• **Suppose you melt a piece of gold so that it becomes a liquid. Have you changed it into a simpler form?** (No, an element cannot be changed.)

Initiate discussion about elements and atoms.
• **What do elements and atoms of any one substance have in common?** (They have the same properties.)
• **Why do you think atoms are considered the basic building blocks of matter?** (They are the smallest particles of elements that have their properties.)
• **Is an atom the smallest particle there is?** (No.)

HISTORICAL NOTE
DISCOVERY OF ELEMENTS

A few elements, such as gold, silver, copper, and sulfur, were known in ancient times. During the Middle Ages and the Renaissance, more elements were discovered. By the time Dmitri Mendeleev developed his periodic table, 63 elements were known. Today the number of natural elements totals 92, and since 1940, 17 more elements have been produced synthetically.

3–3 (continued)

CONTENT DEVELOPMENT

Tell students that like people, every element has its own special name.
• **What are some of the shorthand names (nicknames) of your friends?** (Accept all answers.)

Explain that the shorthand representation of an element is called symbol.
• **If the element's name is oxygen, what logical shorthand symbol would you use?** (Students should answer O.)
• **If the element's name is nitrogen, what logical shorthand symbol would you use?** (Students should answer N.)

Point out that scientists often use the Latin name of an element to create the symbol. Also point out that the symbols for some elements consist of two, not one, letters.

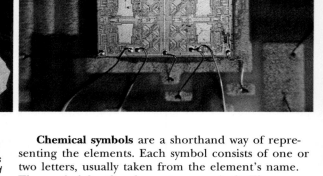

Figure 3–15 *Elements are the simplest type of pure substance. These yellow crystals are made of the element sulfur. Computer chips contain silicon. In what ways would our lives be different if there was no silicon on Earth?* ❶

Figure 3–16 *This table shows the chemical symbols for some of the most common elements. What is the symbol for tin? Why is Fe the symbol for iron?* ❷

Chemical symbols are a shorthand way of representing the elements. Each symbol consists of one or two letters, usually taken from the element's name. The symbol for the element oxygen is O. The symbol for hydrogen is H; for carbon, C. The symbol for aluminum is Al; and for chlorine, Cl. Two letters are needed for a chemical symbol when the first letter of that element's name has already been used as a symbol for another element. For example, the symbol for carbon is C, for calcium it is Ca, and for copper it is Cu. You should note that when two letters are used in a symbol, the first letter is always capitalized but the second letter is never capitalized.

What do you think the symbol for gold is? The symbol for gold is Au. Does that surprise you? Gold is not spelled with an "a" or a "u." But the reason for the symbol is really not so strange. The Latin

COMMON ELEMENTS

Name	Symbol	Name	Symbol	Name	Symbol
Aluminum	Al	Hydrogen	H	Oxygen	O
Bromine	Br	Iodine	I	Phosphorus	P
Calcium	Ca	Iron	Fe	Potassium	K
Carbon	C	Lead	Pb	Silicon	Si
Chlorine	Cl	Lithium	Li	Silver	Ag
Chromium	Cr	Magnesium	Mg	Sodium	Na
Copper	Cu	Mercury	Hg	Sulfur	S
Fluorine	F	Neon	Ne	Tin	Sn
Gold	Au	Nickel	Ni	Uranium	U
Helium	He	Nitrogen	N	Zinc	Zn

● ● ● ● **Integration** ● ● ● ●

Use the discussion on names of elements to integrate the language arts concept that many words in the English language, particularly in the sciences, are derived from Latin words.

GUIDED PRACTICE

Skills Development

Skill: Identifying relationships

Before class, make a chalkboard list of the following elements: oxygen, calcium, copper, carbon, hydrogen, chlorine, aluminum, nickel, and helium. Have students predict the symbol for each element. After students have listed their symbols, write the correct symbols on the chalkboard.

INDEPENDENT PRACTICE
Section Review 3–3

1. A pure substance is made of only one kind of material and has definite properties. Elements are made up of only one kind of atom that cannot be broken down

Figure 3–17 *The top four rows are symbols that were used by ancient alchemists to represent elements. The bottom three rows are part of the system developed by John Dalton. Do you think it would be easier to remember these symbols for the elements or the symbols shown in Figure 3–16?* ❸

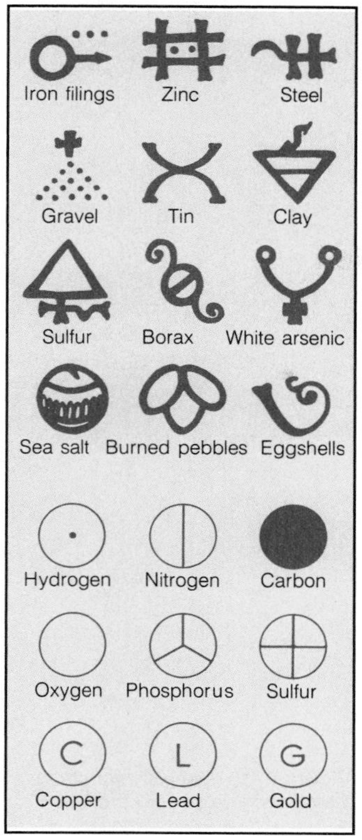

name for gold is *aurum*. Scientists often use the Latin name of an element as its symbol. Here are some other examples. The symbol used for silver is Ag, from the Latin word for silver, *argentum*. The Latin word for iron is *ferrum*, and the symbol for this element is Fe. The symbol for mercury is Hg, from the Latin name *hydrargyrum*. The table in Figure 3–16 lists some common elements and their symbols.

3–3 Section Review

1. What is a pure substance? Why are elements pure substances?
2. What is an atom? How do atoms of the same element compare? Of different elements?
3. Write the chemical symbols for oxygen, nitrogen, lead, sulfur, sodium, and helium.

Critical Thinking—*Relating Facts*

4. Why can elements be thought of as homogeneous matter?

3–4 Compounds

As you just learned, the simplest type of pure substance is an element. But not all pure substances are elements. Water and table salt, for example, are pure substances. Each is made of only one kind of material with definite properties. Yet water and table salt are not elements. Why? They can be broken down into simpler substances. Water can be broken down into the elements hydrogen and oxygen. Table salt can be broken down into the elements sodium and chlorine. Thus water and table salt, like many other pure substances, are made of more than one element.

Iron filings — Zinc — Steel
Gravel — Tin — Clay
Sulfur — Borax — White arsenic
Sea salt — Burned pebbles — Eggshells
Hydrogen — Nitrogen — Carbon
Oxygen — Phosphorus — Sulfur
Copper — Lead — Gold

Guide for Reading

Focus on this question as you read.

▶ *What is a compound?*

3–4 Compounds

MULTICULTURAL OPPORTUNITY 3–4

3–4 Compounds

MULTICULTURAL OPPORTUNITY 3–4

Percy Julian (1899–1975) was one of the nation's most distinguished chemists and is also an advocate for the recruitment of African-American scientists. His work in organic chemistry included the synthesis of physostigmine, a drug used in the treatment of glaucoma, and the invention of "aero-foam," a fire extinguisher derived from soybeans. In 1936, Julian was appointed as chief chemist at the Glidden Company, a significant acceptance for African-American chemists.

ESL STRATEGY 3–4

Write the numbered items on the chalkboard. Tell students to fill in the first blank in each item with the word that is logically related to the word before the colon. Ask students to complete the second blank, giving the reason for making the analogy.

1. Homogeneous:Heterogeneous
Soluble: _____
Reason: _____
2. Substances:Mixtures
Solute and solvent: _____
Reason: _____
3. Atom:Element
_____: Compound
Reason: _____
4. Words:Ideas
Chemical symbols: _____
Reason: _____

REINFORCEMENT/RETEACHING

Monitor students' responses to the Section Review questions. If students appear to have difficulty understanding any of the concepts, review this material with them.

CLOSURE

▶ *Review and Reinforcement Guide*

At this point have students complete Section 3–3 in their *Review and Reinforcement Guide.*

into simpler substances.
2. An atom is the smallest part of an element that has the properties of that element. Atoms of the same element are alike. Atoms of different elements are different.
3. O, N, Pb, S, Na, He.
4. Because they are the same throughout.

TEACHING STRATEGY 3–4

FOCUS/MOTIVATION

Hold up a clean, shiny iron nail and a rusty iron nail.
• **How are these nails alike? Different?** (Answers will vary, but likenesses will probably include solid and iron, whereas differences will include shiny/dull, rusty/smooth.)
• **What is under the rust?** (Pure iron.)
• **What do you think might have caused the rust?** (Answers will vary but may include materials or processes such as water, acid, other rust, chemicals, or weathering.)

Pure substances that are made of more than one element are called compounds. A **compound** is two or more elements chemically combined. Sugar is a compound that is made of the elements carbon, hydrogen, and oxygen. Carbon dioxide, ammonia, baking soda, and TNT are compounds. Can you name some other common compounds? ❶

Unlike elements, compounds can be broken down into simpler substances. Heating is one way to separate some compounds into their elements. The compound copper sulfide, which is also known as the ore chalcocite, can be separated into the elements copper and sulfur by heating it to a high temperature.

Electric energy is often used to break down compounds that do not separate upon heating. By passing an electric current through water, the elements hydrogen and oxygen can be obtained. What elements would you obtain if you passed an electric current through melted table salt? ❷

The properties of the elements that make up a compound are often quite different from the properties of the compound itself. Would you want to flavor your French-fried potatoes with a poisonous gas and a highly active metal? Yet, in a way, this is exactly what you are doing when you sprinkle salt on your potatoes. Chlorine is a yellow-green gas that is poisonous. Sodium is a silvery metal that explodes if placed in water. But when chemically combined, these elements produce a white compound—sodium chloride—that you cannot and probably would not want to live without. And it adds a tasty flavor to foods as well!

Figure 3–18 *The element sodium is often stored under kerosene because it reacts explosively when it comes into contact with water (left). The element chlorine is a poisonous gas (center). When sodium and chlorine combine, sodium chloride forms. What is the common name for sodium chloride?* ❸

Figure 3–19 *As you can see from this diagram, molecules are made of two or more elements chemically bonded together. What are the chemical formulas for these two compounds?* **4**

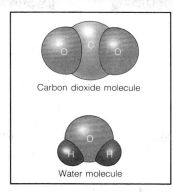

Carbon dioxide molecule

Water molecule

Compounds and Molecules

Most compounds are made of **molecules** (MAHL-ih-kyoolz). A molecule is made of two or more atoms chemically bonded together. A molecule is the smallest particle of a compound that has all the properties of that compound.

Water is a compound. A molecule of water is made up of 2 atoms of hydrogen chemically bonded to 1 atom of oxygen. One molecule of water has all of the properties of a glass of water, a bucket of water, or a pool of water. If a molecule of water were broken down into atoms of its elements, would the atoms have the same properties as the molecule? **5**

Just as all atoms of a certain element are alike, all molecules of a compound are alike. Each molecule of ammonia, for example, is like every other. Because it is made of only one kind of molecule, a compound is the same throughout. So compounds, like elements, are pure substances.

Chemical Formulas

You probably learned the alphabet before you learned to read. Well, you can think of chemical symbols as the letters of a chemical alphabet. Just as you learned to put letters together to make words, chemical symbols can be put together to make chemical "words." Combinations of chemical symbols are called **chemical formulas.** Chemical formulas are a shorthand way of representing chemical substances.

Most chemical formulas represent compounds. For example, ammonia is a compound made of the elements nitrogen (N) and hydrogen (H). The chemical formula for ammonia is NH_3. A molecule of ammonia contains 1 atom of nitrogen and 3 atoms of hydrogen. The formula for rubbing alcohol is C_3H_7OH. What elements make up this compound? How about the compound silver nitrate, $AgNO_3$? **6**

Sometimes a formula represents a molecule of an element, not a compound. For example, the symbol

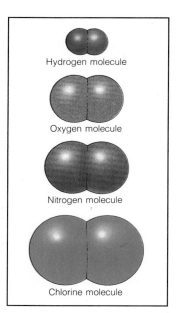

Figure 3–20 *Some elements are found in nature as molecules that are made of 2 atoms of that element. Hydrogen, oxygen, nitrogen, and chlorine are examples of such elements. What is the chemical formula for a molecule of each of these elements?* ❶

Hydrogen molecule

Oxygen molecule

Nitrogen molecule

Chlorine molecule

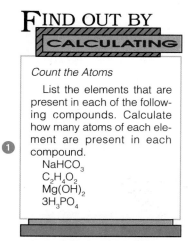

FIND OUT BY

CALCULATING

Count the Atoms

❶ List the elements that are present in each of the following compounds. Calculate how many atoms of each element are present in each compound.

$NaHCO_3$
$C_2H_4O_2$
$Mg(OH)_2$
$3H_3PO_4$

74 ■ N

for the element oxygen is O. But in nature, oxygen occurs as a molecule that contains 2 atoms of oxygen bonded together. So the formula for a molecule of oxygen is O_2. Some other gases that exist only in pairs of atoms are hydrogen, H_2, nitrogen, N_2, fluorine, F_2, and chlorine, Cl_2. Remember that the symbols for the elements just listed are the letters only. The formulas are the letters with the small number 2 at the lower right.

When writing a chemical formula, you use the symbol of each element in the compound. You also use small numbers, called **subscripts.** Subscripts are placed to the lower right of the symbols. A subscript gives the number of atoms of the element in the compound. When there is only 1 atom of an element, the subscript 1 is not written. It is understood to be 1.

Carbon dioxide is a compound of the elements carbon and oxygen. Its formula is CO_2. By looking at the formula, you can tell that every molecule is made up of 1 atom of carbon (C) and 2 atoms of oxygen (O). Sulfuric acid has the formula H_2SO_4. How many hydrogen atoms, sulfur atoms, and oxygen atoms are there in a molecule of sulfuric acid? ❷

Can you now see the advantages of using chemical formulas? Not only does a formula save space, but it tells you a lot about the compound. It tells you the elements that make up the compound. And it tells you how many atoms of each element combine to form the compound.

Chemical Equations

If you think of chemical symbols as "letters" and chemical formulas as "words," then you can write chemical "sentences." Chemical sentences are a way to describe a chemical process, or chemical reaction. As you learned in Chapter 2, during a chemical reaction, substances are changed into new and different substances through a rearrangement of their atoms. New chemical substances with new properties

---

are formed. By using chemical symbols and formulas, you can describe a chemical reaction.

Have you ever seen charcoal burning in a barbecue grill? If so, you were watching a chemical reaction. The carbon atoms in the charcoal were combining with the oxygen molecules in the air to form the gas carbon dioxide. The reaction could be written:

carbon atoms plus oxygen molecules
produce carbon dioxide molecules

By using symbols and formulas, this reaction can be written in a simpler way:

$$C + O_2 \longrightarrow CO_2$$

The symbol C represents an atom of carbon. The formula O_2 represents a molecule of oxygen. And the formula CO_2 represents a molecule of carbon dioxide. The arrow is read "yields," which is another way of saying "produces."

The description of a chemical reaction using symbols and formulas is called a **chemical equation.** An equation is another example of chemical shorthand. Instead of using words to describe a chemical reaction, you can use a chemical equation.

Here is another example. The chemical equation for the formation of water from the elements hydrogen and oxygen is

$$H_2 + O_2 \longrightarrow H_2O$$

PROPERTIES OF ELEMENTS, COMPOUNDS, AND MIXTURES

Elements	Compounds	Mixtures
Made up of only one kind of atom	Made up of more than one kind of atom	Made up of more than one kind of molecule
Cannot be broken down by chemical means	Can be broken down by chemical means	Can be separated by physical means
Has same properties as atoms making it up	Has different properties from elements making it up	Has same properties as substances making it up
Has same properties throughout	Has same properties throughout	Has different properties throughout

Figure 3–21 *This illustration shows the chemical reaction that occurs when carbon and oxygen combine to form carbon dioxide. What is the chemical formula for carbon dioxide?* ③

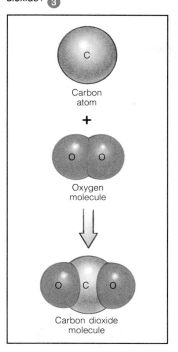

Carbon atom

+

Oxygen molecule

Carbon dioxide molecule

Figure 3–22 *This table shows the common properties of elements, compounds, and mixtures. Which of the three substances does not have the same properties throughout?* ④

BACKGROUND INFORMATION

THE NAMING OF COMPOUNDS

Molecular compounds are named according to systems. What system is used depends on the number of elements present. A pair of nonmetals form only one compound; the name of the element whose symbol appears first in the formula is written first. For this reason we have HF or hydrogen fluoride, HCl or hydrogen chloride, H_2S or hydrogen sulfide. A water solution of hydrogen fluoride, HF, however, is called hydrofluoric acid. A water solution of hydrogen chloride similarly is called hydrochloric acid. If more than one compound is formed by a pair of nonmetals, the Greek prefixes for the numbers 2 to 6 are used: *di-, tri-, tetra-, penta-,* and *hexa-;* for example, N_2O_5 is dinitrogen pentoxide.

There are a number of well-known binary compounds of nonmetals that are simply known by common names, for example: ammonia, nitric oxide, and hydrogen peroxide.

Some of the most important acids contain three elements: hydrogen, oxygen, and a nonmetal such as carbon or sulfur. These compounds have still other systems for naming.

(No. Toothpaste is a mixture, not a compound.)

INDEPENDENT PRACTICE

▶ *Activity Book*

Students who need practice with atomic formulas should be provided with the Chapter 3 activity called Counting Atoms.

GUIDED PRACTICE

Skills Development

Skills: Applying concepts, drawing conclusions, making models

At this point you might want to have students complete the in-text Chapter 3 Laboratory Investigation, Making Models of Chemical Reactions, to reinforce the concepts of atoms and molecule formation.

LEAD POISONING

Lead is an element that even in very small amounts can cause tremendous damage if taken into the body. Some health problems that are caused by lead poisoning include weight loss; dehydration; weakness; inability to sleep; crankiness; inability to absorb and use important substances such as iron, vitamin D, and calcium; and high blood pressure.

In an attempt to reduce the amount of lead found in the environment, the United States government has ordered the production of unleaded gasoline for automobiles and has banned the manufacture of leaded paint. These measures have greatly reduced the problem of lead poisoning. But Americans are still exposed to lead through drinking water, soil, lead-containing fertilizers and pesticides, air pollution, and from the glaze on foreign ceramicware that has not been fired sufficiently.

Those who are most susceptible to lead poisoning are young people, whose growth can be affected; pregnant women, whose unborn children can be affected; and middle-aged men who battle heart disease and high blood pressure.

Individuals can limit their lead intake by replacing lead-based paint in their homes, checking plumbing lines for lead traces, carefully examining foreign ceramicware, and eating a balanced diet to prevent maximum absorption of lead by body tissues.

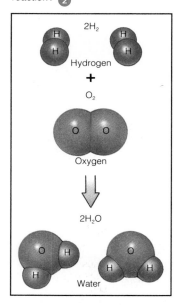

Figure 3–23 *During the formation of water, 2 hydrogen molecules combine with a molecule of oxygen to form 2 water molecules. What is the chemical equation for this reaction?* ②

This equation ($H_2 + O_2 \longrightarrow H_2O$) tells you what elements are combining and what product is formed. But something is wrong with this equation. Do you know what it is? ❶

Look at the number of oxygen atoms on each side of the equation. Are they equal? On the left side of the equation there are 2 oxygen atoms. On the right side there is only 1 oxygen atom. Could 1 oxygen atom have disappeared? Scientists know that atoms are never created or destroyed in a chemical reaction. Atoms can only be rearranged. So there must be the same number of atoms of each element on each side of the equation. The equation must be balanced. The balanced equation for the formation of water is

$$2H_2 + O_2 \longrightarrow 2H_2O$$

Now count the atoms of each element on each side of the equation. You will find that they are the same: 4 atoms of hydrogen on the left side and on the right; 2 atoms of oxygen on the left side and on the right. The equation is correctly balanced.

You have seen that an equation can be balanced by placing the appropriate number in front of a chemical formula in the equation. This number is called a **coefficient** (koh-uh-FIHSH-uhnt). The correctly balanced equation now tells you that 2 molecules of hydrogen combine with 1 molecule of oxygen to produce 2 molecules of water. A balanced equation is evidence of a chemical reaction.

3–4 Section Review

1. What is a compound?
2. How is a compound different from an element?
3. What is a molecule? How is a molecule of an element or a compound represented?
4. Why must a chemical equation be balanced?

Connection—*You and Your World*
5. How is a recipe for baking a cake like a chemical equation? What three things must be included in a good, easy-to-follow recipe?

3–4 (continued)

GUIDED PRACTICE

Skills Development

Skill: Applying definitions

• **How many molecules of water are produced by the chemical reaction?** (2)
• **How many molecules of hydrogen are needed to produce two molecules of water?** (2)
• **How many atoms of hydrogen are needed to produce two molecules of water?** (4)
• **How many atoms of oxygen are need to**

produce two molecules of water? (2)
• **How many molecules of oxygen are needed to produce two molecules of water?** (1)
• **What is the balanced chemical equation for the formation of water from hydrogen and oxygen?** ($2H_2 + O$ $2H_2O$)

INDEPENDENT PRACTICE

▶ *Activity Book*

Students who need to reinforce their understanding of compounds, mixtures, and elements should complete the chap-

ter activity called Elements, Compounds, and Mixtures in the *Activity Book*.

CONTENT DEVELOPMENT

• **What are some examples of chemical reactions that you have observed?** (Answers will vary but might include meat being charcoaled on a grill, wood burning in a fireplace, and a firecracker exploding in the air.)

CONNECTIONS

Time and a Tree

You have to hurry. . . . In three minutes you will be late for class. Time has a way of ruling your days. Time tells you where to be, and when. Time also tells you what to do. Days seem short when you have a lot to do.

Time for a sugar maple is different. You probably do not give much thought to time's effects on a tree. A tree stands tall and proud for so long that time seems to have little impact on its life from one day to the next. Yet if you were able to observe a tree over a year's time, you would notice profound changes.

Take this sugar maple in the photograph. It is the middle of March and the Vermont woods where this tree grows are covered with a winter's blanket of snow. Few birds can be seen or heard, and even fewer other animals are in sight. For most forms of forest life, winter is a time of rest. But deep within the trunk of a maple tree, things are beginning to stir. Sap, a sweet juice conducted in tiny tubes in the tree trunk, is starting to move upward from the roots. Farmers are able to "tap" the tree's trunk and collect buckets of sap. Later the sap will be boiled down into delicious maple syrup. But where did this sweet sap come from?

Actually, the sugars in the sap were made by the tree the year before. In the previous spring, the maple tree leafed out. The beautiful leaves that clothed the maple then are efficient collectors of the sun's energy. The green pigment in the leaves, which is called chlorophyll, ① trapped the energy of sunlight and used it to make food. In a complex series of chemical reactions, water was combined with carbon dioxide to produce sugars. Scientists write a chemical equation to describe the process:

$$6CO_2 + 6H_2O \xrightarrow[\text{(chlorophyll)}]{\text{(sunlight)}} C_6H_{12}O_6 + 6O_2$$

Carbon dioxide plus water plus the energy of the sun trapped by chlorophyll yields sugar plus oxygen—a simple equation that describes the single most important chemical reaction on Earth.

You might wonder why this reaction is so important. It is important because plants are able to use the energy of the sun in ways animals never can. And in so doing, plants produce food (in the form of plant sugars) and oxygen necessary for the survival of animals on Earth.

Laboratory Investigation

MAKING MODELS OF CHEMICAL REACTIONS

BEFORE THE LAB

1. Divide the class into groups of six students.

2. Gather all materials at least one day prior to the investigation. You should have enough supplies to meet your class needs, assuming six students per group.

3. Prepare each color by adding 30 mL food coloring to 500 mL water. Orange can be made by mixing equal parts of red and yellow. Purple can be made by mixing equal parts of red and blue.

4. Prepare two coloring stations for each color. Each station should have marshmallows, 250 mL color, paper towels, and toothpicks on a tray. Each team will need a tray colored with waxed paper.

5. Prepare a place for the trays of colored marshmallows to dry overnight.

PRE-LAB DISCUSSION

Before doing the coloring in Part A, demonstrate how to color the marshmallows by inserting a toothpick into a marshmallow, dipping it into the color, and placing the marshmallow (with the pick) onto the waxed paper to dry. Tell the groups to label their trays for easy retrieval.

Remind the groups to keep each colored marshmallow separate from the others so that the colors do not mix.

Before doing Part B, tell the sudents that they will be making models to help them understand chemical reactions.

Laboratory Investigation

Making Models of Chemical Reactions

Problem

How do atoms and molecules of elements and compounds combine in chemical reactions?

Materials (per group)

> toothpicks
> red, yellow, green, blue, purple (red-blue), and orange (yellow-red) food coloring
> 25 large marshmallows

Procedure

A. *Making Marshmallow Atoms*

1. Prepare model atoms by applying food coloring to the marshmallows as follows:

   N (nitrogen)—red (2)
   H (hydrogen)—blue (6)
   Cu (copper)—green (4)
   O (oxygen)—yellow (6)
   K (potassium)—orange (2)
   Cl (chlorine)—purple (2)

2. Let the marshmallows dry for 2 hours.

B. *Assembling the Marshmallow Molecules*

1. Use a toothpick to join two red marshmallows to make a molecule of N_2. Use a toothpick to join two blue marshmallows to make a molecule of H_2.

2. Ammonia (NH_3) is used in cleaning solutions and in the manufacture of fertilizers. A molecule of ammonia contains 1 nitrogen atom and 3 hydrogen atoms. Use the marshmallow molecules of nitrogen and hydrogen you made in step 1 to form an ammonia molecule. You may use as many nitrogen and hydrogen molecules as you need to make ammonia molecules as long as you do not have any atoms left over. Remember, hydrogen and nitrogen must start out as molecules consisting of 2

atoms each. Now balance the equation for the chemical reaction that produces ammonia:

$$\_\_N_2 + \_\_H_2 \longrightarrow \_\_\_\_\_NH_3$$

3. Use two green marshmallows for copper and one yellow marshmallow for oxygen to make a model of a copper oxide molecule (Cu_2O). With a white marshmallow representing carbon, manipulate the marshmallow models to illustrate the reaction below, which produces metallic copper. Balance the equation.

$$\_\_Cu_2O + \_\_C \longrightarrow \_\_Cu + \_\_CO_2$$

4. Use orange for potassium, purple for chlorine, and white for oxygen to assemble a molecule of potassium chlorate ($KClO_3$).

Observations

1. How many molecules of N_2 and H_2 are needed to produce 2 molecules of NH_3?

2. How many molecules of copper are produced from 2 molecules of Cu_2O?

Analysis and Conclusions

1. Which substances that you made are elements? Which are compounds?

2. If you had to make 5 molecules of ammonia (NH_3), how many red marshmallows would you need? How many blue marshmallows?

TEACHING STRATEGY

1. Have the groups follow the directions carefully as they work in the laboratory.

2. If you have several sessions, you may want to have each session do the coloring on a different day to be sure you have enough storage space for the marshmallows.

3. After the groups have completed the investigation, share and discuss the results. Have groups take turns showing and explaining a model and the balanced equation.

DISCOVERY STRATEGIES

Discuss how the investigation relates to the chapter ideas by asking open questions similar to the following:

• **How do you think it is possible to tell which molecules are most complex?** (By the number of elements and atoms—inferring.)

• **Do you think certain elements when combined to form a compound could develop strong smells?** (Yes, ammonia is an example—inferring, relating.)

Study Guide

Summarizing Key Concepts

3–1 Classes of Matter

▲ Matter is classified according to its makeup as mixtures, solutions, elements, or compounds.

3–2 Mixtures

▲ A mixture is composed of two or more substances mixed together but not chemically combined.

▲ The substances in a mixture can be present in any amount.

▲ The substances in a mixture can be separated by simple physical means.

▲ A mixture that does not appear to be the same throughout is a heterogeneous mixture.

▲ A mixture that appears to be the same throughout is a homogeneous mixture.

▲ The particles in a colloid, a type of homogeneous mixture, are not dissolved.

▲ A solution is a type of homogeneous mixture formed when one substance, called the solute, dissolves in another substance, called the solvent.

▲ The amount of a solute that can completely dissolve in a given solvent is called its solubility.

▲ Alloys are metal solutions in which solids are dissolved in solids.

3–3 Elements

▲ A pure substance is made of only one kind of material, has definite properties, and is the same throughout.

▲ Elements are the simplest type of pure substance. They cannot be broken down into simpler substances without losing their identity.

▲ Elements are made of atoms, which are the building blocks of matter.

3–4 Compounds

▲ Compounds are two or more elements chemically combined.

▲ Most compounds are made of molecules. A molecule is made of two or more atoms chemically bonded together.

▲ A chemical formula, which is a combination of chemical symbols, usually represents a molecule of a compound.

▲ A chemical equation describes a chemical reaction.

Reviewing Key Terms

Define each term in a complete sentence.

3–2 Mixtures
mixture
heterogeneous mixture
homogeneous mixture
colloid
solution
solute
solvent
soluble

insoluble
solubility
alloy

3–3 Elements
pure substance
element
atom
chemical symbol

3–4 Compounds
compound
molecule
chemical formula
subscript
chemical equation
coefficient

OBSERVATIONS

1. 1 molecule of N_2, 3 molecules of H_2.
2. 4.

ANALYSIS AND CONCLUSIONS

1. Elements are nitrogen, hydrogen, and copper. Compounds are NH_3, Cu_2O, CO_2, and $KClO_3$.
2. 5 red and 15 blue.

GOING FURTHER: ENRICHMENT

Discuss how models help scientists and students understand nature. Ask open questions like the following:
• **How do models help you understand chemical reactions?**
• **How are the marshmallow models like real atoms?**
• **How are the marshmallow models different from real atoms?**
• **What is a model?**
• **What other models are useful?**

Chapter Review

ALTERNATIVE ASSESSMENT

The *Prentice Hall Science* program includes a variety of testing components and methodologies. Aside from the Chapter Review questions, you may opt to use the Chapter Test or the Computer Test Bank Test in your *Test Book* for assessment of important facts and concepts. In addition, Performance-Based Tests are included in your *Test Book*. These Performance-Based Tests are designed to test science process skills, rather than factual content recall. Since they are not content dependent, Performance-Based Tests can be distributed after students complete a chapter or after they complete the entire textbook.

CONTENT REVIEW

Multiple Choice
1. d
2. b
3. a
4. d
5. b
6. a
7. a
8. a

True or False
1. F atom
2. F do
3. E heterogeneous
4. T
5. F physical
6. F soluble
7. T
8. T

Concept Mapping
Row 1: Classes
Row 3: Mixtures, Compounds

CONCEPT MASTERY

1. The parts of the solution are not chemically combined. A solution is made up of two or more different kinds of particles. A solution can be separated by physical means. A solution has the same properties as its ingredients.
2. (a) Evaporate water, (b) use magnet for getting iron out, (c) float in water (d) by size.
3. It tells what its elements are and how many atoms of each element it has.

Content Review

Multiple Choice

Choose the letter of the answer that best completes each statement.

1. Matter that consists of two or more substances mixed together but not chemically combined is called a(an)
   a. element.　　　　c. pure substance.
   b. compound.　　　d. mixture.
2. An example of a heterogeneous mixture is
   a. salt water.　　　c. stainless steel.
   b. salad dressing.　d. salt.
3. In a solution, the substance being dissolved is called the
   a. solvent.　　　　c. solubility.
   b. solute.　　　　　d. insoluble.
4. The simplest type of pure substance is a (an)
   a. compound.　　　c. solution
   b. alloy.　　　　　d. element.

5. The chemical formula for a molecule of nitrogen is
   a. N.　　　　　c. N_3.
   b. N_2.　　　　d. Ni.
6. Pure substances that are made of more than one element are called
   a. compounds.　　c. alloys.
   b. mixtures.　　　d. solutions.
7. Which of the following is not an alloy?
   a. zinc　　　　　c. stainless steel
   b. gold jewelry　d. brass
8. Which of the following is not a compound?
   a. H_2　　　　c. H_2SO_4
   b. H_2O　　　d. CO_2

True or False

If the statement is true, write "true." If it is false, change the underlined word or words to make the statement true.

1. The basic building block of matter is the <u>compound</u>.
2. When elements combine to form compounds, their properties <u>do not</u> change.
3. One example of a <u>homogeneous</u> mixture is concrete.
4. Substances in a <u>mixture</u> keep their separate identities and most of their own properties.
5. Mixtures can be separated by simple <u>chemical</u> means.
6. Salt and sugar are <u>insoluble</u> in water.
7. The "best mixed" of mixtures is a <u>solution</u>.
8. The particles in a <u>colloid</u> are mixed together but not dissolved.

Concept Mapping

Complete the following concept map for Section 3–1. Refer to pages N6–N7 to construct a concept map for the entire chapter.

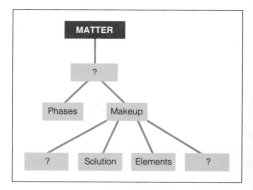

4. (a) Au, (b) O, (c) C, (d) H, (e) Ag, (f) Ca, (g) N. Suggested uses will vary.
5. Subscripts indicate the number of atoms of an element; coefficients indicate how many molecules and atoms are involved in a reaction.
6. A solution is a homogeneous mixture in which one substance dissolves in another. Solute and solvent. Three properties are (1) all particles are evenly spread out, (2) particles are not large enough to be seen, and (3) particles are too small to scatter light.

CRITICAL THINKING AND PROBLEM SOLVING

1. The symbols and conventions of writing chemical equations follow international standards.
2a. $2Mg + O_2 = 2MgO$
  b. $2NaCl = 2Na + Cl_2$
  c. $CH_4 + 2O_2 = CO_2 + 2H_2O$
  d. $2H_2 + O2 = 2H_2O$
3. (a) Pass an electric current through water and collect the O_2 and H_2 into which it decomposes. Test each gas appropriately for identification. (b) Evapo-

Concept Mastery

Discuss each of the following in a brief paragraph.

1. A solution is classified as a mixture instead of a compound. Why?
2. Describe a method you can use to separate the following mixtures. Your method should take into account the physical properties of the substances that make up the mixture.
   a. sugar and water
   b. powdered iron and powdered aluminum
   c. wood and gold
   d. nickels and dimes

3. What two things does a chemical formula indicate about a compound?
4. Write the symbols for the following elements and describe one use for each: (a) gold, (b) oxygen, (c) carbon, (d) hydrogen, (e) silver, (f) calcium, (g) nitrogen.
5. Chemical equations can be balanced by using coefficients but not subscripts. Explain why this is so.
6. What is a solution? What two parts make up a solution? Describe three properties of a solution.

Critical Thinking and Problem Solving

Use the skills you have developed in this chapter to answer each of the following.

1. **Making inferences** Suppose you find a chemistry book that is written in a language you cannot understand. When you look at the book, however, you realize that you can understand and duplicate the chemical reactions printed in the text. Explain how you can do this?
2. **Making calculations** Balance the following equations:
   a. $Mg + O_2 \longrightarrow MgO$
   b. $NaCl \longrightarrow Na + Cl_2$
   c. $CH_4 + O_2 \longrightarrow CO_2 + H_2O$
   d. $H_2 + O_2 \longrightarrow H_2O$
3. **Designing an experiment** Describe an experiment to show that
   a. water is a compound, not an element.
   b. salt water is a solution, not a pure substance.
4. **Relating facts** You learned that mixtures have three important properties. Use the example of a bowl of cereal with milk and strawberries to illustrate each property.
5. **Classifying data** Develop a classification system for the months of the year. State the property or properties that you will use to classify the months. Do not use the four seasons. Try to make your system as useful and as specific as possible.
6. **Making inferences** Explain whether or not you believe there exists a true "universal solvent" capable of dissolving all other substances. Include a description of the kind of container you would need to hold such a solvent.
7. **Using the writing process** Water has been accused of being an element by an assistant district attorney. You are the defense attorney whose job is to convince the jury that water is a compound. Write up a brief summation to the jury to make your case. Use only the very best scientific information in your case.

You might want to assign some of the Concept Mastery and Critical Thinking and Problem Solving questions as homework and have students include their responses to unassigned questions in their portfolio. Students should be encouraged to include both the question and the answer in their portfolio.

ISSUES IN SCIENCE

The following issues can be used as a springboard for class debate or given as a writing assignment:

1. Some scientists think solutions should not exist in the general classification of matter. Other scientists believe that solutions are a definite part of the general classification system. What is your opinion? Explain.

2. Predict the development of classification of matter in the twenty-first century. Who do you think will undertake the investigation into new matter? What will be your role in this scientific research? How will it be important in your life?

rate the water, leaving behind the salt.

4. Substances keep their own identity: You can recognize the milk, strawberries, and cereal by both sight and taste. Substances can be present in any amount; you can use varying amounts of each substance and still have a mixture of the three. Substances are easily separated according to their physical properties: You can filter the cereal flakes and berries from the milk and then pick out the berries from the flakes.

5. Answers will vary. Sample criteria are the first letter of the name of a month; number of letters in the name of a month; average temperature; hours of daylight; number of days; school and nonschool months.

6. Answers will vary, but most students probably will say that no true universal solvent exists. If there were one, no container could hold it. Accept all logical answers.

7. An element cannot be broken down into simpler substances by ordinary means, but water can be broken down into oxygen and nitrogen.

SECTION	LABORATORY INVESTIGATIONS AND DEMONSTRATIONS
4–1 An Atomic Model of Matter pages N84–N91	**Student Edition** Shoe Box Atoms, p. N102 **Laboratory Manual** Making Predictions Using Indirect Evidence
4–2 Structure of the Atom pages N92–N99	**Laboratory Manual** Investigating Rutherford's Model of the Atom Relating Electrons and Probability **Teacher Edition** Testing for Finite Number, p. N82d
4–3 Forces Within the Atom pages N99–N101	**Teacher Edition** Observing Attraction, p. N82d
Chapter Review pages N102–N105	

*All materials in the Chapter Planning Guide are available as part of the Prentice Hall Science Learning System.

OUTSIDE TEACHER RESOURCES

Books

Bohr, Niels. *Theory and the Description of Nature,* AMS Press.

Condon, E. V., and H. Odabasi. *Atomic Structure,* Cambridge University Press.

Conn, G. K. *Atoms and Their Structure,* Cambridge University Press.

Koester, L., and A. Steyerl. *Neutron Physics,* Springer-Verlag.

Audiovisuals

Electrons and Protons in Chemical Change, two filmstrips with two cassettes, PH Media

The Geneva Event, video, Media Guild

Matter and Molecular Theory, video, Coronet

Matter and Molecules: Into the Atom, filmstrip with cassette, SVE

Measuring Electron Charge and Mass, two filmstrips with two cassettes, PH Media

The Nucleus: Composition, Stability, and Decay, filmstrip or slides with cassette, PH Media

OTHER ACTIVITIES	MULTIMEDIA

Activity Book
    Chapter Discovery: Using Indirect Evidence
Student Edition
    Find Out by Doing: Shine a Little Light On It, p. N85
    Find Out by Doing: Making a Model Atom, p. N89
Review and Reinforcement Guide
    Section 4–1
	Transparency Binder
	    Rutherford's Experiment
	English/Spanish Audiotapes
	    Section 4–1

Activity Book
    ACTIVITY: Counting Atoms
    ACTIVITY: Drawing Atoms
    ACTIVITY: Atomic Structure
    ACTIVITY: Making Models of Isotopes
    ACTIVITY: Isotopes or Different Elements?
Student Edition
    Find out by Calculating: The Mystery Element, p. N97
Review and Reinforcement Guide
    Section 4–2
	Courseware
	    The Atomic Nucleus (supplemental)
	Transparency Binder
	    Structure of the Atom
	    Isotopes of Carbon
	    Energy Levels
	English/Spanish Audiotapes
	    Section 4–2

Activity Book
    ACTIVITY: Atomic Dimensions
Product Testing Activity
    Glue
Review and Reinforcement Guide
    Section 4–3
	English/Spanish Audiotapes
	    Section 4–3

Test Book
    Chapter Test
    Performance-Based Tests
	Test Book

Chapter 4 — ATOMS: BUILDING BLOCKS OF MATTER

CHAPTER OVERVIEW

Have you ever put together a model airplane, baked cookies, or built a tower out of blocks? In these activities individual parts are combined to form a new object. The airplane is made up of parts such as wings and propellers. Flour and oatmeal are some of the ingredients that go into cookies. And wooden blocks of various shapes, sizes, and colors fit together to make a tower.

All objects are made up of tiny building blocks. Scientists call these basic building blocks atoms. But unlike model parts, cookie ingredients, and colorful blocks, atoms cannot be seen.

Atoms are very, very small. Look at the period at the end of this sentence. A trillion atoms could fit into it!

Today, atomic-theory scientists have powerful instruments that help them see atoms. And although scientists still think of the atom as the basic building block of all things, they know now that the atom is made up of even smaller particles. At the center of each atom is a nucleus, and this nucleus contains electrically positive protons and electrically neutral neutrons. Whirling about the nucleus are electrically negative electrons.

This chapter will explain an atomic model of matter and describe how this model has evolved over time. The structure of the atom will also be explained, and the forces of nature as they relate to atomic structure will be identified.

4–1 AN ATOMIC MODEL OF MATTER
THEMATIC FOCUS

The purpose of this section is to describe how the atomic model has changed over time. Since the time of the early Greeks, various atomic models have been proposed to account for the structure of matter. The Greek atomists believed the atom to be indivisible, and the work of later scientists helped to discover that the atom was made up of smaller particles.

Students will learn that scientists have used observations, or indirect evidence, to create models. Models help to explain unfamiliar facts observed in nature.

The themes that can be focused on in this section are unity and diversity and scale and structure. These themes are connected because we live in a world composed of very small pieces of matter that mostly remain unseen.

Unity and diversity: Stress that atoms are considered to be the smallest pieces of matter. For thousands of years, scientists and philosophers have wondered and speculated about what matter was made of. Because atoms in matter remained unseen for many years, models of atoms were created to help explain this unseen world.

*Scale and structure: Make sure students understand that even though atoms are considered to be the smallest pieces of matter, scientists have observed, created models, and proved that the atom itself is composed of smaller particles.

PERFORMANCE OBJECTIVES 4–1
1. Relate indirect evidence to the steps involved in the development of a model of an atom.
2. Describe how the atomic model has changed over time.

SCIENCE TERMS 4–1
nucleus p. N88

4–2 STRUCTURE OF THE ATOM
THEMATIC FOCUS

The purpose of this section is to introduce students to the structure of the atom and the particles that compose the atom. Students will learn that the nucleus of an atom is about one hundred thousand times smaller than the atom itself, yet it contains two of the three subatomic particles found in an atom. The nucleus of the atom contains positively charged protons and uncharged neutrons, each of which is thought to be made up of smaller particles, called quarks. Whirling about the nucleus of an atom are electrons. Isotopes of an element contain an equal number of protons but different numbers of electrons.

The themes that can be focused on in this section are scale and structure, stability, patterns of change, and energy. These themes are connected because atoms are made up of smaller particles, and the combination of these smaller particles determines the atomic number and the mass number of that atom.

*Scale and structure: All atoms are made up of smaller particles—protons, neutrons, and electrons. Protons carry positive charges, and the number of protons in the nucleus of an atom determines the atomic number of the atom. Neutrons are electrically neutral particles in the nucleus. Electrons move about the nucleus, and their number combines with the number of protons to determine the electrical charge of the atom.

*Stability: Stress that the number of protons in an atom of an element never changes, but the number of neutrons in the nucleus of that atom can change. This change creates an isotope of that element.

*Patterns of change: Each increase in the number of protons in an atom results in a new kind of atom.

Energy: Make students aware that the energy content of an electron (which can increase or decrease) determines its energy level in an atom.

PERFORMANCE OBJECTIVES 4–2
1. Classify the three main subatomic particles.
2. Explain the structure of the atom.

SCIENCE TERMS 4–2
subatomic particle p. N92
proton p. N92
atomic mass unit p. N93
neutron p. N93
atomic number p. N94
isotope p. N94

4–3 FORCES WITHIN THE ATOM
THEMATIC FOCUS

The purpose of this section is to introduce students to the forces associated with atomic structure. Students will learn that these four forces (gravity, electromagnetic force, strong force, and weak force) account for the behavior of subatomic particles and govern all the interactions of matter and energy.

The themes that can be focused on in this section are systems and interactions and unity and diversity.

*Systems and interactions: The forces that govern the behavior of subatomic particles are electromagnetic, strong, weak, and gravity. Explain and discuss how each of these forces interacts and combines to keep atoms together.

Unity and diversity: Stress that atoms are the smallest pieces of matter and that none of these pieces can be seen by the naked eye. Even though they remain unseen, atoms and the forces and components within atoms seem to function in an orderly fashion. Researchers and scientists have learned many things about atoms, but there are many more questions than answers remaining. Their quest for knowledge about this unseen world never ceases.

PERFORMANCE OBJECTIVES 4–3
1. Identify the four forces associated with atomic structure.
2. Explain the four forces associated with atomic structure.

SCIENCE TERMS 4–3
electromagnetic force p. N99
strong force p. N100
weak force p. N100
gravity p. N100

Discovery *Learning*

TEACHER DEMONSTRATIONS MODELING
Observing Attraction

Divide the class into teams of four to six students per team. Give each team a magnet and a small paper clip. Tell the class that in this model, the magnet represents the positive charge of a proton in the nucleus of an atom and the paper clip represents the negative charge of an electron whirling about the nucleus of that same atom.

Have each team investigate how close they can move the paper-clip electron past the magnet proton without being "captured" by the magnet.
• **What did you discover?** (When the paper-clip electron gets too close and/or moves too slowly, it is pulled into the magnet proton.)
• **What can you conclude about the speed of a negatively charged electron that allows it to move around the positively charged proton without being pulled into the nucleus?** (The electron must be moving very fast and have a great deal of energy.)

Testing for Finite Number

The number of electrons that can fit into a given orbital of an atom is finite. This can be demonstrated with books and bookshelves.

Obtain a bookcase with several shelves that can hold a finite number of books. Make sure the bookcase is empty. Also obtain a selection of random-sized books, enough to fill several shelves of the bookcase.

Have a volunteer fit as many books as possible onto the lowest shelf. Record the results. Have another volunteer fit as many books as possible onto the second-lowest shelf. Record the results. Continue until the bookcase is filled.

The bookcase can be emptied and the process repeated any number of times
• **What did you notice?** (Students should notice that the size and the arrangement of the books determined how many books each shelf could hold. Each shelf may hold a different number of books, but that number appears to be finite.)

Explain that students will learn in future lessons how finite numbers of electrons, not books, can fit into the orbitals of an atom, not a bookshelf.

CHAPTER 4
Atoms: Building Blocks of Matter

INTEGRATING SCIENCE

This physical science chapter provides you with numerous opportunities to integrate other areas of science, as well as other disciplines, into your curriculum. Blue numbered annotations on the student pages and integration notes on the teacher wraparound pages alert you to areas of possible integration.

In this chapter you can integrate social studies (pp. 85, 86), fine arts (pp. 85, 88), life science and cells (p. 89), architecture (p. 91), mathematics (pp. 93, 96, 97), life science and evolution (p. 94), and life science and ecology (p. 101).

SCIENCE, TECHNOLOGY, AND SOCIETY/COOPERATIVE LEARNING

The superconducting supercollider (SSC), a large machine for crashing atoms together and observing the resulting debris, is being built in Texas. The SSC will enable physicists to observe new phenomena and new subatomic particles.

The SSC is actually two different machines—a collider and a series of detectors. Two beams of protons will travel in opposite directions through a 54-mile-long tunnel 3000 times per second. Approximately every sixteen billionth of a second, the two beams will intersect at predetermined collision sites. A small percentage of the protons will collide but still generate roughly 100 million collisions per second and produce dozens of

INTRODUCING CHAPTER 4

DISCOVERY LEARNING

▶ *Activity Book*

Begin your teaching of the chapter by using the Chapter 4 Discovery Activity from your *Activity Book.* Using this activity, students will discover the role indirect evidence plays in drawing conclusions.

USING THE TEXTBOOK

Have students observe the photograph on page N82. Point out that it shows beads of mercury.
• **What is mercury?** (Students might suggest that mercury is the "liquid" in a thermometer.)
• **What phase do you guess mercury to be? Why?** (Liquid, because it has no definite shape.)

Have students read the chapter introduction.

• **Is there some tiny bead of mercury in the picture that if sliced one more time would no longer be mercury?** (No.)

Point out that mercury is a liquid and is made of one kind of particle. Explain that after observing, collecting facts, and experimenting, scientists developed a theory that some substances were made of only one kind of particle. Tell students that first the scientists had to determine what the particle was.

Atoms: Building Blocks of Matter

Guide for Reading

After you read the following sections, you will be able to

4–1 An Atomic Model of Matter

- Describe how the atomic model has changed over time.

4–2 Structure of the Atom

- Classify subatomic particles.
- Identify the relationships among atomic number, isotope, mass number, and atomic mass.
- Describe the structure of an atom according to modern atomic theory.

4–3 Forces Within the Atom

- Identify how the four forces in nature are related to atomic structure.

Beads of mercury gleam on a sheet of cloth. Some beads are small; others are large. But they are all still mercury, a pure substance. If you were to take the smallest bead of mercury and slice it in half once, twice, three times, even a thousand times, you would still be left with mercury—or would you?

Is there some incredibly tiny bead of mercury that if sliced one more time would no longer be mercury? It was just this kind of question that sparked the imagination and curiosity of early scientists. They hypothesized and argued as the years passed—for more than 2000 years, in fact.

Then, slowly, clues were found. Experiments were performed. New ideas were explored. And finally an answer was developed. In many ways it was quite a simple answer. To find it out, let's begin at the beginning.

Journal *Activity*

You and Your World Have you ever seen pictures of the Great Pyramids that were built in Egypt thousands of years ago? Block upon block, these great tombs were constructed with few tools and great effort. Even the tallest building is made of small parts. Draw a picture in your journal of a building you like. Next to your drawing, make another drawing of one of the pieces that make up your building.

Silvery beads of liquid mercury gleam in the photographer's lights.

N ■ 83

---

new subatomic particles. The detectors must capture the birth and death of these subatomic particles.

Particle detectors monitor the subatomic particles that appear and disappear within trillionths of a second. They measure the momentum, direction, charge, and energy of the particles released by the collisions. Vertex detectors trace very short-lived particles. Tracking chambers measure their momentum. Calorimeters measure the energy of particles, and muon detectors trace the path of particles similar to electrons. Scientists collect the data and try to produce a profile of each particle's behavior.

Congressional approval for the SSC followed much debate. Many scientists argued that the cost would drain research dollars away from other programs; that only a few specialists would understand the results; and that in the future the SSC could be built at less cost. Proponents of the SSC argued that the information gained from the SSC would increase understanding of the universe; would further knowledge of the atom and the tremendous energy contained in its bonds; and would give clues to how nature works at the most basic level.

Cooperative learning: Using preassigned lab groups or randomly selected teams, have groups complete one of the following assignments:

• Using the information presented in this chapter, prepare an illustrated time line that traces the evolution of the atomic model from Democritus to the SSC. Assign each group one section of the time line and one model of the atom to illustrate and explain.

• Write a letter to your representative in Congress stating your position on continued funding for the SSC.

See Cooperative Learning in the *Teacher's Desk Reference.*

JOURNAL ACTIVITY

You may want to use the Journal Activity as the basis of a class discussion. As students discuss their buildings, lead them to the idea that the building of pyramids can be related to atomic structure. Students should be instructed to keep their Journal Activity in their portfolio.

• **What would you do to identify the single smallest particle of any substance?** (Name it.)

Point out that scientists also needed to name the single smallest particle of matter. Have students read the chapter title.

• **What did scientists name this single smallest particle of matter?** (An atom.)

Explain that after scientists found this very tiny particle, they had to test the theory of the atom over and over again. Point out that a great many experiments over 2400 years changed and rechanged the idea of what an atom was.

• **Why would it take such a long time to research the atom?** (Students might suggest that the atom is too small to see, or that because it was a new idea, other scientists were reluctant to accept it.)

Point out to students that as the chapter title says, the atom is the basic building block of all matter.

4–1 An Atomic Model of Matter

MULTICULTURAL OPPORTUNITY 4–1

Discuss with students the idea that knowledge is a cumulative process. Often we view science as the work of individuals (usually European or American males). More often, scientific discoveries represent the cumulative work of many different people, male and female, including individuals from different countries and cultures. The atomic model is an example of an idea that scientists contemplated for more than 2000 years.

ESL STRATEGY 4–1

Point out the words beginning with the prefix *in-* that are used in this section in connection with the atom: *indivisible, infinite, indestructible.*

Explain the meaning of the prefix *in-* and ask students to define each of the words. Have them use the words to
1. Describe why Democritus gave the name *atamos* to the smallest piece of matter.
2. Describe how the atomists imagined the atom.
3. Describe Dalton's theory about these particles.

Have students work in pairs or small groups as they prepare their answers.

Guide for Reading

Focus on this question as you read.

▶ *How has the modern atomic model changed over time?*

Figure 4–1 *Scientists often depend on indirect evidence to develop a model of something that cannot be observed directly. Use the two drawings in this figure to develop a model that might explain what happened during the few hours that separate the two drawings.* ❶

4–1 An Atomic Model of Matter

In the last few chapters, you learned several important facts about matter. All materials are made of matter. Matter is anything that has mass and volume. And the basic building blocks of matter are atoms. You have learned all of this in a rather short time. But the story of how scientists have come to know what they do about matter spans a much greater time period—thousands of years to be sure!

For more than 2400 years, philosophers and scientists have tried to determine the composition of matter using a variety of experiments and observations. Because the basic building blocks of matter (atoms) could not until recently be seen, researchers have relied on observations of how matter behaves. Such observations are called indirect evidence.

Indirect evidence about an object is evidence you get without actually seeing or touching the object. As you gather indirect evidence, you can develop a mental picture, or model. A model uses familiar ideas to explain unfamiliar facts observed in nature. A model can be changed as new information is collected. As you read further, you will learn how a model of matter was developed and changed over many years. From the early Greek concept of the atom to the modern atomic theory, scientists have built on and modified existing models of the atom. Let's see just how.

TEACHING STRATEGY 4–1

FOCUS/MOTIVATION

Distribute a 6-inch by 6-inch sheet of paper to each student. Using only their hands, have each student fold the square into halves, then tear the sheet into halves along the line of the crease. This creasing and tearing should be continued as many times as possible. While students are working, remind them that the paper represents a pure substance and that they are

attempting to divide that paper or substance as many times as possible.
• **How many different pieces of paper were you able to create?** (Answers will vary.)
• **What prevented you from creating more pieces?** (Responses might include the large size of their hands and fingers when compared to the small size of the pieces.)
• **Using different equipment like microscopes and special cutting tools, how many times do you think a piece of paper could be divided until just the smallest possible piece of paper remains?** (Answers will vary.)

Remind students that the smallest possible piece of paper that still has properties of that paper is called an atom.

CONTENT DEVELOPMENT

As you discuss the characteristics of the atomic models of the Greeks, point out that the outlook of a Greek philosopher-scientist such as Democritus was basically nonexperimental and relied on untested speculation. Remind students of the scientific method—in particular, the role of experimentation in testing hypotheses.

Figure 4–2 *Unlike many artists working today, ancient Greek artists did not paint on canvas. This vase painting, showing a warrior carrying the body of a dead companion, was made about the time Democritus lived.*

The Greek Model

The search for a description of matter began with the Greek philosopher Democritus (dih-MAHK-ruh-tuhs) more than 2000 years ago. He and many other philosophers had puzzled over this question: Could matter be divided into smaller and smaller pieces forever, or was there a limit to the number of times a piece of matter could be divided?

After much observation and questioning, Democritus concluded that matter could not be divided into smaller and smaller pieces forever. Eventually the smallest possible piece would be obtained. This piece would be indivisible. Democritus named this smallest piece of matter an atom. The word *atom* comes from the Greek word *atomos,* meaning "not to be cut," or "indivisible."

The Greek philosophers who shared Democritus' belief about the atom were called atomists. The atomists had no way of knowing what atoms were or how they looked. But they hypothesized that atoms were small, hard particles that were all made of the same material but were of different shapes and sizes. Also, they hypothesized that they were infinite in number, always moving, and capable of joining together.

Although Democritus and the other atomists were on the right trail, the theory of atoms was ignored and forgotten. Few people believed the idea. In fact, it took almost 2100 years before an atomic model of matter was accepted.

FIND OUT BY
DOING

Shine a Little Light on It

Indirect evidence about an object is evidence you get without actually seeing or touching the object. As you gather indirect evidence, you can develop a model, or mental picture.

1. Fill two glasses almost completely full with water. Leave one glass as is. Add a piece of soap about the size of a pea to the other glass. Stir the water to dissolve the soap.

2. Turn off the lights in the room. Make sure that the room is completely dark.

3. Shine a flashlight beam horizontally from the side of the glass into the soapy water. Aim the light beam so that it enters the water just below the surface. Repeat this procedure with the glass of plain water. Observe and record the effect of the light beam in each glass.

What was the effect in the plain water? What was the effect in the soapy water? What caused the effect in the soapy water? What was the role of the glass of plain water in this activity?

N ■ 85

Figure 4–3 *The Rosetta Stone was discovered in 1799, a few years before Dalton's atomic theory was proposed. In his work, Dalton tried to explain the mysteries of atomic structure. Do you know how the Rosetta Stone helped to explain the mysteries of Egyptian writing?* ❶

Dalton's Model

In the early 1800s, the English chemist John Dalton performed a number of experiments that eventually led to the acceptance of the idea of atoms. Dalton had long been interested in meteorology, the study of weather. His observations about the composition of air led him to investigate the properties of gases. He discovered that gases combine as if they were made of individual particles. These particles were the atoms of Democritus.

In 1803, Dalton combined the results of his experiments with other observations about matter and proposed an atomic theory. The basic ideas of Dalton's atomic theory are as follows:

- **All elements are composed of atoms. Atoms are indivisible and indestructible particles.**
- **Atoms of the same element are exactly alike.**
- **Atoms of different elements are different.**
- **Compounds are formed by the joining of atoms of two or more elements.**

Dalton's atomic theory of matter became one of the foundations of modern chemistry. But like many scientific theories, Dalton's theory had to be modified as scientists gained more information about the structure of matter.

Figure 4–4 *The atoms of relatively few elements make up everything in the world around you—whether it be a tranquil country landscape or a vibrant (but smoggy) city.*

86 ■ N

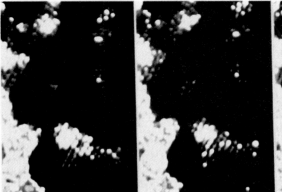
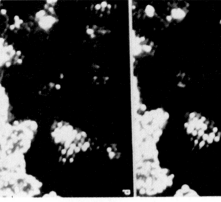

Thomson's Model

Was Dalton's theory correct? Is an atom indivisible? In 1897, the English scientist J. J. Thomson provided the first hint that an atom is made of even smaller particles. Thomson was studying the passage of an electric current through a gas. The gas gave off rays that Thomson showed were made of negatively charged particles. But the gas was known to be made of uncharged atoms. So where had the negatively charged particles come from? From within the atom, Thomson reasoned. A particle smaller than the atom had to exist. The atom was divisible! Thomson called the negatively charged particles "corpuscles." Today these particles are known as electrons.

As often happens in science, Thomson's discovery of electrons created a new problem to solve. The atom as a whole was known to be uncharged, or neutral. But if electrons in the atom were negatively charged, what balanced the negative charge? Thomson reasoned that the atom must also contain positively charged particles. But try as he might, he was unable to find this positive charge.

Thomson was so certain that these positively charged particles existed that he proposed a model of the atom that is sometimes called the "plum pudding" model. Figure 4–6 shows Thomson's model. **According to Thomson's atomic model, the atom was made of a puddinglike positively charged material throughout which negatively charged electrons were scattered, like plums in a pudding.** Thomson's

Figure 4–5 *These photographs of uranium atoms were taken by scientists working at the University of Chicago. The blue, yellow, and red spots are uranium atoms magnified more than 5 million times. In this remarkable series of photographs, you can observe the actual movement of the atoms.*

Figure 4–6 *Thomson's model of the atom pictured a "pudding" of positively charged material. Negatively charged electrons were scattered throughout like plums in a pudding. What is the overall charge on this atom? Why?* ②

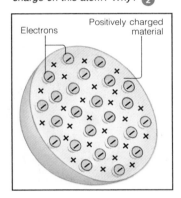

N ■ 87

HISTORICAL NOTE

JOSEPH JOHN THOMAS

In 1906, Sir Joseph John Thomson received the Nobel prize in physics for his discovery of the electron.

FACTS AND FIGURES

THE ROSETTA STONE

The Rosetta Stone is 28 centimeters thick, almost 114 centimeters high, and 72 centimeters across—too large to be lost forever.

how atoms behave, scientists can find out what the building blocks consist of, where they are located, and how to use them.

● ● ● ● **Integration** ● ● ● ●

Use the information on the Rosetta Stone to integrate social studies into your lesson.

GUIDED PRACTICE

Skills Development

Skills: Making observations, making inferences

At this point have students complete the in-text Chapter 4 Laboratory Investigation, Shoe Box Atoms. They will determine how indirect evidence can be used to build a model.

CONTENT DEVELOPMENT

Ask students to think about a shopping mall or other shopping area.

• **Name some stores in the shopping mall.** (Student responses will vary.)

Point out that a shopping mall is made up of a collection of stores.

• **Is it important to know what is in a collection of things? Why?** (Yes. You can use those things or make those things available to other people.)

• **Why would it be important to know what each store in the mall does?** (To be able to go to the right business when you need to.)

• **Would it be important to know where each store is located? Why?** (Yes. To be able to find and use a certain type of product or service.)

• **Why is it important to know what the building blocks of matter, atoms, are made of?** (If you know what the atoms are made of, then you can better understand how they work and how to use them.)

Explain to students that by studying

NIELS BOHR

Niels Bohr was a Danish physicist who lived from 1885 to 1962. Bohr studied under J. J. Thomson in England and then worked with Ernest Rutherford. In 1916, he became professor of physics at the University of Copenhagen. He became director of the Institute of Theoretical Physics in 1920 and won the Nobel prize in physics in 1922.

During World War II, in 1943, Bohr left Copenhagen to escape from the Nazis and went to Los Alamos, New Mexico, to serve as an advisor on the development of the first atomic bomb. After the war, he returned to Copenhagen and worked to promote peaceful uses of nuclear energy. Bohr received the first Atoms for Peace award in 1957.

FACTS AND
FIGURES

CELLS

All living things—plants and animals—are made of cells. Cells are a variety of shapes and sizes. Most averaged-sized cells are about 0.0025 centimeters long. Almost 500 of these cells would fit within the dot of this *i*.

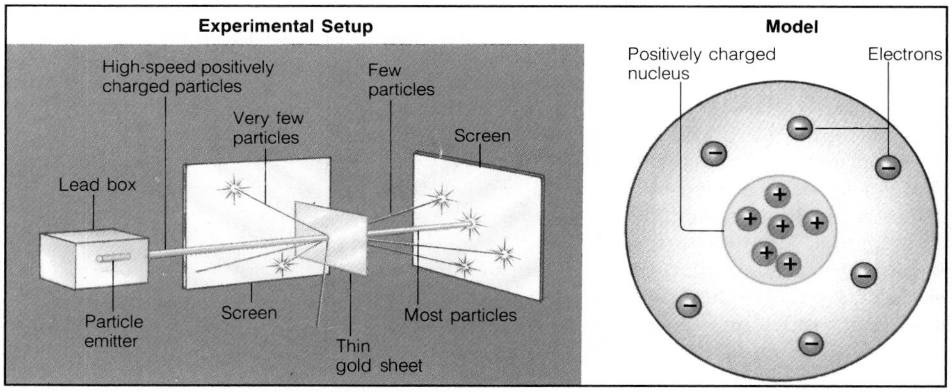

4-1 (continued)

CONTENT DEVELOPMENT

Review the early model of the indivisible atom and ask students to consider the difficulty of testing it experimentally, given the incredible smallness of the atom. Remind them of the role of indirect evidence in the experimentation. Then tell them that in the case of the divisibility of atoms, such evidence is actually relatively easy to obtain.

GUIDED PRACTICE

▶ *Laboratory Manual*

Skills Development

Skills: Observing, making predictions

At this point you may want to have students complete the Chapter 4 Laborato-

Figure 4–7 *Artist and physicist Bill Parker created this "electric art" by passing an electric current through a glass sphere that contained certain gases. The light is produced when electrons in the gases absorb energy and release it. Who is credited with the discovery of the electron?* ❶

Figure 4–8 *In Rutherford's experiment, most of the positively charged material passed right through the gold sheet (left). A few particles were slightly deflected, and even fewer particles bounced straight back. From these observations, Rutherford concluded that the atom was mostly empty space with a dense positively charged nucleus in the center (right).*

Experimental Setup

High-speed positively charged particles

Few particles

Very few particles

Screen

Lead box

Particle emitter

Screen

Thin gold sheet

Most particles

Model

Positively charged nucleus

Electrons

---

model, while far from correct, was an important step in understanding the structure of the atom.

Rutherford's Model

In 1908, the English physicist Ernest Rutherford was hard at work on an experiment that seemed to have little to do with unraveling the mysteries of atomic structure. Rutherford's experiment involved firing a stream of tiny positively charged particles at a thin sheet of gold foil. (Although the gold foil was hammered very thin, it was still 2000 atoms thick!) Rutherford discovered that most of the positively charged "bullets" passed right through the gold atoms in the sheet of foil without changing course at all. This could only mean that the gold atoms in the sheet were mostly empty space! Atoms were not a pudding filled with a positively charged material, as Thomson had thought.

Some of the "bullets," however, did bounce away from the gold sheet as if they had hit something solid. In fact, a few bounced almost straight back. What could this mean? Rutherford knew that positive charges repel other positive charges. So he proposed that an atom had a small, dense, positively charged center that repelled his positively charged "bullets." He called this center of the atom the **nucleus** (NOO-klee-uhs; plural: nuclei, NOO-klee-igh). The nucleus is tiny compared to the atom as a whole. To get an idea of the size of the nucleus in an atom, think of a marble in a baseball stadium!

---

ry Investigation in the *Laboratory Manual* called Making Predictions Using Indirect Evidence. Students will use indirect evidence to determine the properties of an object they cannot see.

CONTENT DEVELOPMENT

Discuss Rutherford's experiment with students. His experiment, which is classic in its simplicity, may be difficult for students to grasp without a step-by-step discussion of what Rutherford did and observed.

• **What did the deflection of particles that Rutherford observed indicate?** (An atom has a small, dense, positively charged center, which he named the nucleus.)

● ● ● ● **Integration** ● ● ● ●

Use the information on electric art to integrate fine arts appreciation into your lesson.

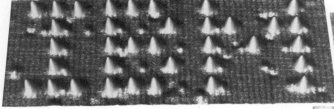

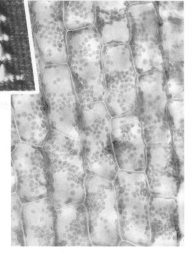

Rutherford reasoned that all of an atom's positively charged particles were contained in the nucleus. The negatively charged electrons were scattered outside the nucleus around the atom's edge. Between the nucleus and the electrons was mostly empty space! Although this model was useful in many ways, it did not adequately explain the arrangement of the electrons. It would be the job of future scientists to improve on the Rutherford atomic model.

The Bohr Model

Rutherford's model proposed that negatively charged electrons were held in an atom by the attraction between them and the positively charged nucleus. But where exactly were the electrons in the atom? In 1913, the Danish scientist Niels Bohr proposed an improvement on the Rutherford model. In his model he placed each electron in a specific energy level. **According to Bohr's atomic model, electrons move in definite orbits around the nucleus, much like planets circle the sun. These orbits, or energy levels, are located at certain distances from the nucleus.**

The Wave Model

Bohr's model worked well in explaining the structure and behavior of simple atoms such as hydrogen. But it did not explain more complex atoms.

Today's atomic model is based on the principles of wave mechanics. The basic ideas of wave mechanics are complicated and involve complex mathematical equations. Some of the conclusions of this theory, however, will help you understand the arrangement of electrons in an atom.

According to the theory of wave mechanics, electrons do not move about an atom in a definite path

Figure 4–9 *Atoms are the incredibly small building blocks of matter. This photograph shows the first structure ever built atom by atom (left). Cells are the building blocks of all living things (right). But even the largest cells are made of tiny atoms.*

FIND OUT BY DOING

Making a Model Atom

1. Use materials such as cardboard, construction paper, colored pencils, string, and cotton to construct models of the Thomson atom and the Rutherford atom.

2. Label the models and place them on display in your classroom. Write a brief description of the experiment that each model was based on.

FIND OUT BY DOING

MAKING A MODEL ATOM

Skills: Making models, manipulative

Materials: string, colored pencils, cotton, cardboard, construction paper

By completing this activity, students reinforce what they have learned about atomic models. Check student models carefully for accuracy, labels, and mode of display.

Suggest that students put their descriptions of the experiments the models were based on in their portfolios.

▶ *Multimedia* ◀

Use the transparency in your *Transparency Binder* called Rutherford's Experiment to help students understand a facet of the history of the atomic model.

GUIDED PRACTICE

Skills Development

Skill: Developing a model

Divide students into teams of four to six students per team. Have each team choose an atomic model and construct a physical representation of it. Encourage teams to use their ingenuity in choosing materials. Completed models may be exchanged, discussed, and displayed.

CONTENT DEVELOPMENT

Impress upon students that as the atomic model evolved and became more sophisticated over the centuries, the equipment used to test the model also became more sophisticated.

• **Why would complicated pieces of equipment be needed in experimentation?** (The processes being studied are difficult to observe, so experimentation must involve great precision. Devices must also be highly sophisticated, and great care must be taken that undesirable complications, such as contamination, false recordings by instruments, and confusion created by other processes, do not interfere with the experiment or scientists' interpretation of it.)

• **How can findings that involve such tiny bits of matter as atoms reveal anything about the universe as a whole?** (The laws of nature that these findings reveal are believed to apply to matter as a whole and govern the behavior and evolution of the universe, which is made up of these tiny particles.)

● ● ● ● **Integration** ● ● ● ●

Use the information on cells to integrate concepts from life science into your lesson.

MICROCOSM AND MACROCOSM

Rutherford and Bohr, in their proposals of atomic models—with their electrons circling a central nucleus—were influenced in this regard by their knowledge of the structure of the solar system. Powerful images (such as that of orbiting planets) developed in one area of thought have often served as a basis for constructing models in other areas. This fact stems in part from a philosophical belief, common among scientists and artists since the Renaissance, that a small structure—the so-called microcosm—and a very large structure—the macrocosm—mirror each other.

BACKGROUND INFORMATION

WAVE MECHANICS

Wave mechanics, or quantum mechanics, is based in part on the concept formulated by Louis de Groglie that particles in motion, such as electrons, also have wavelike properties. Wave mechanics permits calculations of the probabilities that an electron in a given energy state will have certain locations or velocities at a given time. Werner Heisenberg in his Uncertainty Principle points out that increased precision regarding one variable, such as position, results necessarily in decreased precision regarding other variables, such as velocity. For example, he demonstrated that exact information on the position of an electron at a given time can be obtained only by sacrificing the ability to obtain any information about the electron's velocity at the same time.

Figure 4–10 *This atomic model shows the nucleus with its neutrons and protons. Surrounding the nucleus are rapidly moving electrons. Can scientists know with certainty where a particular electron is located in an atom?* ❶

Figure 4–11 *When atomic particles collide, new and unusual particles may be produced. By studying the tracks made by these particles in a bubble chamber, scientists can learn more about the nature and interactions of atomic particles.*

like planets around the sun. In fact, it is impossible to determine the exact location of an electron. Scientists can only predict where an electron is most likely to be found. The probable location of an electron is based on how much energy the electron has.

As you can see, the modern atomic model is based on the models of Rutherford and Bohr, and on the principles of wave mechanics. **According to the modern atomic model, an atom has a small positively charged nucleus surrounded by a large region in which there are enough electrons to make the atom neutral.**

4–1 Section Review

1. How has the model of the atom changed over time?
2. Why is indirect evidence important in studying the structure of the atom?
3. What atomic particle did J. J. Thomson discover?
4. What is the center of the atom called? How was it discovered?
5. How does the wave model of electron placement differ from the model of electron position proposed by Niels Bohr?

Critical Thinking—*Science and Technology*
6. The model that explains atomic structure has changed over time. How has technology contributed to this change?

4–1 (continued)

CONTENT DEVELOPMENT

It is important to make clear to students that the atomic models they are studying were well supported by the experimental evidence available at the time the models were proposed. The point in presenting them is not to belittle the work of earlier scientists, but rather to show the logic that underlay their work and scientific method that allowed for the re-

placement of each model by a more adequate model. Stress the nature of science as a logical and creative process rather than as an unchanging body of facts.
• **Thinking back about each model we discussed, why did each person propose that model? How does the development of the model illustrate scientific method? Why was the model replaced by another?** (The point is that each model was proposed to overcome the inadequacies of an older model. These inadequacies were revealed by experimentation, which also

served to support the new model, whose inadequacies would, in time, be revealed by later experimentation. Once again, logic, scientific method, and scientific process are to be stressed.)

INDEPENDENT PRACTICE

Section Review 4–1

1. Early models of the atom were characterized by conclusions based on indirect evidence. Through the years, atomic models were characterized more and more by conclusions based on an increasing quan-

CONNECTIONS

Data In . . . A Building Out

You now know that as a result of many, many years of research, scientists have developed a model that describes the structure of the atom—and they have done so without ever having seen an actual atom. Today, scientists have abundant evidence that this model of the atom is accurate.

But making a model has other, more practical uses. You can see examples of these uses almost daily as you walk down streets in your town or city. Today, models developed by *computers* serve as blueprints for the houses and buildings you see around you. Such a model can show how a building will look while it is still

Computers have become invaluable tools in many different professions. The final designs and plans for this building were developed with the help of a computer.

only a series of ideas in an architect's mind and a few quick sketches on a sheet of paper.

Computer programs offer architects and building engineers a wide range of applications: designing a building, determining air flow and people movement, measuring wind effect on structure, to name a few. Some computer programs can even show the effects of light and shadow that will exist in a finished building. If such effects are undesirable, changes in the location and number of windows and doors, for example, can be made long before construction of the building begins.

Remember, however, that computer-assisted designs are only a tool to make the work of architects and engineers easier. The design of a wonderful building—a building that stirs the heart and lifts the spirit—still begins deep within the human mind and results from the combined talents of its creators.

tity of solid, scientific data.

2 Indirect evidence is evidence about an object that is gathered without actually having seen or touched the object. It is based on observations of how the object behaves. It helps in the development of a model, which explains observed facts.

3. J. J. Thompson discovered the negatively charged atomic particle called the electron.

4. The center of the atom is called the nucleus. It was discovered by Ernest Rutherford. He fired a stream of positively charged particles at a thin sheet of gold foil. Most of the particles passed right through the atoms in the gold sheet. But some particles did bounce away from the gold sheet as if they had hit something solid. Rutherford proposed that these solid areas were in the centers of the atoms.

5. According to Bohr's atomic model, electrons move in definite orbits, or energy levels, around and at certain distances from the nucleus. According to the wave model, electrons do not move about an atom in a definite path. It is im-

4-2 Structure of the Atom

Guide for Reading

Focus on these questions as you read.
▶ What are the particles that make up the atom?
▶ What is the structure of the atom?

4-2 Structure of the Atom

When Thomson performed his experiments, he was hoping to find a single particle smaller than an atom. This task is similar to finding a particular grain of sand among the grains of sand making up all the beaches of the Earth! Certainly Thomson would be surprised to learn that today about 200 different kinds of such particles are known to exist! Because these particles are smaller than an atom, they are called **subatomic particles.**

The three main subatomic particles are the proton, the neutron, and the electron. As you read about these particles, note the location, mass, and charge of each. In this way, you will better understand the modern atomic theory. Let's begin with the nucleus, or center, of the atom.

The Nucleus

The nucleus is the "core" of the atom, the center in which 99.9 percent of the mass of the atom is located. Yet the nucleus is about a hundred thousand times smaller than the entire atom! In fact, the size of the nucleus compared to the entire atom has been likened to the size of a bee compared to a football stadium! Two of the three main subatomic particles are found in the nucleus.

PROTONS Those positively charged "bullets" that Rutherford fired at the gold sheet bounced back because of **protons** in the nucleus of the gold atoms. Protons are positively charged particles found in the nucleus. All protons are identical, regardless of the element in which they are found.

Figure 4-12 *A lithium nucleus contains 3 protons and 4 neutrons. A carbon nucleus contains 6 protons and 6 neutrons. How many electrons does a lithium nucleus contain? A carbon nucleus?* ❶

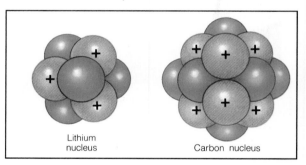

Lithium nucleus

Carbon nucleus

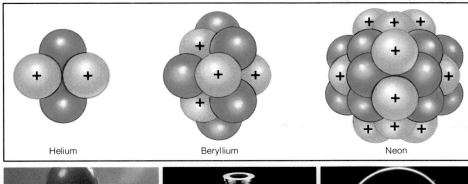

Because the masses of subatomic particles are so small, scientists use a special unit to measure them. They call this unit an **atomic mass unit,** or amu. The mass of a proton is 1 amu. To get a better idea of how small a proton is, imagine the number 6 followed by 23 zeros. It would take that many protons to equal a mass of just 1 gram!

NEUTRONS Sharing the nucleus with the protons are the electrically neutral **neutrons.** Neutrons have no charge. Like protons, all neutrons are identical. Neutrons have slightly more mass than protons. But the mass of a neutron is still considered to be 1 amu.

Atomic Number

You read before that atoms of different elements are different. But if all protons are identical and all neutrons are identical, what accounts for these differences? The answer lies in the particles found in the nucleus—more specifically, in the number of protons in the nucleus. Because it is the number of

Figure 4–13 *The nuclei of helium, beryllium, and neon atoms all contain protons and neutrons. Yet helium, beryllium, and neon are very different elements. What accounts for these differences?* ❷

FACTS AND FIGURES
OTHER SUBATOMIC PARTICLES

Protons, neutrons, and electrons are not the only subatomic particles. Others are called baryons, mesons, leptons, and bosons.

BACKGROUND INFORMATION
BERYLLIUM

Beryllium was discovered in the same year, 1928, by two scientists in two different places—Friedrich Wohler in Germany and A. A. Bussy in France.

Beryllium is a gray-white metal. Although it is the lightest of the rigid metals, it is very strong and hard.

Because X-rays pass easily through pure beryllium, it is used to make airtight windows in X-ray tubes and to make electrodes inside neon light bulbs. Beryllium is also used in building rockets and spacecraft because it is light in weight and can absorb large amounts of heat.

Investigation in the *Laboratory Manual* called Investigating Rutherford's Model of the Atom. Students will duplicate Rutherford's experiment.

ENRICHMENT

Have students consider how subatomic particles would be affected if the particles were passed in a beam between oppositely charged plates (similar to allowing them to move in the magnetic field of a bubble chamber).

• **How might a relatively massive, positively charged proton be affected, as compared to a very low-mass negatively charged electron moving at the same velocity?** (The proton and the electron would be deflected in different directions—the proton toward the negatively charged plate, the electron toward the positively charged plate. The proton, because it is more massive (or has greater inertia), is deflected less than the electron. The uncharged neutron is not deflected.)

▶ *Multimedia* ◀

Use the transparency in your *Transparency Binder* called Structure of the Atom to help develop the concept of atomic structure.

REINFORCEMENT/RETEACHING

▶ *Activity Book*

Students who need practice with the different subatomic particles should complete the chapter activity Drawing Atoms.

protons in the nucleus that determines what the element is. For example, an atom of carbon has 6 protons in its nucleus. Carbon is a dark solid. Much of the sooty remains of a burned piece of wood are made up of atoms of carbon. An atom of nitrogen has 7 protons in its nucleus—only one more proton than carbon. Nitrogen is a colorless gas that makes up most of the Earth's atmosphere.

The number of protons in the nucleus of an atom is called the **atomic number.** The atomic number identifies the element. All hydrogen atoms—and only hydrogen atoms—have 1 proton and an atomic number of 1. Helium atoms have an atomic number of 2. There are 2 protons in the nucleus of every helium atom. Oxygen has an atomic number of 8, and 8 protons are in the nucleus of each atom. How many protons does an atom of uranium—atomic number 92—have? And what are the atomic numbers of the elements carbon and nitrogen that you just read about? ●

Isotopes

The atomic number of an element will never change. This means that there is always the same number of protons in the nucleus of every atom of that element. But the number of neutrons is not so constant! Atoms of the same element can have different numbers of neutrons.

Atoms of the same element that have the same number of protons but different numbers of neutrons are called **isotopes** (IGH-suh-tohps). Look at Figure 4–15. You will see three different isotopes of

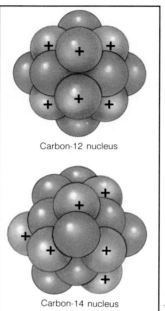

Carbon-12 nucleus

Carbon-14 nucleus

Figure 4–14 *These two isotopes of carbon have the same atomic number, 6. Although it cannot speak, this fossil fish can be made to divulge its age. To do this, scientists analyze the proportions of carbon isotopes present in the fish. What is the difference between the two carbon isotopes?* ●

94 ■ N

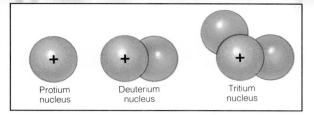

Protium nucleus Deuterium nucleus Tritium nucleus

Figure 4–15 *The three isotopes of hydrogen are protium, deuterium, and tritium. Which isotope contains 2 neutrons? What is the atomic number of each isotope?* ③

the element hydrogen. Note that the number of protons does not change. Remember that the atomic number, or number of protons, identifies a substance. No matter how many neutrons there are in the nucleus, 1 proton always means the atom is hydrogen. How many neutrons does each hydrogen isotope have? ④

Mass Number and Atomic Mass

All atoms have a **mass number.** The mass number of an atom is the sum of the protons and neutrons in its nucleus. The mass number of the carbon isotope with 6 neutrons is 6 (protons) + 6 (neutrons), or 12. The mass number of the carbon isotope with 8 neutrons is 6 (protons) + 8 (neutrons), or 14. To distinguish one isotope from another, the mass number is given with the element's name.

Two common isotopes of the element uranium are uranium-235 and uranium-238. The atomic number—or number of protons—of uranium is 92. Since the mass number is equal to the number of protons plus the number of neutrons, the number of neutrons can easily be determined. The number of neutrons is determined by subtracting the atomic number (number of protons) from the mass number (number of protons + neutrons). Here are two problems for you to try. How many neutrons are there in uranium-235? In uranium-238? ⑥

Any sample of an element as it occurs in nature contains a mixture of isotopes. As a result, the **atomic mass** of the element is the average mass of all the isotopes of that element as they occur in nature. For this reason, the atomic mass of an element is not usually a whole number. For example, the atomic mass of carbon is 12.011. This number indicates that there are more atoms of carbon-12 than there are of carbon-14. Can you explain why this conclusion is reasonable? ⑦

Figure 4–16 *This chart shows the symbol, atomic number, and mass number for some common elements. Why is the mass number always a whole number but the atomic mass is not?* ⑤

COMMON ELEMENTS

Name		Atomic Number	Mass Number
Hydrogen	H	1	1
Helium	He	2	4
Carbon	C	6	12
Nitrogen	N	7	14
Oxygen	O	8	16
Fluorine	F	9	19
Sodium	Na	11	23
Aluminum	Al	13	27
Sulfur	S	16	32
Chlorine	Cl	17	35
Calcium	Ca	20	40
Iron	Fe	26	56
Copper	Cu	29	64
Zinc	Zn	30	65
Silver	Ag	47	108
Gold	Au	79	197
Mercury	Hg	80	201
Lead	Pb	82	207

N ■ 95

each isotope is simply multiplied by the decimal form of its percent occurrence, and all the results are added. Consider as an example isotopes of a fictitious element that has the following atomic masses: 8 amu (20 percent), 9 amu (50 percent), and 10 amu (30 percent). The atomic mass of the element is 8 amu (0.20) + 9 amu (0.50) + 10 amu (0.30) = 9.1 amu.

Have students apply the method to other elements, both fictitious and real. Simply provide them with the mass of each isotope and its percent occurrence in nature (taking care that the percents total 100 for each element).

▶ *Activity Book*

Students will be challenged by the chapter activity Isotopes or Different Elements?

7. T atom—1 proton and 1 neutron (2 amus.)

INDEPENDENT PRACTICE

▶ *Activity Book*

Students who need practice on the concept of the isotopes should complete the chapter activity called Making Models of Isotopes.

CONTENT DEVELOPMENT

Using a periodic table, prepare a list of selected elements along with their number of protons. Then have students write the atomic number for each element.

You may also wish to reverse the procedure by listing the atomic number and having students give the number of protons in the nucleus.

ENRICHMENT

Demonstrate for students a method that can be used to calculate the atomic mass of an element, given the atomic masses and the percent of natural occurrence of its isotopes. The atomic mass of

PROBLEM SOLVING
IMPROVING THE ODDS

This simple activity enables students to relate the concept of probability to a common experience—the location of a friend. Students should recognize that informed guessing is the basis of probability. Have them construct their charts several times, reflecting changes in the weather, day of the week, and season. Students will gain a better appreciation of the concept of probability by relating it to a real-life situation. They can predict only the probable location of their friend, just as only the *probable* location of an electron in an atom can be determined.

Integration: Use the Problem Solving feature to integrate mathematics into your lesson.

COMMON ERRORS

Students who did not get the correct answer may have confused some of the numbers asked for in the directions, or they may have made mistakes in a simple arithmetic. Go over these students' calculations with them and point out what they did wrong.

PROBLEM ??? Solving

Improving the Odds

You are trying to locate a friend on a sunny Saturday afternoon. Although you cannot say with absolute certainty where your friend is, you can estimate the chance of finding your friend in various places. Your estimates are based on past experiences.

Create a chart that lists at least seven possible locations for your friend. Next to each location, give the probability of finding your friend there. Express the probability in percent. For example, there is a 50-percent probability that your friend ❶ is at the school yard playing soccer. Remember that the total probability for the seven events should equal 100 percent.

Would a change in the weather influence your probability determination? How about a change in the day of the week? In the season of the year?

Relating Concepts

How does this activity help you better understand the concept of probability? How does it relate to an electron's location in an atom?

The Electrons

If you think protons and neutrons are small, picture this. Whirling around outside the nucleus are particles that are about 1/2000 the mass of either a proton or a neutron! These particles are **electrons.** Electrons have a negative charge and a mass of 1/1836 amu. In an uncharged atom, the number of negatively charged electrons is equal to the number of positively charged protons. The total charge of the atom is zero. Thus the atom is said to be neutral.

As you have learned, electrons do not move in fixed paths around the nucleus. In fact, the exact location of an electron cannot be known. Only the probability, or likelihood, of finding an electron at a particular place in an atom can be determined.

4–2 (continued)

CONTENT DEVELOPMENT

Explain that the negatively charged electrons in the atom are found within a "cloud" around the nucleus. Point out that most of the cloud is empty space.

• **What is meant by "an electron fills the cloud"?** (That the electron can be anywhere within the space around the nucleus.)

Point out that the number of electrons in an atom equals the number of protons. Explain that the mass of an electron is much less than that of a proton. Tell students that the mass of an electron is 1/1836 amu.

• **How may electrons would it take to equal the mass of 1 proton?** (1836 electrons.)

Students may imagine that the electron cloud of an atom is actually a cloudy smear of spread-out electrons. But the "cloudlike" description of the real structure relates only to the appearance of a probability diagram in which specific locations of electrons at different times are plotted simultaneously as points. The many points give a cloudlike appearance to the diagram.

GUIDED PRACTICE
▶ *Laboratory Manual*

Skills Development

Skills: Relating concepts, making calculations

At this point you may want to have students complete the Chapter 4 Laboratory Investigation in the *Laboratory Manual* called Relating Electrons and Probability. Students will gain a better understanding of probability and how it relates to electrons.

In fact, the entire space that the electrons occupy is what scientists think of as the atom itself. Sometimes this space is called the **electron cloud.** But do not think of an atom as a solid center surrounded by a fuzzy, blurry cloud. For the electron cloud is a space in which electrons are likely to be found. It is somewhat like the area around a beehive in which the bees move. Sometimes the electrons are near the nucleus; sometimes they are farther away from it. In a hydrogen atom, 1 electron "fills" the cloud. It fills the cloud in the sense that it can be found almost anywhere within the space.

Although the electrons whirl about the nucleus billions of times in one second, they do not do so in a random way. Each electron seems to be locked into a certain area in the electron cloud. The location of an electron in the cloud depends upon how much energy the electron has.

According to modern atomic theory, electrons are arranged in **energy levels.** An energy level represents the most likely location in the electron cloud in which an electron can be found. Electrons with the lowest energy are found in the energy level closest to the nucleus. Electrons with higher energy are found in energy levels farther from the nucleus.

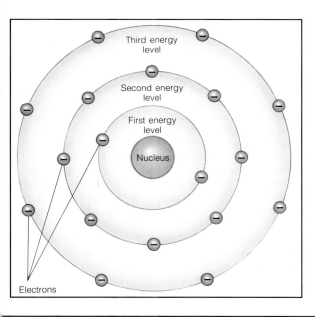

Electrons

Third energy level

Second energy level

First energy level

Nucleus

Figure 4–17 *Each energy level in an atom can hold only a certain number of electrons. How many electrons are in the first, second, and third energy levels shown here?* ❶

FIND OUT BY CALCULATING

The Mystery Element

You can identify the mystery element by performing the following mathematical calculations. ❷

a. Multiply the atomic number of hydrogen by the number of electrons in mercury, atomic number 80.

b. Divide this number by the number of neutrons in helium, atomic number 2, mass number 4.

c. Add the number of protons in potassium, atomic number 19.

d. Add the mass number of the most common isotope of carbon.

e. Subtract the number of neutrons in sulfur, atomic number 16, mass number 32.

f. Divide by the number of electrons in boron, atomic number 5, mass number 11.

Which of the following elements is the mystery element: fluorine, atomic number 9; neon, atomic number 10; or sodium, atomic number 11?

SUBATOMIC PARTICLES			
Particle	**Mass (amu)**	**Charge**	**Location**
Proton	1	+	Nucleus
Neutron	1	Neutral	Nucleus
Electron	1/1836	−	Electron cloud

Figure 4–18 *The mass, charge, and location of the three basic subatomic particles are shown in this chart. Which subatomic particle has a neutral charge and a mass of 1 amu? Where is this subatomic particle located?* ❶

BACKGROUND INFORMATION
LITHIUM BONDING

Lithium, a soft, silvery-white metallic element, is the lightest known metal. Lithium metal combines readily with other metals, and for that reason, it does not occur pure in nature. To obtain lithium metal, scientists pass electricity through fused lithium chloride.

FACTS AND FIGURES
QUARKS

According to current theory, quarks are thought to possess properties called "flavors" and "color." The six different quark flavors are up, down, strange, charm, truth, and beauty. The three colors are red, blue, and green. These names, however, do not refer to actual flavors or colors.

4–2 (CONTINUED)

ENRICHMENT

Students may wish to do some library research on quarks and on related characteristics such as quarks' "colors" and "flavors." Advise them to consult up-to-date popular-science magazines rather than difficult technical journals.

GUIDED PRACTICE

▶ *Activity Book*

Students who need practice on the concept of the structure of an atom should complete the chapter activity Atomic Structure.

▶ *Multimedia* ◀

Use the transparency in your *Transparency Binder* called Energy Levels to help

---

CAREERS

Science Teacher

The weather on Saturday afternoon was ideal for gardening. But the teacher's mind was back in the classroom rather than on the tender bean sprouts that had just pushed their way through the soil's surface.

Science teachers spend much of their time developing plans to teach different topics. They try to create interesting ways to present information to their students. Activities such as lectures, demonstrations, laboratory work, and field trips are often used.

Science teachers also attend professional meetings, conferences, and workshops. If you are interested in this career, you can learn more by writing to the American Federation of Teachers, 1012 Fourteenth Street NW, Washington, DC 20005.

Each energy level within an atom can hold only a certain number of electrons. The energy level closest to the nucleus—the lowest energy level—can hold no more than 2 electrons. The second and third energy levels can each hold 8 electrons. See Figure 4–17 on page 97.

The properties of the different elements depend upon how many electrons are in the various energy levels of their atoms. In fact, the electron arrangement of its atoms is what gives an element its chemical properties. One of the most important chemical properties of an element is its bonding (combining) ability. Some elements easily form bonds with other elements. Some elements hardly ever form bonds. An element's bonding ability is determined by the arrangement of the electrons in its atoms—more specifically, the arrangement of the electrons in the outermost energy level, or the level farthest from the nucleus.

Can the atom be "cut"? The existence of protons, neutrons, and electrons proves it can. In fact, two of these particles can be separated into even smaller particles. It is now believed that a new kind of particle makes up all the other known particles in the nucleus. This particle is called the **quark** (kwork). There are a number of different kinds of quarks. All nuclear particles are thought to be combinations of three quarks. One group of three quarks will produce a neutron. Another group of three quarks will produce a proton. According to current theory, quarks have properties called "flavor" and "color." There are six different flavors and three different colors.

---

develop understanding of electrons' behavior.

INDEPENDENT PRACTICE
Section Review 4–2

1. A proton is located in the nucleus of an atom, having a positive electrical charge and a mass of 1 amu. A neutron is located in the nucleus of an atom, having a neutral electrical charge and a mass of 1 amu. An electron travels about the nucleus of an atom and has a negative electrical charge and a mass of 1/1836 amu.

2. The nucleus, or core, of an atom contains 99.9 percent of the mass of an atom because the heaviest subatomic particles are located there.

3. The number of protons in the nucleus of an atom is its atomic number. Atoms of the same element that have the same number of protons but different numbers of neutrons are called isotopes. The atomic mass of an element is the average mass of all the isotopes of that element as they occur in nature. The mass number of an atom is the sum of the protons and neu-

4-2 Section Review

1. Classify the three main subatomic particles according to location, charge, and mass.
2. Why does the nucleus account for 99.9 percent of the mass of an atom?
3. Define atomic number; isotope; atomic mass; mass number.
4. Describe the arrangement of electrons in an atom. Why is electron arrangement so important?
5. Nitrogen-14 and nitrogen-15 are isotopes of the element nitrogen. Describe how atoms of these isotopes differ from each other.

Connection—*You and Your World*

6. How does a scientific model—such as the model of the structure of an atom—differ from a model airplane or boat that you might build?

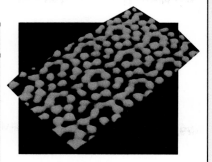

Figure 4–19 *This is the first image taken of atoms and their bonds. The bright round objects are single atoms. The fuzzy areas between atoms represent bonds.*

4-3 Forces Within the Atom

What keeps an atom together? Why don't the electrons fly out of their orbits around the nucleus? Why don't the protons move away from each other? Why don't all the atoms in the universe explode?

The answers to these questions can be found in the forces within the atom. **The four forces that account for the behavior of subatomic particles are the electromagnetic force, the strong force, the weak force, and gravity.**

The **electromagnetic force** can either attract or repel the particles on which it acts. If the particles have the same charge, such as two protons, the electromagnetic force is a force of repulsion. If the particles have opposite charges—such as an electron and a proton—the electromagnetic force is a force of attraction.

Electrons are kept in orbit around the nucleus by the electromagnetic force. The negatively charged electrons are attracted to the positively charged nucleus.

Guide for Reading

Focus on this question as you read.

▶ What four forces are associated with atomic structure?

---

trons in its nucleus.
4. Electrons are found whirling about the nucleus of an atom. They do not move in fixed paths, and only a probability or likelihood of their location can be determined.
5. Both nitrogen-14 and nitrogen-15 contain 7 protons. Nitrogen-14, however, contains 7 neutrons, and nitrogen-15 contains 8 neutrons.
6. Students should consider the differences between a scientific model of something that cannot be seen and a model of a concrete object.

REINFORCEMENT/RETEACHING

Review students' responses to the Section Review questions. Reteach any material that is still unclear, based on students' responses.

CLOSURE

▶ *Review and Reinforcement Guide*
Students may now complete Section 4–2 in their *Review and Reinforcement Guide.*

4-3 Forces Within the Atom

MULTICULTURAL OPPORTUNITY 4–3

Encourage students to explore the life of Dr. Lloyd N. Ferguson. Dr. Ferguson has received many honors in the field of chemical education. He is the first African-American scholar to earn a PhD in chemistry from the University of California at Berkeley. He has authored six textbooks, including the landmark *Modern Structural Theory of Organic Chemistry*.

ESL STRATEGY 4–3

Have students state orally
1. The four phases of matter.
2. The four classes of matter (according to makeup).
3. The four forces that account for behavior.

Ask students to describe briefly how each force works to keep the atom intact.

TEACHING STRATEGY 4–3

FOCUS/MOTIVATION

Remind students of the important experiments described in the chapter. Point out that the attempt to solve these basic mysteries about nature is an attempt to understand not only the nature of matter but also the forces that account for its behavior and structure. Give students a length of glass, a fur and cloth glove, some bits of paper, and several magnets and let them manipulate them and make discoveries about electromagnetic force.

Ask students to create a situation that could demonstrate gravitational force.

FORCE

Force can generally be thought of as a measure of the ability to produce a change in the motion of an object. Force is equal to the product of the mass of the affected object and the acceleration (rate of change of velocity) produced in the object. Mathematically, this is represented as $F = ma$.

Forces are carried, or mediated, by particles. The electromagnetic force is carried by photons. The weak nuclear force is carried by particles called weak bosons. The strong force is believed to be carried by hypothetical particles called gluons. Gravitational force is believed to be carried by hypothetical particles called gravitons. The electromagnetic and weak forces have already successfully been combined into the so-called electro-weak force. The other forces have yet to be combined.

Combination of forces is demonstrated by interconversion between one type of particle that carries one type of force and another type of particle that carries another type of force. It is believed that in the earliest moments of time after the "big bang" in which the universe is generally thought to have begun, conditions of such high energy existed that the four forces were truly unified. At that time, neutrons and protons had not yet come into existence, and the entire universe was compacted into a tiny space.

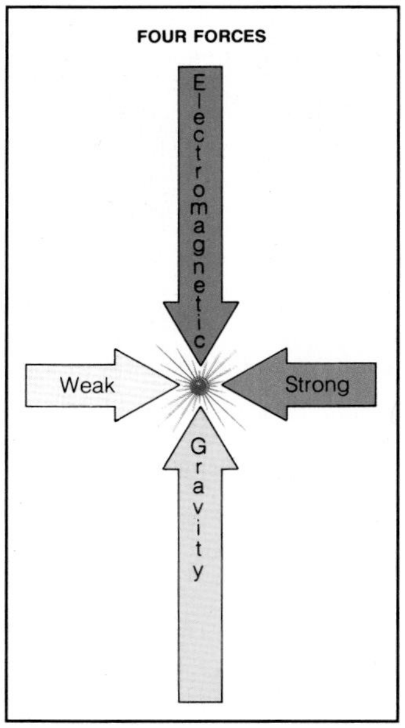

4–3 (continued)

CONTENT DEVELOPMENT

Forces within an atom are subject matter that can be difficult to understand. This section displays only a topical look at such forces, presenting the basic information students might need to appreciate the importance of the scientific issues involved. Deeper treatment of the subject matter would require a sophisticated mathematical approach. Stress with students the issue of basic forces and the possible large-scale consequences of the reduction of the forces to one fundamental force. To help do so, remind students that progress in science generally involves accounting for more and more kinds of phe-

Figure 4–20 *The four known forces that govern all the interactions of matter and energy are the strong force, the electromagnetic force, the weak force, and gravity. Which of the four forces is the weakest?* ❶

The electromagnetic force acts in the nucleus as a force of repulsion between positively charged protons. What keeps the protons from repelling each other and causing the atom to explode?

The **strong force** opposes the electromagnetic force of repulsion between protons. The strong force "glues" protons together to form the nucleus. Without the strong force, there would be no atoms. The strong force works only when protons are very close together, however. Although the strong force is the greatest of the four forces, it has a limited range. See Figure 4–21.

The **weak force** is the key to the power of the sun. The weak force is responsible for a process known as radioactive decay. During radioactive decay, a neutron in the nucleus changes into a proton and an electron.

The final force, **gravity,** is by far the weakest force known in nature. Yet it is probably the force most familiar to you. Gravity is the force of attraction exerted between all objects in nature. Gravity causes apples to fall from a tree and planets to remain in orbit around the sun. The effects of gravity are most easily observed in the behavior of large objects. Inside the nucleus of an atom, the effect of gravity is small compared to the effects of the other three forces. The role of gravity in the atom is not clearly understood.

As you can see, the four forces—electromagnetic, strong, weak, and gravity—are quite different. Yet physicists have tried to develop a single principle

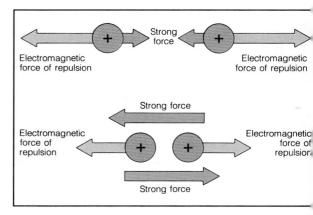

Figure 4–21 *The strong force opposes the electromagnetic force of repulsion between two protons (top). The strong force becomes powerful enough to overcome the repulsive force and bind protons in the nucleus only when the protons are very close together (bottom).*

nomena on the basis of fewer, more powerful, and more comprehensive and unified theories and models.

● ● ● ● **Integration** ● ● ● ●

Use the photograph of the tropical rain forest to integrate ecology in your lesson.

ENRICHMENT

▶ *Activity Book*
Students will be challenged by the chapter activity Atomic Dimensions.

CONTENT DEVELOPMENT

Sometimes a clear distinction is not drawn between the terms *electromagnetic force* and *electromagnetic energy*. Electromagnetic force is the force within an atom that can either attract or repel particles on which it acts. Electromagnetic energy is a moving electric charge. Power lines carry electromagnetic energy into our homes in the form of electricity. Electric motors are driven by electromagnetic energy. Other examples include light in the form

that would account for the differences between these forces. Such a principle would explain all four forces in terms of one fundamental force and all varieties of particles in terms of one basic particle. It is an awesome endeavor, indeed. But it is one that continues to challenge the knowledge and imagination of many scientists.

4–3 Section Review

1. What four forces govern the behavior of subatomic particles?
2. Which two forces are responsible for holding the atom together?
3. How does the electromagnetic force differ from the other three forces?

Critical Thinking—*Relating Concepts*
4. Gravity is the weakest of the four forces. However, it is one of the most easily observed forces in your daily life. Explain why this is so.

Figure 4–22 *In trying to unlock nature's secrets, physicists in a laboratory often study the tiny structure of the atom. Other scientists often find themselves in more precarious positions! These biologists are studying life in the treetops of a large tropical rain forest. As a result of their work, they may discover a previously unknown animal or plant, or even a new chemical that can be used to treat a once incurable disease. Often these new chemicals are analyzed atom by atom in a laboratory. Thus the knowledge uncovered in one scientific field often has applications in others.*

ECOLOGY NOTE
TROPICAL RAIN FORESTS

Tropical rain forests are extremely important to the Earth. The vast number of trees in these forests help to "clean" the air by taking carbon dioxide out of it and putting oxygen into it. Some plants in tropical rain forests produce chemicals for medicines that can be obtained from no other sources.

In some places, people are destroying the tropical rain forests. Trees are being cut down and turned into lumber and other commercial products. Land is being cleared to provide farmland for the rapidly expanding populations that live near the rain forests. And, of course, roads are being constructed to enable people to travel through the forests to get to the newly cleared land, thus causing more destruction of the forests.

4. Explanations will vary. Gravity is the most easily observed force because everything is held on our world by its force. The effects of this force are clearly visible, as when we drop an object, unlike other forces, which act in the unseen subatomic world.

REINFORCEMENT/RETEACHING

Monitor students' responses to the Section Review questions. If students appear to have difficulty with any of the questions, review the appropriate material in the section.

CLOSURE

▶ *Review and Reinforcement*

At this point have students complete Section 4–3 in their *Review and Reinforcement Guide*.

of rainbows and lasers, and X-rays and radio waves.

INDEPENDENT PRACTICE

▶ *Product Testing Activity*

Have students perform the product test on glue from the Product Testing Activity worksheets. Ask students to relate the activity concepts and results to the nature of attractive forces.

INDEPENDENT PRACTICE
Section Review 4–3

1. The four forces that govern the behavior of subatomic particles are the electromagnetic force, the strong force, the weak force, and gravity.
2. The electromagnetic force and the strong force are responsible for holding the atom together.
3. The electromagnetic force differs from the other forces in that it can either attract or repel the particles on which it acts.

Laboratory Investigation

SHOE BOX ATOMS

BEFORE THE LAB

1. Obtain one shoe box for each student group and set out the other materials needed.
2. Into each shoe box, place one or more relatively small familiar objects of the same kind, such as pencils, large nails, erasers, chalk, or large paper clips. Different boxes should contain different objects. Number each box and keep a record of what is in each. Tape the boxes securely shut.

PRE-LAB DISCUSSION

Before beginning this investigation, remind students of the important role of indirect evidence in scientific investigation. Review with them the general steps involved in the scientific method and stress the care that must be taken in formulating and testing hypotheses. Make it clear that the main point is not to determine conclusively exactly what is in the box but rather to proceed in a scientific manner with the investigation and with the development of a reasonable model.

TEACHING STRATEGY

1. Refrain from making comments on the procedures being followed (assuming they are safe and reasonably appropriate).
2. Discourage students from calling out guesses on what is in the box or from attempting to seek hints from you.

Laboratory Investigation

Shoe Box Atoms

Problem

How can indirect evidence be used to build a model?

Materials (per group)

shoe box, numbered and taped shut, containing unidentified object(s)
balance
magnet

Procedure

1. Your teacher will give you a shoe box with an object or objects inside. Do not open or damage the box.
2. Use a magnet to determine if the objects in the box have any magnetic properties.
3. Determine the mass of an empty shoe box. Then determine the mass of your shoe box. The difference between the two masses is the mass of the object(s) inside your shoe box.
4. You may be able to determine something about the object's shape by tilting the box. Does the object slide? (flat) Does it roll? (rounded) Does it collide inside? (more than one object)
5. Shake the box up and down to determine if the object bounces. How hard does it bounce? Does it flip?
6. For each test you perform, record your observations in a data table similar to the one shown here.

Observations

1. How many objects are in your shoe box?
2. Is the object soft? Magnetic? Fragile?
3. Is the object flat, or rounded?

Test Performed	Results	
	Trial 1	Trial 2
Magnet brought near		
Mass of object(s) determined		
Box tilted		
Box shaken		

Analysis and Conclusions

1. Make a sketch of what you think is in the shoe box. Draw the object(s) to show relative size.
2. What other indirect evidence did you gather to help you make the drawing?
3. How does your sketch compare with the actual objects as reported by your teacher? Make a sketch of the actual contents of the box.
4. Describe how you can develop a model of an object without directly observing the object.
5. **On Your Own** Prepare a shoe box model with two items that you select. Have a classmate see if he or she can determine what is in your shoe box.

DISCOVERY STRATEGIES

Discuss how the investigation relates to the chapter ideas by asking open questions similar to the following:
• **What can you tell about the objects in the box without opening the box?** (A general idea of size, weight, composition—predicting, analyzing.)
• **How can you use the data you collect to describe the objects in the box?** (Relate the data about size, weight, composition, and other properties to the properties of objects you are familiar with—observing,

comparing, relating.)
• **How is figuring out what the objects are in the box like using a model to show atomic structure?** (In each case, answers are based on indirect evidence because the objects involved cannot be seen or touched—comparing, relating.)

OBSERVATIONS

1.–3. All observations will depend on the items in the boxes. Observations should be checked to see if they are consistent with hidden items.

Study Guide

Summarizing Key Concepts

4–1 An Atomic Model of Matter

▲ More than 2400 years ago, the Greek philosopher Democritus theorized the existence of the atom, the smallest particle of matter.

▲ John Dalton's atomic theory was based on experimental evidence about the behavior of matter. His theory stated that all matter is made of indivisible particles, or atoms.

▲ The discovery of the electron by J. J. Thomson proved that the atom is divisible.

▲ Thomson's model pictured the atom as being made of a positively charged, puddinglike material throughout which negatively charged electrons were scattered.

▲ Rutherford's experiments led him to propose an atomic model that states that an atom has a small, dense, positively charged nucleus surrounded by negatively charged electrons.

▲ The Bohr model of the atom pictured electrons as moving in definite orbits, or energy levels, around the nucleus.

▲ According to the theory of wave mechanics, electrons do not move about an atom in definite orbits. The exact location of an electron in an atom is impossible to determine.

4–2 Structure of the Atom

▲ Protons and neutrons are found in the nucleus.

▲ Protons have a positive charge and a mass of 1 amu.

▲ Neutrons are electrically neutral and have a mass of 1 amu.

▲ The number of protons in the nucleus of an atom is the atomic number.

▲ Atoms of the same element that have the same number of protons but different numbers of neutrons are called isotopes.

▲ The mass number of an atom is the sum of the protons and neutrons in its nucleus.

▲ The atomic mass of an element is the average mass of all the naturally occurring isotopes of that element.

▲ Electrons have a negative charge.

▲ Within the electron cloud, electrons are arranged in energy levels.

4–3 Forces Within the Atom

▲ Four forces—electromagnetic, strong, weak, and gravity—govern the behavior of subatomic particles.

Reviewing Key Terms

Define each term in a complete sentence.

4–1 An Atomic Model of Matter
nucleus

4–2 Structure of the Atom
subatomic particle
proton
atomic mass unit

neutron
atomic number
isotope
mass number
atomic mass
electron
electron cloud
energy level
quark

4–3 Forces Within the Atom
electromagnetic force
strong force
weak force
gravity

Part 1

Ask student groups to switch boxes after they have completed their procedures and have written their conclusions. Students can then attempt to evaluate critically and constructively one another's methods, reasoning, and conclusions and can debate differences in suggested models.

Part 2

Ask students to consider how the experiment might be run "in reverse." Students should choose an object (or objects) to be placed into the box and should predict which of its properties are revealed by the various tests and how clearly the properties are revealed. Ask students to consider which objects might reveal essentially the same properties. This will help to bring out the point that in many cases, more than one model can effectively account for a given body of indirect evidence.

ANALYSIS AND CONCLUSIONS

1. Check student sketches to see if they are logical, based on observations. Students should not be graded on whether or not they were correct but on the scientific method employed.

2. Answers will vary but will likely include responses such as smell.

3. Students should be able to give valid reasons for any differences between their original sketch and the actual contents of the box.

4. Answers will vary but should be logical and demonstrate scientific method.

5. Partners should be careful not to give any hints about the contents of their shoe boxes. Trade the boxes among the rest of your classmates.

Chapter Review

ALTERNATIVE ASSESSMENT

The *Prentice Hall Science* program includes a variety of testing components and methodologies. Aside from the Chapter Review questions, you may opt to use the Chapter Test or the Computer Test Bank Test in your *Test Book* for assessment of important facts and concepts. In addition, Performance-Based Tests are included in your *Test Book*. These Performance-Based Tests are designed to test science process skills, rather than factual content recall. Since they are not content dependent, Performance-Based Tests can be distributed after students complete a chapter or after they complete the entire textbook.

CONTENT REVIEW

Multiple Choice
1. b
2. b
3. d
4. d
5. a
6. c
7. a
8. d
9. a
10. d

True or False
1. F, nucleus
2. F, closest to
3. T
4. F, electrons
5. T

Concept Mapping
Row 2: Atomic model
Row 3: Proton

CONCEPT MASTERY

1. An atom is composed of protons, neutrons, and electrons. A proton is located in the nucleus of an atom, having a positive electrical charge and a mass of 1 amu. A neutron is located in the nucleus of an atom, having a neutral electrical charge and a mass of 1 amu. An electron travels about the nucleus of an atom and has a negative electrical charge and a mass of 1/1836 amu.

2. The four forces that govern the behavior of subatomic particles are the electromagnetic force, the strong force, the weak force, and gravity. These four forces help to keep an atom together by not letting the electrons fly out of their orbits and not letting protons move away from each other.

3. Answers will vary. A possible response is that scientific method allowed a faster evolution of the atomic model by requiring conclusions that were based on the best possible data at that time. Lack of scientific method may have caused the evolution to occur in a more random, sporadic fashion.

4. Sulfur will have 2 electrons in the first level, 8 electrons in the second level, and 6 electrons in the third level. Fluorine will have 2 electrons in the first level and 7 electrons in the second level. Argon will have 2 electrons in the first level, 8 electrons in the second level, and 8 electrons in the third level. Lithium will have 2 electrons in the first level and 1 electron in the second level.

5. The number of protons in the nucleus of an atom is its atomic number. The mass number of an atom is the sum of

---

Content Review

Multiple Choice

Choose the letter of the answer that best completes each statement.

1. The name Democritus gave to the smallest possible particle of matter is the
a. molecule.   c. electron.
b. atom.   d. proton.

2. The scientist J. J. Thomson discovered the
a. proton.   c. neutron.
b. electron.   d. nucleus.

3. The small, heavy center of the atom is the
a. neutron.   c. electron.
b. proton.   d. nucleus.

4. Particles smaller than the atom are called
a. molecules.   c. ions
b. elements.   d. subatomic particles.

5. The nucleus of an atom contains
a. protons and neutrons.
b. protons and electrons.
c. neutrons and electrons.
d. protons, neutrons, and electrons.

6. The number of protons in an atom with an atomic number of 18 is
a. 10.   b. 36.   c. 18.   d. 8.

7. An isotope of oxygen, atomic number 8, could have
a. 8 protons and 10 neutrons.
b. 10 protons and 10 neutrons.
c. 10 protons and 8 electrons.
d. 6 protons and 8 neutrons.

8. All nuclear particles are thought to be made of a combination of three
a. electrons.   c. molecules.
b. isotopes.   d. quarks.

9. Which of the following forces within the atom is responsible for keeping electrons in orbit around the nucleus?
a. electromagnetic   c. weak
b. strong   d. gravity

10. The arrangement and location of what subatomic particles determine the chemical properties of an atom?
a. protons   c. quarks
b. neutrons   d. electrons

True or False

If the statement is true, write "true." If it is false, change the underlined word or words to make the statement true.

1. Most of the mass of the atom is located in the electron cloud.

2. Electrons that have the least amount of energy are located farthest from the nucleus.

3. The idea that matter is made up of indivisible particles called atoms was proposed by Democritus.

4. In Thomson's experiment, the gas in the tube gave off rays that were made of negatively charged particles called neutrons.

5. The element chlorine has an atomic number of 17. It has 17 protons in its nucleus.

Concept Mapping

Complete the following concept map for Section 4–1. Refer to pages N6–N7 to construct a concept map for the entire chapter.

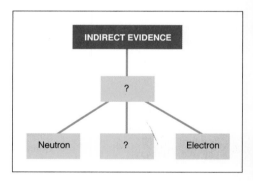

Concept Mastery

Discuss each of the following in a brief paragraph.

1. Describe the structure of the atom in terms of the three main subatomic particles. Include information about the location, charge, and atomic mass of each particle.
2. Describe the four forces and explain their role in the structure of the atom.
3. The model of the structure of the atom has changed over time. How does this illustrate the strength of the scientific method? Use specific examples in your explanation when appropriate.
4. Describe the electron configuration of each element based on atomic number: sulfur, 16; fluorine, 9; argon, 18; lithium, 3.

5. Explain how the following terms are related: atomic number, isotope, mass number, atomic mass. Be sure to define each term as you explain the relationships.
6. A certain element contains 82 percent of an isotope of mass number J and 18 percent of an isotope of mass number K. Is the atomic number of this element closer to J or to K? Explain your answer.
7. Why must scientists use the concept of probability in describing the structure of an atom?
8. What is the significance of the atomic number of an element?

Critical Thinking and Problem Solving

Use the skills you have developed in this chapter to answer each of the following.

1. **Making inferences** Why are models useful in the study of atomic theory?
2. **Analyzing diagrams** The accompanying illustration shows the nucleus of a helium atom. Why is the nucleus positively charged? What is the mass of the nucleus? What is the atomic number of helium?

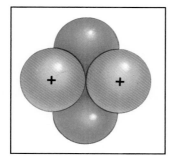

3. **Applying definitions** If the letter Z represents the atomic number of an atom and

the letter A represents the mass number, explain how you could use these symbols to calculate: the number of protons, the number of electrons, and the number of neutrons.
4. **Making inferences** The element Einsteinium (named after the famous physicist Albert Einstein) has an atomic mass of 252. Einsteinium is a synthetic element, or an element that has been artificially made. How does this fact explain why the atomic mass of Einsteinium is a whole number?
5. **Using the writing process** Use the information presented in this chapter to write an update letter to Democritus. In your letter, explain how his early ideas about the atom have been modified as new pieces of indirect evidence have been uncovered. Be sure to include the names of the scientists who contributed to our current ideas about the atom and a description of their experiments.

protons (atomic number) and neutrons in its nucleus. An isotope of an element has the same number of protons but different numbers of neutrons in the nucleus. The atomic mass of an element is the average mass of all its isotopes as they occur in nature.

6. The atomic number of this element is closer to J. The average is weighted toward J because 82 percent of that isotope is used to find an average.

7. Probability must be used to describe the structure of an atom because the ex-

act location of a subatomic particle at any given moment is not known exactly. Its location is estimated in terms of probability.

8. The atomic number of an element is significant because it will never change.

CRITICAL THINKING AND PROBLEM SOLVING

1. Answers will vary. A possible response would suggest that models are useful in the study of atomic theory because the actual subatomic world is relatively invisible.

2. The nucleus is positively charged be-

cause it contains protons. The mass number of the nucleus is the sum of its protons and neutrons. The atomic number of helium is 2.

3. The letter Z would yield the number of protons. A - Z would yield the number of neutrons. The letter Z would yield the number of electrons.

4. Answers will vary. A possible response might suggest that the atomic mass of an element refers to the average mass of all the isotopes of that element as they occur in nature. For this reason, the atomic mass of an element is usually not a whole number. The atomic mass of a single element, like Einsteinium, is a whole number because no known isotopes of the element occur or have been found in nature.

5. Answers may vary. Responses should explain how and why early models have been modified and should detail the contributions of other scientists.

KEEPING A PORTFOLIO

You might want to assign some of the Concept Mastery and Critical Thinking and Problem Solving questions as homework and have students include their responses to unassigned questions in their portfolio. Students should be encouraged to include both the question and the answer in their portfolio.

ISSUES IN SCIENCE

The following issue can be used as a springboard for discussion or given as a writing assignment:

Scientists tend to assume that what they learn here on Earth about the basic nature of matter is applicable to matter everywhere in the universe. Is this belief justified? Supporters usually adhere to an underlying assumption that the "laws" that govern nature will apply everywhere, but some scientists and philosophers of science have questioned this, pointing out the limited nature of the evidence gathered so far. What do you think?

Chapter 5 CLASSIFICATION OF ELEMENTS: THE PERIODIC TABLE

SECTION	LABORATORY INVESTIGATIONS AND DEMONSTRATIONS
5–1 Arranging the Elements pages N108–N112	**Teacher Edition** Organization and Function, p. N106d
5–2 Design of the Periodic Table pages N112–N121	**Teacher Edition** Comparing Elements, p. N106d
5–3 Chemical Families pages N122–N131	**Student Edition** Flame Tests, p. N136 **Laboratory Manual** The Alkaline Earth Elements
5–4 Periodic Properties of the Elements pages N131–N135	**Laboratory Manual** Investigating the Activity Series of Metals
Chapter Review pages N136–N139	

*All materials in the Chapter Planning Guide Grid are available as part of the Prentice Hall Science Learning System.

OUTSIDE TEACHER RESOURCES

Books

Ahrens, L. H., ed. *The Origin and Distribution of the Elements,* Pergamon.

Donohue, J. *Structure of the Elements,* Wiley.

Klein, M. L., and J. A. Venables, eds. *Rare Gas Solids,* Academic Press.

Kuper, C. G., et al., eds. *Liquid and Solid Helium,* Halsted.

Poda, J. S. *The Periodic Table: Experiments and Theory,* Halsted.

OTHER ACTIVITIES	MULTIMEDIA
Activity Book 　Chapter Discovery: Chemical Pursuit 　ACTIVITY: Classifying Objects **Review and Reinforcement Guide** 　Section 5–1	**English/Spanish Audiotapes** 　Section 5–1
Activity Book 　ACTIVITY: Metals and Nonmetals Around Home 　ACTIVITY: Heat Conductivity in Metals 　ACTIVITY: Metal or Nonmetal? 　ACTIVITY: Some Common Elements 　ACTIVITY: An Alien Periodic Table **Student Edition** 　Find Out by Doing: Classifying Objects—My Way, p. N116 　Find Out by Doing: A Hot Time, p. N118 　Find Out by Doing: An Elemental Hunt, p. N121 **Review and Reinforcement Guide** 　Section 5–2	**Transparency Binder** 　The Periodic Table **Courseware** 　The Periodic Table (Supplemental) **English/Spanish Audiotapes** 　Section 5–2
Activity Book 　ACTIVITY: Halogens 　ACTIVITY: Identifying Substances 　ACTIVITY: Interpreting the Periodic Table **Student Edition** 　Find Out by Doing: Homely Halogens, p. N130 **Review and Reinforcement Guide** 　Section 5–3	**English/Spanish Audiotapes** 　Section 5–3
Activity Book 　ACTIVITY: Element Code 　ACTIVITY: Identifying Unknown Elements 　ACTIVITY: Valence Clues 　ACTIVITY: Element Maze **Review and Reinforcement Guide** Section 5–4	**Video/Videodisc** 　Periodic Table and Periodicity **English/Spanish Audiotapes** 　Section 5–4
Test Book 　Chapter Test 　Performance-Based Tests	**Test Book** 　Computer Test Bank Test

Audiovisuals

Atomic Structure and the Periodic Chart: An Introduction, filmstrip or slides, PH Media
Classification of the Elements: Metals, Non-Metals, Metalloids, filmstrip, PH Media

Elements Discovered, video, Media Guild
Family of Halogens, film, CRM/McGraw-Hill
Matter and Molecules: The Matter of Elements, filmstrip, Singer Educational Division

The Origin of the Elements, film, CRM/McGraw-Hill
The Periodic Table, video, Media Guild

CHAPTER OVERVIEW

The first periodic table was developed in the mid-1800s when only 63 elements were known. Russian scientist Dmitri Mendeleev developed the first periodic table of the elements by arranging the elements according to increasing atomic mass. The table seemed to misplace some items according to their properties.

The modern periodic table resolved the problem by arranging the elements according to increasing atomic number. The modern table orders 109 elements, 17 of which were produced in laboratories and do not naturally occur. The modern periodic table is a valuable tool used by chemists and other scientists.

The information given for each element in the table includes chemical symbol, name, atomic number, and atomic mass. The elements are arranged in vertical columns called families or groups and in horizontal rows called periods. The elements are broadly classified as metals, nonmetals, and metalloids. The elements classified as metals are on the left of the periodic table. Metals are good conductors of heat and have high melting points. The nonmetals are on the right of the table. Nonmetals are poor conductors of heat and have low melting points. The metalloids are positioned between the metals and the nonmetals. Metalloids exhibit properties of both the metals and the nonmetals.

5–1 ARRANGING THE ELEMENTS
THEMATIC FOCUS

The purpose of this section is to review the history of the development of the periodic table of the elements.

By the mid-1800s, 63 elements were known. Dmitri Mendeleev, a Russian chemist, devised a method by which these elements were put into order. Using their physical and chemical properties, Mendeleev found a pattern in the elements. When he arranged them in order of increasing atomic mass, the valence numbers always occurred in a pattern.

Today the period table is based on the periodic law, which states that the physical and chemical properties of the elements are periodic functions of their atomic numbers. Unlike Mendeleev's table, which was based on atomic masses, the modern table uses atomic numbers—the number of protons in the nucleus of the atom of an element.

The themes that can be focused on in this section are patterns of change and systems and interactions.

*Patterns of change: The periodic law states that the physical and chemical properties of the elements are predictable. Mendeleev used atomic masses to arrange the elements, and his table led to the discovery of new elements to fill the gaps. Using atomic numbers, the periodic table became an even more powerful predictor of the existence and properties of new elements.

*Systems and interactions: The periodic table not only served to help scientists discover or produce new elements, but its logical arrangement clarifies the way in which elements interact with one another to form compounds. The ways in which chemical interactions occur are important to an understanding of both living and nonliving phenomena.

PERFORMANCE OBJECTIVES 5–1

1. **Explain how Mendeleev developed his periodic table.**
2. **Explain the concepts of atomic mass, valence, and atomic number.**
3. **Describe Henry Moseley's contributions to the modern periodic table.**

SCIENCE TERMS 5–1
periodic law p. N111

5–2 DESIGN OF THE PERIODIC TABLE
THEMATIC FOCUS

The purpose of this section is to show students how to use the modern periodic table. Information about an individual element included in the table consists of chemical symbol, element name, atomic number, and atomic mass.

The vertical columns in the table, called families or groups, illustrate the similarity in properties of elements that result from the same number of valence electrons. The horizontal rows, called periods, show the changes in the properties as the number of valence electrons increases across each period.

The themes that can be focused on in this section are systems and interactions and unity and diversity.

*Systems and interactions: The modern periodic table presents the elements in such a way that properties such as combining power, atomic mass, and electron configuration occur in regular patterns. Help students understand how the underlying atomic structures of elements result in a table with eight principal columns.

Unity and diversity: The periodic table helps to make sense of what was, in the past, an overwhelming number of different elements and compounds, each with its own characteristics. All elements obey certain scientific principles dictating the ways in which they combine to make compounds. Yet each element is distinguished by individual attributes such as its atomic number.

PERFORMANCE OBJECTIVES 5–2

1. **Describe the design of the modern periodic table.**
2. **Discuss how families contain elements with similar properties.**
3. **Explain how properties of elements vary across a horizontal row, or period.**
4. **Compare the properties of metals, nonmetals, and metalloids.**

PERFORMANCE OBJECTIVES 5–4
1. Describe some periodic properties of the elements.
2. Explain how electron arrangement changes across a period.
3. Identify the change in metallic properties across a period.
4. Explain how atomic size changes across a period.

5–3 CHEMICAL FAMILIES
THEMATIC FOCUS

The purpose of this section is to present an overview of the main families of elements in the periodic table. Starting at the left with the most active metals, students will learn the principal properties of the metals in each family. As you move across the table, the elements become less and less metallic. On the right side are the noble gases, elements so nonreactive that they are also referred to as inert.

The themes that can be focused on in this section are unity and diversity and stability.

Unity and diversity: The elements in each family on the periodic table share certain characteristics. But the individual properties of each element set it apart from the others in its column. Understanding the ways in which elements are alike and different will help students appreciate the organizing power of the periodic table.

*Stability: The atoms of a given element are characterized by a certain number of valence electrons in the outermost energy level. Any sample of the element will always have this characteristic, regardless of the conditions of temperature and pressure.

PERFORMANCE OBJECTIVES 5–3
1. Locate the families of elements on the periodic table.
2. Describe the properties of each of the eight families of elements in the periodic table.

5–4 PERIODIC PROPERTIES OF THE ELEMENTS
THEMATIC FOCUS

The purpose of this section is to discuss the properties of the elements that vary in a regular way from left to right across the periodic table. These properties include electron arrangement, reactivity, atomic size, and metallic properties.

Students will learn about the pattern of valence electrons that recurs in each period. They also will discover that the tendency of an element to lose or gain electrons in chemical combinations is related to its position in a period.

The themes that can be focused on in this section are energy and scale and structure.

Energy: As elements combine with one another to form compounds, energy is used. Some elements have only one or two valence electrons in the outermost energy layer, and thus relatively little energy is needed when they form compounds. Similarly, elements at the right of the periodic table need only one or two electrons to complete the outer layers. They also are highly active, combining easily to form compounds.

*Scale and structure: The periodic table also gives information about the size of the atoms in the elements. As you move from left to right or bottom to top in the table, atomic size decreases. All atoms, however, regardless of size, combine to form compounds in the same manner.

Discovery *Learning*

TEACHER DEMONSTRATIONS MODELING
Organization and Function

Show students a photograph of the outside or inside of a fast-food restaurant. Discuss some ways in which organization helps such a restaurant run smoothly.
• **Does each person have a specific job to do?** (Yes.)
• **What would happen at a busy time if the fry-cook disappeared from his or her position?** (Students might suggest that the restaurant would become disorganized because order takers would not be able to get their orders filled.)
• **Is food organized and placed in separate bins or locations?** (Yes.)
• **Do you think it would be easier for a new employee to learn the procedures of the restaurant if things were always kept in the same places?** (Yes.)

Point out that when there is an organized method of operation, things are often easier to learn.

Comparing Elements

Show the class a piece of black carbon, such as the carbon rod from a dry cell, and a piece of lead, such as a lead fish sinker.
• **How are these two substances different?** (One is black and nonmetallic; the other is silver and metallic.)
• **How are these two substances similar?** (Both are solids.)
• **What do you notice about carbon and lead on the periodic table?** (They are in the same column—Family 13.)

Explain that the elements in some families may be either metallic or nonmetallic.

CHAPTER 5

Classification of Elements: The Periodic Table

INTEGRATING SCIENCE

This physical science chapter provides you with numerous opportunities to integrate other areas of science, as well as other disciplines, into your curriculum. Blue numbered annotations on the student page and integration notes on the teacher wraparound pages alert you to areas of possible integration.

In this chapter you can integrate music (p. 110), life science and zoology (p. 110), social studies (pp. 112, 118), earth science and geology (pp. 120, 126), fine arts (p. 124), life science and plants (p. 128), life science and ecology (p. 134), and mathematics (p. 131).

SCIENCE, TECHNOLOGY, AND SOCIETY/COOPERATIVE LEARNING

Heavy metals are metals with a relatively high atomic mass. Examples are platinum, gold, lead, and mercury. Heavy metals are used in dental fillings, electrical devices, processing and refining other metals, as catalysts in many industrial processes, and as fungicides.

Heavy metals are toxic to living things because they are readily inhaled or absorbed into the body. Once inside, they combine with and inhibit the functioning of enzymes.

Heavy metal elements, especially mercury, are particularly dangerous when

INTRODUCING CHAPTER 5

DISCOVERY LEARNING

▶ *Activity Book*
Begin your teaching of the chapter by using the Chapter 5 Discovery Activity from your *Activity Book*. In this activity students will discover that elements have various physical and chemical properties.

USING THE TEXTBOOK

Begin your introduction of Chapter 5 by having as many colored compounds as possible on display in the room. Have students discuss the different colors used in paintings. Point out that the compounds are often composed of metals and nonmetals. Using a periodic table, point out the location of metals contained in various compounds.

• **Why do you suppose some substances have a bright color while others do not?** (The energy levels in the atomic structures are the key to this. If valence electrons can absorb some of the wavelengths of visible light, then the substances will reflect back unabsorbed colors to the observer.)

Explain that the periodic table of the elements has some things in common with a calendar. Days of the week on a calendar are grouped into columns. Discuss the things that Fridays have in common—last day of the school week, payday in

Classification of Elements: The Periodic Table

Guide for Reading

After you read the following sections, you will be able to

5–1 Arranging the Elements
- Discuss the role Mendeleev played in the development of the periodic table.

5–2 Design of the Periodic Table
- Recognize how the modern periodic table is designed.
- Describe some differences between metals and nonmetals.

5–3 Chemical Families
- Describe some properties of the eight families of elements.

5–4 Periodic Properties of the Elements
- Identify how the periodic law explains the physical and chemical properties of the elements.

Mary Cassatt, an American artist, lived in Paris toward the end of the nineteenth century. At that time artists were developing a "new" style of painting called Impressionism. Impressionist painters felt they no longer needed to paint with great realism. They used bright colors to give the "impression" of light and shadow in their paintings. Often, Impressionist painters moved out of their studios and into the daylight. Mary Cassatt began to paint in this new style. Today her paintings rightly share a place of honor in the history of human expression in art.

The origins of this painter's talents were firmly rooted in the human spirit. However, her paints' wondrous colors—colors that artists call pigments—have a much more ordinary origin. They are all part of the storehouse of elements in the Earth. A list of pigments reads like a chemistry textbook—zinc white, cadmium yellow, cobalt blue, iron oxide red, chromium green. All of these pigments are made from a group of elements known as the transition metals. In this chapter you will read about the transition metals and about many other groups of elements. Each group has its own properties and its own interesting—and often surprising—uses.

Journal *Activity*

You and Your World Artists often "speak" to people through drawings, paintings, and sculpture. Think back to the last time you were moved by a work of art. Maybe it was your own. Express your thoughts and feelings in your journal. Did you have any questions about what the artist was "saying"?

Mary Cassatt painted this picture entitled Susan on a Balcony Holding a Dog.

---

some instances. Ask students what they will be doing on a future Saturday. Point out that they can use the predictive power of a calendar to make some assumptions about the day Saturday.

The periodic table also has predictive properties. The elements are grouped into columns and rows. By knowing the location of an element in the table, a person can predict some of the properties of that element.

• **What familiar metals on the periodic table might have properties similar to those of lead and nickel?** (Possible answers are tin and platinum.)

---

they get into a food chain because of biomagnification. Mercury is non-biodegradable—a substance that cannot be broken down by chemical processes in the body. The body filters out the mercury that passes through the digestive system and accumulates it. As organisms at the higher levels of the food chain eat lower organisms, they accumulate much more mercury than the original environmental concentration.

Cooperative learning: Using preassigned lab groups or randomly selected teams, have groups complete one of the two assignments below. Have the groups use the information in this chapter's Connections feature as well as the scenario that follows.

In a small fishing village near Minamata, Japan, animals were behaving strangely. Birds would sometimes drop from the sky onto the ground, and cats would exhibit spastic movements for several days and then become paralyzed and die. Eventually, the people of the village began experiencing symptoms similar to those of the cats. Over time, mental retardation, insanity, and babies born with severe birth defects were also observed in larger numbers. Scientists finally discovered that "Minamata disease" was actually mercury poisoning. A chemical plant was discharging mercury-containing waste into the bay where the villagers caught their fish.
• Have groups illustrate the method of environmental contamination and the food web that led to the mercury poisoning in Minamata.
• Write a letter to a company in your area requesting information on how metal elements are used in their industry and how they dispose of any waste materials containing dangerous metal elements.

See Cooperative Learning in the *Teacher's Desk Reference.*

JOURNAL ACTIVITY

You may want to use the Journal Activity as the basis of class discussion. As students discuss their experiences with drawings, paintings, and sculpture, lead them to think about the types of physical materials that are used to create these products. Students should be instructed to keep their Journal Activity in their portfolio.

5-1 Arranging the Elements

Discuss with students the notion of periodicity. What are some other examples of periodic trends in science (moon phases, tides, weather patterns)? How do scientists use periodicity for predictions? If it were not for regular patterns in nature, it would be impossible to make predictions.

ESL STRATEGY 5-1

Dictate the following questions. Ask students to make some notes in order to be prepared to answer the questions aloud. Have them work in small groups. One student reads the question, another student answers it, and a third confirms or corrects the answer.

1. What were the properties Mendeleev listed on the cards he used to organize his classification system of chemical elements? (Atomic mass, density, color, melting point, valence.)

2. What did Mendeleev do in order to arrange chemical elements so that those with similar properties would be grouped together? (He first put the elements in order by increasing atomic mass. Then he noticed a pattern in the valence numbers.)

3. When and how was Mendeleev's periodic table replaced by the modern periodic table? (It was 50 years after Mendeleev's table that Henry Moseley arranged the elements by atomic number rather than by atomic mass.

Guide for Reading

Focus on these questions as you read.
▶ *How was the periodic table of the elements developed?*
▶ *What is the importance of the periodic law?*

5-1 Arranging the Elements

In some ways, your daily life contains many of the qualities of a good detective story. Unanswered questions and unexplained problems challenge your thoughts and actions all the time. And so you often act like a good detective. You discover places to go with friends and family. You learn about people who come from different cultures. You explore and gather evidence about the world around you. Like a good detective, you often try to make sense out of a series of clues and find meanings in seemingly unrelated observations.

Chemists, too, are good detectives. They gather evidence, analyze clues, follow their hunches, and make predictions. One of the most successful detective stories in the history of chemistry is the development of the periodic table of the elements. The periodic table of the elements represents a system of classifying, or logically grouping, all of the known elements. The arrangement of the elements in the periodic table was a milestone in the history of chemistry because it brought order to what had seemed to be a collection of thousands of unrelated facts. And it did something even more important: It helped chemists predict the existence of elements that had yet to be discovered!

Figure 5-1 *Each element has its own characteristic chemical and physical properties. Potassium is a soft, silvery metal that reacts explosively with water (right). Aluminum, also a silvery metal, does not easily combine with oxygen in water or in the air (left). Thus aluminum can be used for a variety of purposes, including drain pipes.*

TEACHING STRATEGY 5-1

FOCUS/MOTIVATION

Have students discuss the following situation:

• **Suppose you want to line up a group of people. What are some ways you can arrange them?** (Possible answers include according to height, age, or the alphabetical order of their names.)

• **Would you expect to get the same results from each method?** (No.)

Have students take turns lining up members of the class according to various methods and then compare the results.

CONTENT DEVELOPMENT

Use the Motivation activity to lead into a discussion of the challenge that faced Mendeleev—to order the elements in a way that would reveal a pattern among them. Point out that several scientists before Mendeleev had tried to do the same thing.

• **Why was it important to Mendeleev to organize the elements?** (He believed that if he could order the elements correctly, elements with similar properties would be grouped together.)

• **How did Mendeleev decide to arrange the elements?** (According to increasing atomic mass.)

• **What important pattern did he discover?** (The valence numbers occurred in the order 1, 2, 3, 4, 3, 2, 1.)

A Hidden Pattern

The detective in this fascinating story was the Russian chemist Dmitri Mendeleev (duh-MEE-tree mehn-duh-LAY-uhf). The evidence he uncovered consisted of a huge collection of facts about the 63 elements that had been discovered by the mid-1800s. His clues were the physical and chemical properties of these elements. Based on these properties, it seemed clear to Mendeleev that some elements were similar to others. For example, sodium and potassium were both soft silver-white metals that reacted violently with water.

Mendeleev had a hunch that there had to be some order or relationship among all the elements. He was convinced that he could find a way to arrange the elements so that those with similar properties were grouped together. But what could the pattern of this arrangement be? ①

In his search for the pattern, Mendeleev first decided to organize his data. He did this by making a card for each of the known elements. On the card, he wrote the properties of each element. Some of the properties he included were atomic mass, density, color, and melting point. He also included the element's valence, or bonding power. Atoms form bonds with other atoms during chemical reactions (processes in which atoms join together to form molecules). When atoms form bonds, they either lose electrons, gain electrons, or share electrons. The valence, or valence number, of an element indicates the number of electrons that will be lost, gained, or shared in the bonding process.

Always looking for a pattern, Mendeleev arranged the cards in order of increasing atomic mass. If he started with lithium, the next element would be beryllium. Then would come boron, carbon, nitrogen, oxygen, and fluorine. With the cards arranged in this order, Mendeleev noticed the startling pattern of the valences: 1 2 3 4 3 2 1. Seven elements in a row, and the pattern of valences repeated itself.

As he arranged all 63 cards in order of atomic mass, Mendeleev saw the same pattern of rises and falls of valence again and again. He also saw something even more remarkable. When the elements were arranged in this way, they fell into columns,

Figure 5–2 *Mendeleev's greatest scientific contribution was the development of the periodic table. But his interests were not limited to chemistry. In 1887, he attempted to study a solar eclipse from a hot-air balloon.*

HISTORICAL NOTE
BEFORE MENDELEEV

Several scientists before Mendeleev attempted to order the elements according to similar properties. In 1817, German scientist Johann Dobereiner classified the elements in triads, or groups of three elements with similar properties. Three of Dobereiner's triads include calcium, barium, strontium; chlorine, iodine, bromine; and sulfur, tellurium, selenium.

In 1863, six years before Mendeleev's periodic table, English chemist John Newlands arranged the known elements according to increasing atomic mass, then created seven groups of seven elements each. He observed that every eighth element had similar properties. He called his observation the Law of Octaves.

curve in mathematics that shows a frequency distribution of 1 2 3 4 3 2 1; a group of objects or people in which the first four increase in height and the next three decrease.)

REINFORCEMENT/RETEACHING

Review the idea of atomic mass by reminding students that an atom is made up of a positively charged nucleus surrounded by one or more negatively charged orbiting electrons. Almost all of the mass of an atom is in the nucleus, which is made up of protons (positively charged) and neutrons (electrically neutral). Atomic mass is measured in very small units called atomic mass units.

Because any sample of an element that occurs in nature will contain a mixture of isotopes, the atomic mass of the element is the average of the masses of all the atoms in the sample.

Explain that an element's valence number refers to the arrangement of electrons in the outermost energy level of an atom of that element. Point out that elements with similar outer-level structures have similar properties.

GUIDED PRACTICE

Skills Development
Skill: Identifying patterns

Write the pattern 1 2 3 4 3 2 1 on the chalkboard. Ask students to describe the pattern in words. (It begins at 1, goes up to number 4, then goes back down to 1.)

Have several volunteers come to the chalkboard and draw visual representations of the pattern. They might, for example, draw an up-and-down series of steps or a series of vertical lines 1 to 4 cm each.

• **Can you think of situations outside chemistry in which you might find a similar pattern?** (Possible answers include a seven-note musical motif that goes up four notes, then back down; a bell-shaped

SEPTEMBER						
S	**M**	**T**	**W**	**Th**	**F**	**S**
1	2	3	4	5	6	7
8	9	10	11	12	13	14
15	16	17	18	19	20	21
22	23	24	25	26	27	28
29	30					

Figure 5–3 *The days of the month are periodic because they repeat themselves according to a definite pattern. What is that pattern? Some animals also behave in a periodic manner. Geese and other birds migrate every fall and spring. What other examples of periodic behavior have you observed?* ❶

one under the other. All the elements in a column had the same valence! All the elements in a column showed similar physical and chemical properties!

It was obvious to Mendeleev that the properties of the elements recurred at regular intervals. In Mendeleev's words, he found that "the properties of the elements were periodic functions of their atomic masses." When used this way, the word periodic means repeating according to some pattern. The days of the week are periodic because every seven days the pattern recurs. The months of the year are periodic because they also occur in a regular, repeating pattern. The notes of the musical scale are periodic, ❷ repeating a pattern with every eighth tone. In fact, you may already understand the word periodic from your familiarity with the word periodical. Sometimes magazines and newspapers are called periodicals. Their appearance on a newsstand, in a library, or at your home occurs according to a recognized repeating pattern. (You probably know when your favorite periodical is due to appear and eagerly anticipate its arrival.) Animals and plants also exhibit periodic behaviors. Birds fly south when winter's cold limits their food supply, and they return north the following spring when warmth signals an abundance of food. Can you think of other examples of periodic occurrences? ❷

A Bold Prediction

Mendeleev designed a periodic table in which the elements were arranged in order of increasing atomic mass. Confident of the accuracy of his discovery, he left spaces in the table in order to make the known elements fit into the proper columns. Then he boldly announced that the empty spaces would be filled with elements that were not yet discovered! Indeed, he even went so far as to predict the physical and chemical properties of the unknown elements. He based his predictions on the properties of the elements above and below and to the left and right of the spaces in the table. Was he correct?

Yes, in fact, he was. Three of the unknown elements were discovered and placed in their correct positions in the periodic table during his lifetime. And the properties of the newly discovered elements

MENDELEEV'S PREDICTIONS AND ACTUAL PROPERTIES OF ELEMENT 32			
"Ekasilicon"		Germanium	
Date predicted	1871	Date discovered	1886
Atomic mass	72	Atomic mass	72.6
Density	5.5 g/cm³	Density	5.47 g/cm³
Bonding power	4	Bonding power	4
Color	Dark gray	Color	Grayish white

Figure 5–4 *The discovery of the element germanium in 1866 made Mendeleev the most famous chemist of the time. Notice how his predictions about the properties of element 32, or "ekasilicon," were incredibly close to the actual properties. How could Mendeleev predict the properties of an "unknown" element with such accuracy?* ③

were in close agreement with Mendeleev's predictions. You can see for yourself how well Mendeleev's predictions were fulfilled by looking at Figure 5–4.

The Modern Periodic Table

Despite the importance of Mendeleev's work, his periodic table was not perfect. When the elements are arranged in order of increasing atomic mass, several elements appear to be misplaced in terms of their properties. Mendeleev assumed that this was because the atomic masses of these elements had been incorrectly measured. Yet new measurements reconfirmed the original masses. What could be the problem?

It was not until 50 years after Mendeleev had developed his periodic table that the answer to the problem became clear. It was then that the British scientist Henry Moseley determined for the first time the atomic numbers of the elements. As you will recall, the atomic number of an element is the number of protons in the nucleus of each atom of that element.

The discovery of atomic numbers led to an important change in Mendeleev's periodic table. It turns out that when the elements are arranged in order of increasing atomic number (rather than increasing atomic mass), elements with similar physical and chemical properties fall into place without exception. Thus, Mendeleev's periodic table was replaced by the modern periodic table. The **periodic law** forms the basis of the modern periodic table.

Figure 5–5 *Great contributions are often made by the young. Henry Moseley was only 27 when he died in a famous battle during World War I, but his work in developing the modern periodic table lives long after him. What was Moseley's contribution?* ④

the modern periodic table is ordered according to increasing atomic number.)

ENRICHMENT

Challenge students to explain why the order of the elements is similar, but not exactly the same, when arranged according to atomic number instead of atomic mass. (Answers may vary, but should include the idea that because protons have mass, atoms with higher atomic numbers tend also to have greater masses. The presence of neutrons in the nucleus of an atom, however, can affect the mass without affecting the atomic number. Thus, atomic masses do not increase in exactly the same order as atomic numbers do.)

● ● ● ● **Integration** ● ● ● ●

Use the discussion of the patterns in a musical scale to integrate music into your lesson.

GUIDED PRACTICE

Skills Development

Skill: Analyzing data

Provide students with the atomic number and atomic mass of the following pairs of elements: tellurium and iodine (52, 127.60 and 53, 126.905); cobalt and nickel (27, 58.9332 and 28, 58.69); argon and potassium (18, 39.948 and 19, 30.098). Ask them to determine the order in which the elements in each pair would have been placed in Mendeleev's periodic table. (Iodine before tellurium; nickel before cobalt; potassium before argon.)

• **How are the elements ordered in the modern periodic table?** (The order of each pair is reversed.)

• **What accounts for the difference?** (Mendeleev ordered the elements according to increasing atomic mass, while

5–2 Design of the Periodic Table

In the eighteenth century, Spain and South America were sites of important research in the area of mining and metallurgy. Encourage students to research the life and work of Don Fausto D'Elhuyar (1755–1833). During his investigations of a mineral called wolframite, he extracted a new metal, wolfram. This metal is also called tungsten. In later years, D'Elhuyar and his older brother Juan José spent time in South America and Mexico as supervisors of mining operations in those countries.

ESL STRATEGY 5-2

Ask students to work in pairs or in small groups. Have them refer to the periodic table in their textbooks as they write answers for the following activities. Selectively check students' work by asking them to read aloud what they have written.

1. List the four parts in each square that describe the element. (Symbol, name, atomic number, atomic mass.)

2. State the physical properties of metals and where they are found in the periodic table. (Metals have luster and are good conductors of heat and electricity. Many metals are ductile and malleable. The metals are found to the left of the dark zigzag line in the periodic table.)

3. Describe the location and physical properties of nonmetals. (Nonmetals are dull and conduct heat and electricity poorly. They are found to the right of the dark zigzag line.)

4. Give the name and location of the elements that have the properties of both metals and nonmetals. (Metalloids; next to the zigzag line.)

Figure 5–6 *Mendeleev recognized that the properties of elements are repeated in a periodic way. Thus certain elements have similar properties. Silver (top), gold (center), and copper (bottom) are all shiny, hard elements that are good conductors of electricity. What are some other uses of these elements?* ①

Guide for Reading

Focus on these questions as you read.

▶ *Why is the periodic table an important tool of science?*

▶ *How do the properties of metals and nonmetals compare?*

The periodic law states that the physical and chemical properties of the elements are periodic functions of their atomic numbers.

Just in case you have the impression that all scientists are strange old people working mysteriously in musty laboratories, you might be interested to learn that Henry Moseley completed his historic work before his twenty-eighth birthday. Sadly, he ① died during World War I at the battle of Gallipoli. It must be left to our imaginations to wonder what other contributions to human knowledge this brilliant chemist might have made had he survived.

5–1 Section Review

1. Describe Mendeleev's periodic table. What are some properties he used to order the elements?
2. What does the word periodic mean?
3. How did Mendeleev predict the existence of undiscovered elements?
4. According to the modern periodic law, what determines the order of the elements?

Connection—*You and Your World*

5. An important series of reference books found in most libraries is entitled *Readers' Guide to Periodical Literature.* From the title, can you infer what kinds of information can be found in these books? Why do you think this series of books is important?

5–2 Design of the Periodic Table

The periodic table of the elements is one of the most important tools of a scientist, especially a chemist. Why? Because the periodic table is a classification system—a way of organizing vast amounts of information in a logical, usable, and meaningful way. In some ways the periodic table is like the system used to organize books in a library. Imagine how

---

5–1 (continued)

CONTENT DEVELOPMENT

● ● ● ● **Integration** ● ● ● ●

Use the information about Henry Moseley to integrate social studies concepts into your lesson.

INDEPENDENT PRACTICE

Section Review 5–1

1. Mendeleev arranged the elements in order of increasing atomic mass. Some of the properties he used were atomic mass, density, color, melting point, and valence.
2. Repeating according to a pattern.
3. He believed that the blank spaces in his table showed undiscovered elements with certain predictable properties.
4. Atomic number.
5. Periodical literature includes maga-

confusing it would be if all the books in a library were placed on shelves in no particular order. You would have a hard time trying to locate the book on magic tricks, stamp collecting, or rocketry you were looking for.

Fortunately, the books in a library are arranged by subject in a system that uses numbers and letters. You can look up a book in the card catalog, find its classification number, and locate it on the shelves. As you can see, such organization makes a book easy to locate. There is another advantage to a library's classification system. The classification number is a key to a book's subject matter. It identifies the broad topic of a book. All books with the same or similar subject matter will have essentially the same classification number. So without ever having seen a certain book, you can predict its topic from its classification number or its placement on a shelf.

The periodic table organizes the elements in a particular way. A great deal of information about an element can be gathered from its position in the periodic table. For example, you can predict with reasonably good accuracy the physical and chemical properties of the element. You can also predict what other elements a particular element will react with chemically. This means that it is not necessary to memorize a whole list of facts about many different elements. Understanding the organization and plan of the periodic table will help you obtain basic information about each of the 109 known elements. A periodic table is found on pages 114 and 115. Refer to the table often as you read about it.

Columns in the Periodic Table

If you look at the periodic table in Figure 5–8, you will notice that it consists of vertical columns of elements. Each column is numbered. There are eighteen main columns of elements. Columns of elements are called **groups** or **families**. Elements within the same group or family have similar but not identical properties. For example, lithium (Li), sodium (Na), potassium (K), and the other members of Family 1 are all soft, white, shiny metals. They are all highly reactive elements, which means they readily combine with other elements to form compounds.

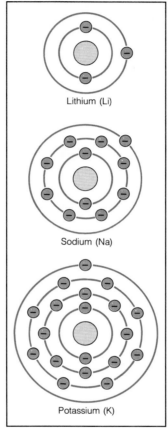

Figure 5–7 *Elements in the same family of the periodic table have similar properties. Here you see the electron arrangement of the elements lithium, sodium, and potassium. How is the electron arrangement in each element similar?*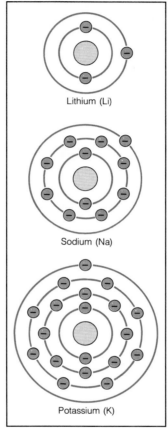

Lithium (Li)

Sodium (Na)

Potassium (K)

• **What is the purpose of an ID?** (To identify a person by listing certain types of information.)

• **What kind of information may be found on an ID?** (Possible answers are name, address, age, sex, height, weight, eye color.)

Use the discussion to lead into the idea that each square of the periodic table is like an element's ID; that is, it contains information that can be used to identify the element.

Display a copy of the modern periodic table, preferably a large, wall-sized model. Point to the element sodium (Na; atomic number 11) and explain that sodium reacts violently with water. Then move down the column to potassium (K) and explain that potassium reacts even more violently with water. Point to the next two elements in the column, rubidium and cesium.

• **What do you think will happen when these elements are brought into contact with water?** (They, too, will react violently with water.)

CONTENT DEVELOPMENT

▶ *Multimedia* ◀

Use the transparency called The Periodic Table in your *Transparency Binder* to help students understand how the elements are classified.

zines, newspapers, and other items published at predictable intervals. The *Readers' Guide to Periodical Literature* contains information on articles, subjects, and authors in periodicals.

REINFORCEMENT/RETEACHING

Review students' responses to the Section Review questions. Reteach any material that is still unclear, based on their responses.

CLOSURE

▶ *Review and Reinforcement Guide*

Have students complete Section 5–1 in their *Review and Reinforcement Guide*.

TEACHING STRATEGY 5–2

FOCUS/MOTIVATION

Lead a discussion about the uses and importance of identification cards.

A few elements were known in ancient times. During the Middle Ages and the Renaissance, more elements were discovered. By the time Mendeleev developed his periodic table, around 60 elements were known. Today, the number of natural elements totals 92; and since 1940, 17 more elements have been produced synthetically.

BACKGROUND INFORMATION
NEW LABELS FOR FAMILIES

Until recently, the families or groups in the table were labeled with a Roman numeral and the capital letter A or B. (There is more than one system of this type.) Now, based on a decision made of the International Union of Pure and Applied Chemistry (IUPAC), the families are labeled with the numbers 1 through 18. The older systems had some advantages; in particular, it was more obvious that Family 6 and Family 4, for example, shared certain properties. If students have access to a periodic table that shows the electronic configurations of the elements, you might challenge them to find the reasons behind the older systems of labeling.

Also, in accordance with IUPAC, the names lanthanide and actinide have been changed to lanthanoid and actinoid.

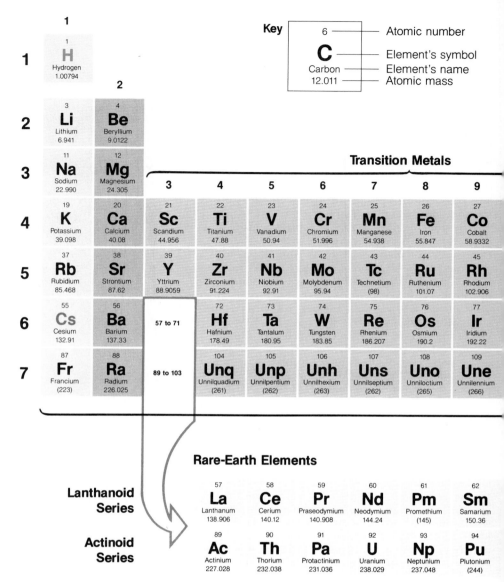

Figure 5–8 *The modern periodic table of the elements is shown here.*

5–2 (continued)

GUIDED PRACTICE

Skills Development

Skill: Interpreting charts

Have students study the periodic table. Explain that the table shows the state of each element (solid, liquid, or gas) under normal conditions of temperature and atmospheric pressure.

• **How are solids designated on this copy of the periodic table?** (By black lettering.)
• **How are liquids designated?** (By green lettering.)

• **How are gases designated?** (By red lettering.)
• **How many elements are solids?** (94.)
• **About what percentage of all elements does this represent?** (86 percent.)
• **How many elements are liquids?** (4.)
• **What percentage of all elements is this?** (About 4 percent.)
• **How many elements are gases?** (11.)
• **What percentage of all elements does this represent?** (About 10 percent.)

CONTENT DEVELOPMENT

Explain to students that the first 92 elements, from hydrogen to uranium, are known as natural elements. This means that they are found either free or combined in nature. These elements are sometimes referred to as the pre-atomic elements. The elements beyond uranium, from number 93 to number 109, are called the transuranium elements. They are artificial elements produced from other elements by nuclear reactions.

OF THE ELEMENTS

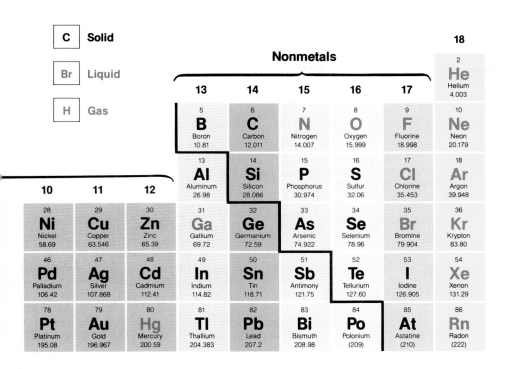

C	Solid
Br	Liquid
H	Gas

Nonmetals

The symbols shown here for elements 104-109 are being used temporarily until names for these elements can be agreed upon.

Metals

Mass numbers in parentheses are those of the most stable or common isotope.

| | 63 Eu Europium 151.96 | 64 Gd Gadolinium 157.25 | 65 Tb Terbium 158.925 | 66 Dy Dysprosium 162.50 | 67 Ho Holmium 164.93 | 68 Er Erbium 167.26 | 69 Tm Thulium 168.934 | 70 Yb Ytterbium 173.04 | 71 Lu Lutetium 174.967 |
| | 95 Am Americium (243) | 96 Cm Curium (247) | 97 Bk Berkelium (247) | 98 Cf Californium (251) | 99 Es Einsteinium (252) | 100 Fm Fermium (257) | 101 Md Mendelevium (258) | 102 No Nobelium (259) | 103 Lr Lawrencium (260) |

In the early 1930s, a team of physicists led by the Italian Enrico Fermi undertook an experimental study of atomic structure. Fermi had proclaimed that it should be possible to produce elements 93 and 94 from uranium. True to his assertion, element 93 was produced in 1940 in the laboratories of the University of California at Berkeley, and later, element 94 was produced in the same laboratories.

Between 1941 and 1961, elements 95 through 103 were produced. The production of elements 104 through 109 in the 1960s and 1970s was surrounded by controversy because both Soviet and American scientists claimed to be the "discoverers" of these elements. Since the country that produces an element traditionally proposes the element's name, no names for these elements could be agreed upon. Thus, IUPAC devised the names shown in the table until official names can be established.

INTEGRATION
LANGUAGE ARTS

Have students try to figure out how the IUPAC decided on the names for elements 104 through 107. (The names are the Latin words for the atomic numbers.) If students need a hint, ask them to recall the geometrical figures quadrilateral, pentagon, and hexagon.

• **Why has it taken so many centuries for all the natural elements to be discovered? Were not these same substances just as abundant in ancient times as they are today?** (Answers may vary. An important point to consider is that many of the elements are not found free in nature; thus it is difficult to isolate them without fairly sophisticated scientific techniques.)

INDEPENDENT PRACTICE

▶ *Activity Book*

Students who need further practice can use the periodic table in an informal manner by completing the Chapter 5 activity called Some Common Elements in the *Activity Book*.

ENRICHMENT

Explain that alchemists were scientists and philosophers who lived in medieval times. Among their objectives were changing base metals into gold and discovering a universal cure for all diseases. Alchemy as a science produced discoveries that led the way to modern chemistry.

Ask students to consider the production of artificial elements in light of the dreams of the alchemists. It is an intriguing topic for discussion to consider the idea that modern science has fulfilled the alchemists' vision. It is just as valid for students to come to the conclusion that the hocus-pocus of the alchemists bears little relationship to modern nuclear science.

FIND OUT BY DOING

Classifying Objects—My Way

Mendeleev's table and the modern periodic table are systems of classifying the elements based on similarities and differences in properties.

Choose a set of objects that are familiar to you. You can use coins, stamps, marbles, leaves, playing cards, or jelly beans. Devise your own system of classifying the objects. Put your system of classification in a table for others to use.

■ What is the most important advantage of your classification system?

Fluorine (F), chlorine (Cl), bromine (Br), and iodine (I) are four of the elements in Family 18. Although fluorine and chlorine are both gases, bromine is a liquid, and iodine is a solid, they all still have many similar properties. In fact, both bromine and iodine become gases very easily. All four elements react to form the same kinds of compounds. You will learn more about each family and its properties later in this chapter.

Rows in the Periodic Table

As you look at the periodic table once again, observe that each horizontal row of elements is called a **period.** Unlike the elements in a family, the elements in a period are not alike in properties. In fact, the properties of the elements change greatly across any given row.

But there is a pattern to the properties of the elements as one moves across a period from left to right. The first element in a period is always an extremely active solid. The last element in a period is always a particularly inactive gas. You can see this pattern by looking at the elements in Period 4 of the periodic table. The first element, potassium (K), is an active solid. The last element, krypton (Kr), is an inactive gas (and bears no relationship to the fictional element Kryptonite, which is the only thing feared by Superman!). The symbols for the elements potassium and krypton should remind you of a rule for writing chemical symbols that you learned about in Chapter 3. The chemical symbol for an element consists of one or two letters. If it consists of one letter, the letter is always capitalized. If it consists of two letters, the first letter is always capitalized, but the second never is.

As you can see, there are seven periods of elements. You will also notice that one row has been separated out of Period 6 and one out of Period 7. Even though these two rows are displayed below the main part of the table, they are still part of the periodic table. They have been separated out to make the table shorter and easier to read. Elements in these two rows are rare-earth elements. You will read about these elements in just a little while.

Element Key

Look closely at the periodic table. Each element is found in a separate square. **Important information about an element is given in each square of the periodic table: its atomic number, chemical symbol, name, and atomic mass.**

The number at the top of each square is the atomic number of the element. Remember that the atomic number of an element is the number of protons in an atom of that element. The atomic number is unique to that element. In other words, no two elements have the same atomic number. Look closely at the element squares of the periodic table to see for yourself that this is true. And as you're looking, notice that the elements are arranged in order of increasing atomic number.

Just below the atomic number, near the center of the square, is the chemical symbol for the element. Below the chemical symbol, the name is spelled out. The number near the bottom of the square is the atomic mass of the element.

Figure 5–9 *The properties of elements in the same period are not alike. Reading from left to right are the elements potassium, iron, copper, gallium, and bromine. In what ways do the properties change across the period?* ❶

6

C

Carbon

12.011

Figure 5–10 *Four important facts about an element are supplied in each square of the periodic table: the atomic number, symbol, name, and atomic mass of that element. The element carbon is found in many things. It makes up the lead in your pencil, most of the foods you eat, and also the Hope diamond.*

N ■ 117

HISTORICAL NOTE
CHEMICAL SYMBOLS

Students may wonder why some of the elements have symbols so different from their names. In fact, some of the best-known elements fall into this category. Examples are gold (Au), silver (Ag), lead (Pb), and sodium (Na).

The French chemist Antoine Lavoisier is given credit for cleaning up chemical terminology by creating a new system for naming chemical compounds. Lavoisier published one of the first modern chemistry books in 1789. His book was translated into many languages and helped to standardize chemical terminology.

In many ways, however, Lavoisier was too late. Many elements already had more than one name in different countries. So, although chemists agreed to standardize the symbols for the elements, the element names are often different in different languages. And some elements have more than one name.

Have students use the periodic table to discover the more commonly used name for each of these elements: natrium (sodium), kalium (potassium), ferrum (iron), argentum (silver), aurum (gold), plumbum (lead).

• **Name three elements in group 2.**
• **Name two elements in period 4.**
• **Name three elements in period 2.**
• **Name two elements in group 17.**

CONTENT DEVELOPMENT

Reproduce on the chalkboard the enlarged element key for carbon (C) shown in the textbook. Ask a student volunteer to go to the chalkboard and reproduce the element key for chlorine (Cl). Use the enlarged models to point out the location of the element's name, symbol,

atomic number, and atomic mass. Emphasize to students that the first letter of a chemical symbol is always capitalized, while the second letter is not.

ENRICHMENT

Divide the class into two teams. Then divide each team in half. Give one half of each team a set of cards marked with the atomic numbers from 1 to 18. Give the other half of each team a set of cards marked with the chemical symbols for the first 18 elements. Challenge the teams

to see how quickly they can match the atomic numbers with the chemical symbols. The first team to complete the task correctly wins.

ENRICHMENT

▶ *Activity Book*

Students who understand the structure of the periodic table will be challenged by the Chapter 5 activity in the *Activity Book* called an Alien Periodic Table.

FIND OUT BY DOING

A Hot Time

1. Roll a piece of aluminum foil into a small cylinder about the shape of a pencil.

2. Stand a stainless steel teaspoon, a strip of wood, a plastic spoon, and the aluminum cylinder you made in a plastic cup.

3. Add hot water to the cup. Be careful to leave the tops of the objects above the water level.

4. Wait one minute. Carefully touch the exposed ends of each object in the cup. What are your observations?

■ What conclusions does this activity help you discover?

Figure 5–11 *Unlike some metals, pure gold is actually quite soft and easily worked. This gold pin, hammered from a flat sheet of almost pure gold, can be bent out of shape with little effort. Gold used for jewelry is often combined with copper and other metals to give it strength.*

Now practice using what you have just learned. Locate the element boron in the periodic table. What is its atomic number? Its symbol? What element has the symbol Cd? What element has an atomic number of 38? What is the atomic mass of magnesium? Of bromine? ●

Metals

When you hear the word **metal,** what do you think of? You probably think of silver, iron, or copper. These are all familiar metals. Kitchen pots, trumpets, knives and forks, and pocket change are all familiar items made of metals. However, there are other elements that are classified as metals that you may not have thought of as metals—such as calcium, sodium, and potassium.

Of the 109 known elements, most are metals. If you look at the periodic table, you will see a dark zigzag line running like steps down the right side of the table. The 88 elements to the left of this line are metals or metallike elements.

PHYSICAL PROPERTIES OF METALS The physical properties of metals make them easy to identify. One such property is **luster,** or shininess. Hold a brand-new penny in your hand, and its gleam will convince you of this important property of metals. Most metals also allow heat and electricity to move through them easily. Therefore, metals are good conductors of heat and electricity. In general, metals have a high density. This means that they are heavy for their size. Trying to lift a metal dumbbell can easily convince you of this! Finally, metals usually have fairly high melting points. Now that you know about some of the properties of metals, explain why metal pots are used for cooking.

There are two other physical properties that are common to many metals. Most metals are **ductile,** which means they can be drawn out into thin wires. And most metals are **malleable,** which means they can be hammered into thin sheets. The ease with which metals can be drawn into wire and hammered into sheets contributes, in large part, to their use in making jewelry. The pin in Figure 5–11 is made of a thin gold sheet that was hammered by an ancient Peruvian native. ●

Figure 5–12 *Some of the physical properties of metals and their alloys are evident in these photographs. What properties can you identify in the cooling slabs of steel (left), steel girders (center), stainless steel artificial human hip joint (inset), and copper tubes (right)?* ②

CHEMICAL PROPERTIES OF METALS The chemical properties of metals are not as easily observed as are the physical properties. The chemical properties of any element depend upon the electron arrangement in the atoms of the element—more specifically, on the number of electrons in the outermost energy level. (Remember that the electrons in the outer energy level, or the valence electrons, are involved in forming bonds with other atoms.) An atom of a metal can have 1, 2, 3, or 4 electrons in its outermost energy level. The electrons in the outermost energy level of a metal are rather weakly held. So metals are elements that tend to lose their outermost electrons when they combine chemically.

Because they tend to lose electrons, most metals will react chemically with water or with elements in the atmosphere. Such a chemical reaction often results in **corrosion.** Corrosion is the gradual wearing away of a metal due to a chemical reaction in which the metal element is changed into a metallic compound. The rusting of iron is an example of corrosion. When iron rusts, it combines with oxygen in the air to form the compound iron oxide. The

Figure 5–13 *The rusting of iron and steel is actually a form of corrosion. This abandoned car shows the dramatic effects of corrosion.*

N ■ 119

HISTORICAL NOTE
ALUMINUM

The most abundant metal, and the third-most abundant element in the Earth's crust, is aluminum. Aluminum compounds occur in garnets, granite, basalt, feldspar, mica, lapis lazuli, clay, and loam. Because aluminum compounds are so common, one might expect that aluminum metal would also be common and very cheap. But, at first, that was not the case. The atoms in the aluminum compounds are tightly bound to other elements and thus difficult to separate. Aluminum was not isolated until about 1825, and it was 30 or 40 years later before it could be prepared inexpensively for commercial use.

At the beginning, aluminum cost $90 a pound or more, which made it more expensive than silver and almost as expensive as gold. Napoleon III of France, who had supported the research of French chemists, used an aluminum fork and dreamed of the day when all French cavalry troops would wear aluminum armor.

GUIDED PRACTICE

Skills Development

Skill: Identifying patterns

After outlining a periodic table on the chalkboard, have a student outline the areas where metals are found. Then ask another student to outline the areas where metalloids are found.

REINFORCEMENT/RETEACHING

Divide the class into two teams. Name an element and challenge the first member of team A to use the periodic table to determine whether the element is a metal, a nonmetal, or a metalloid. Repeat the process with the first member of team B, and so on. Each correct answer scores one point for the team. The team that finishes with the greatest number of points wins.

INDEPENDENT PRACTICE

▶ *Activity Book*

Students who are having difficulty understanding the differences between metals and nonmetals should be provided with the Chapter 5 activities called Metals and Nonmetals Around Home and Metal or Nonmetal? in the *Activity Book.*

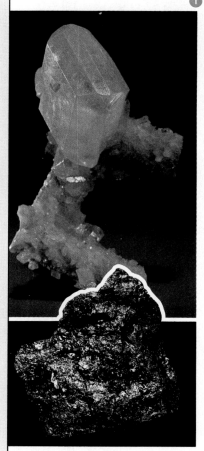

Figure 5–14 *Sulfur (top) is a nonmetal that can form beautiful crystals. Boron (bottom) is a metalloid, a word that means metallike. What are some properties of nonmetals and metalloids?* **2**

tarnishing of silver is another example of corrosion. Tarnishing results when silver reacts with compounds of sulfur in the air or in certain foods. Have you ever observed examples of rusting and/or tarnishing? How would you describe what you observed? **1**

Nonmetals

Elements that are **nonmetals** are located to the right of the zigzag line in the periodic table. Fewer elements are classified as nonmetals than as metals in the periodic table. In general, the physical and chemical properties of nonmetals tend to be opposite those of metals.

PHYSICAL PROPERTIES OF NONMETALS Nonmetals usually have no luster and are dull in appearance. Nonmetals do not conduct heat and electricity well. Nonmetals are brittle and thus break easily. They cannot be drawn out into wire or hammered into thin sheets. In other words, nonmetals are neither ductile nor malleable. Nonmetals usually have lower densities and lower melting points than metals.

Nonmetals are not as easy to recognize as a group as are metals. Nonmetals can be noticeably different from one another. For example, bromine is a brown liquid, oxygen is a colorless gas, and sulfur is a yellow solid. Yet all are nonmetals.

CHEMICAL PROPERTIES OF NONMETALS Remember, the chemical properties of elements are determined by the number of electrons in the outermost energy level. Atoms of most nonmetals have 5, 6, 7, or 8 electrons in their outermost energy level. Atoms with 5, 6, or 7 valence electrons gain 3, 2, or 1 electron, respectively, when they combine chemically. Thus nonmetals are elements that tend to gain electrons. Perhaps you are wondering about the nonmetals whose atoms have 8 valence electrons. Atoms with 8 valence electrons have a complete outermost energy level. So elements whose atoms have 8 valence electrons tend to be nonreactive or rarely react with atoms of other elements. Knowing what you do now about metals and nonmetals, do you think they can form compounds with each other if one gives up electrons and one takes electrons? **3**

Figure 5–15 *Both silicon (left) and antimony (right) are metalloids. All metalloids are solids that can be shiny or dull. The silicon in the photograph has been made into a computer chip.*

Metalloids

The dividing line between metals and nonmetals is not quite as definite as it appears. For along both sides of the dark zigzag line are elements that have properties of both metals and nonmetals. These elements are called **metalloids** (MEHT-uh-loidz). The word metalloid means metallike. All metalloids are solids that can be shiny or dull. They conduct heat and electricity better than nonmetals but not as well as metals. Metalloids are ductile and malleable. The metalloids include boron, silicon, germanium, arsenic, antimony, tellurium, polonium, and astatine. Do any of these elements sound familiar to you? If so, in what way? ④

5–2 Section Review

1. What important information is given in each square of the periodic table?
2. What are the horizontal rows in the periodic table called? What are the vertical rows called?
3. What are some physical and chemical properties of metals? Of nonmetals?
4. What is a metalloid?

Critical Thinking—*Applying Concepts*
5. Electricity is, in large part, responsible for our modern lifestyle. How are some of the physical properties of metals related to the fact that a steady supply of electricity is able to reach our homes from electric generating plants?

FIND OUT BY DOING

An Elemental Hunt

1. Collect some samples of elements that are easily obtained, such as copper, iron, aluminum, nickel, and carbon.

2. Attach each element to a large square of paper or cardboard. Make each square of paper or cardboard look like a square of the periodic table.

3. On the paper square, include the atomic mass, atomic number, name, and chemical symbol of the element displayed.

Working along with your classmates, see how complete a periodic table you are able to create.

5-3 Chemical Families

Guide for Reading

Focus on these questions as you read.
▶ *What is the basis for the placement of elements in the periodic table?*
▶ *What are the properties of chemical families?*

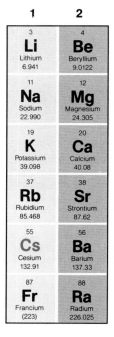

Figure 5–16 *Family 1 metals are called the alkali metals. Family 2 metals are called the alkaline earth metals. How many electrons are in the outermost energy level of each alkali metal? Of each alkaline earth metal?* ①

5-3 Chemical Families

You are about to go on a "tour" of the periodic table. This trip will help you become more familiar with the basic properties of the families of elements. Remember, it is not necessary to memorize lots of facts about the elements. What we hope you will be able to do is recognize the value of the periodic table in organizing information about the elements. We also hope that you will appreciate how these elements—some of which may be unfamiliar to you—are a part of your world. After all, your world is made up of matter, and matter is ultimately made up of atoms of elements. So in some way, each and every one of the 109 elements in the periodic table is a part of your life. To help you on your tour, keep in mind the following principle: **Elements within the same family of the periodic table have similar properties because they have the same number of valence electrons.**

The Most Active Metals

The elements in Family 1, with the exception of hydrogen, are called the **alkali** (AL-kuh-ligh) **metals.** Atoms of the alkali metals have a single electron in their outermost energy level. In other words, they have 1 valence electron. Hydrogen also has 1 electron in its outer shell. In many ways, it behaves like the alkali metals.

The alkali metals are soft, silver-white, shiny metals. They are so soft, in fact, that they can be cut with a knife. The alkali metals are good conductors of heat and electricity. Because they have only 1 valence electron, these elements bond readily with other substances. In fact, they are so reactive that they are never found uncombined in nature. In other words, they are never found as free elements. In the laboratory, samples of these elements are stored in oil in order to keep them from combining with water or oxygen in the air. The reaction is violent when the alkali metals react with water. Hydrogen gas is produced, as well as extreme heat. Because of the heat produced, the hydrogen gas can begin to burn and may explode.

---

easily with other elements. The elements underneath hydrogen in Family 1 are called the alkali metals.

CONTENT DEVELOPMENT

• **Find potassium in the periodic table. Where is it located?** (In Family 1 underneath sodium.)

Explain that potassium is even more active than sodium is. Both sodium and potassium are so eager to combine with other elements that they are hardly ever found alone. And once they have been

separated as elements, they will combine quickly (and often dangerously) with other elements.

If a piece of sodium or potassium is exposed to air, it tarnishes immediately because the outer atoms combine with oxygen. If a piece of sodium or potassium no larger than a match head is put in water, it combines with the oxygen in water and liberates one of the hydrogen atoms. The heat of the reaction is so great that the hydrogen often catches fire.

ALKALI METALS		
Element	**Properties**	**Uses of Compounds**
Lithium (Li)	m.p. 179°C b.p. 1336°C Soft; silvery; reacts violently with water	Medicine; metallurgy
Sodium (Na)	m.p. 97.8°C b.p. 883°C Soft; silvery white; reacts violently with water	Soap; table salt; lye
Potassium (K)	m.p. 62.5°C b.p. 758°C Soft; silvery white; reacts violently with moisture	Fertilizer; medicine; photography
Rubidium (Rb)	m.p. 39.0°C b.p. 700°C Soft; lustrous; reacts violently with moisture	Space vehicle engines; photocells
Cesium (Cs)	m.p. 28.6°C b.p. 670°C Silvery white; ductile; reacts with moisture	Photocells
Francium (Fr)	Extremely rare; radioactive isotopes	Not widely used

Figure 5–17 *This table shows some of the properties of the alkali metals and the uses of their compounds. Which alkali metal has radioactive isotopes?* 2

Although the alkali metals themselves have few familiar uses, the compounds they form are some of the most important substances you use every day. Table salt and baking soda are two compounds you may be familiar with. Soap, which forms when alkali compounds react with fats, is another. Now look at the periodic table and identify the alkali metals.

Family 2 consists of the six elements known as the **alkaline** (AL-kuh-lihn) **earth metals.** Like the alkali metals, the alkaline earth metals are never found in nature as uncombined elements. Instead, they exist bonded with other elements in compounds. The alkaline earth metals have 2 valence electrons. Atoms of these elements lose their 2 electrons easily when they combine with other atoms. But since they must lose 2 electrons, they are not quite as reactive as the alkali metals.

Two of the alkaline earth metals—magnesium and calcium—are probably familiar to you. Magnesium is often combined with aluminum to make alloys that are strong yet light in weight. These alloys are used to make ladders and airplane parts. They are used where light yet strong metal parts are needed. Other compounds of magnesium are used in medicines, flares, and fireworks. Calcium is an abundant substance in the Earth's crust. Calcium compounds

ANNOTATION KEY

Answers

1 Each alkali metal has 1 electron in the outermost energy level; each alkaline earth metal, 2 electrons. (Applying definitions)

2 Francium. (Interpreting charts)

FACTS AND FIGURES

IF YOU COULD FIND IT

Francium should be the most active metal on the periodic table, but it has been difficult to investigate its properties because it is so rare. Scientists estimate that there is less than 1 ounce of francium in the entire Earth's crust.

Because it is so difficult to find, the element with the atomic number 87 has had several different names. Dr. Fred Allison thought he had isolated this element in 1929 and named it virginium for his native state. Ten years later, a chemist named Horia Hulubey stated he had finally found the element and proposed naming it moldavium after the river Moldau in Bohemia. Finally, Marguerite Prey in Paris found a certain unstable isotope with a mass of 223 and a half-life of 22 minutes. She proposed the now-accepted name francium.

CONTENT DEVELOPMENT

Have students find magnesium in the periodic table. Explain that magnesium and the other five elements in Family 2 are called the alkaline earth metals. These metals are also very active, but not quite as active as those in Family 1.

• **Strontium-90 is a compound in fallout. Why are scientists concerned about the appearance of strontium-90 in milk products?** (Strontium-90 would have similar properties to calcium and could be absorbed into our bones.)

INDEPENDENT PRACTICE

▶ *Activity Book*

Students who need practice using the periodic table should be provided with the Chapter 5 activity in the *Activity Book* called Identifying Substances.

GUIDED PRACTICE

▶ *Laboratory Manual*

Skills: Making observations, applying concepts, classifying

At this point you may want to have students complete the Chapter 5 Laboratory Investigation, The Alkaline Earth Elements, in the *Laboratory Manual.* In this investigation students will compare the abilities of alkaline earth elements to form precipitates as a result of a chemical reaction.

The rusting of iron is actually the oxidation of iron. This means that in the process of rusting, iron gives up electrons to oxygen. Rusting will not occur, however, without moisture. One part of the iron surface acts as an anode (source of electrons) because the surface of most iron structures is not homogeneous. When the iron atoms of that area lose electrons, they form iron +2. These ions travel through the moisture on the surface to an area where oxygen is found and form a compound (Fe_2O_3) known as rust.

Iron rust is a crumbly substance that flakes away from the metal and exposes fresh iron to the oxygen and moisture of the air. The fresh iron then rusts and flakes away. Eventually, the entire piece of iron will rust and crumble into flakes. It is for this reason that iron and most forms of steel must be painted to protect them from rusting. Often the steel used in construction is an orange-red color. The color is paint, however, and not rust.

5–3 (continued)

REINFORCEMENT/RETEACHING

Remind students that elements in vertical columns, or families, have similar properties. For example, point out that all the elements in Family 2 have 2 electrons in their outer energy levels.

Point out that the elements in the horizontal rows, or periods, do not have similar properties. Explain that in each horizontal row the electrons in the outermost energy level increase from 1 to 8. The elements range from the metals on the left to the nonmetals on the right.

FOCUS/MOTIVATION

Have students find the transition metals (Family 3 through Family 12) on the periodic table.

ALKALINE EARTH METALS

Element	Properties	Uses of Compounds
Beryllium (Be)	m.p. 1285°C b.p. 2970°C Poisonous	Radio parts; steel
Magnesium (Mg)	m.p. 650°C b.p. 1117°C Burns with very bright flame; strong but not dense	Medicine; photographic flashbulbs; auto parts; space vehicle parts; flares
Calcium (Ca)	m.p. 851°C b.p. 1487°C Silvery; important part of bones and teeth; tarnishes in moist air	Plaster and plasterboard; mortar and cement; water softeners; metal bearings
Strontium (Sr)	m.p. 774°C b.p. 1366°C Least abundant alkaline earth metal; reactive in air	Fireworks; flares
Barium (Ba)	m.p. 850°C b.p. 1537°C Extremely reactive in air	Medicine; paints; glassmaking
Radium (Ra)	m.p. (700°C) b.p. (1525°C) Silvery white but turns black in air; radioactive	Treatment of cancer; medical research

Values in parentheses are physical properties of the most stable isotope.

Figure 5–18 *The properties and uses of alkaline earth metals are shown in this table. Which alkaline earth metal is important for strong teeth and bones?* ❶

make up limestone and marble rock. Calcium is also an essential part of your teeth and bones.

The Transition Metals

Look at the periodic table between Family 2 and Family 13. What do you see? You should see several groups of elements that do not seem to fit into any other family. These elements are called the **transition metals.** Transition metals have properties similar to one another and to other metals, but they are different from the properties of any other family.

The names of the transition metals are probably well known to you. These are the metals with which you are probably most familiar: copper, tin, zinc, iron, nickel, gold, and silver, for example. You may

Figure 5–19 *An artist uses a palette of different colors to paint a picture. Many of the colors are made from the transition metals. Tungsten is a transition metal whose importance in your life is immediately apparent when you switch on an incandescent light. The tungsten wire in a light bulb glows as electricity passes through it.*

• **How many of these elements do you recognize?** (Students will be familiar with some of the elements.)
• **What uses are made of these metals?** (Accept all logical responses.)

CONTENT DEVELOPMENT

Explain that transition metals are good conductors of heat and electricity. They combine with other elements to form many different compounds.

Explain that many of the transition metals are used to make alloys. An alloy is a mixture of two elements—both metals or a metal and a nonmetal—that has the properties of a metal. Copper and zinc are made into the alloy brass. Copper mixes with tin to make bronze, and chromium is used with iron to make stainless steel.

The transition metals are often brightly colored and thus are frequently found in paints.

also know that the transition metals are good conductors of heat and electricity. The compounds of transition metals are usually brightly colored and are often used to color paint. (Remember Mary Cassatt and the other Impressionist painters you read about at the beginning of the chapter?) Gold and silver are used to make jewelry and eating utensils. These two metals are often used in dental fillings to replace decayed areas of a tooth. Silver is essential in the making of photographic film and paper. Mercury is an interesting transition metal because it is a liquid at temperatures above −38.8°C. How do you think this fact relates to the use of mercury in household thermometers? 2

Most transition elements have 1 or 2 valence electrons. When they combine with other atoms, they lose either 1 or both of their valence electrons. But transition elements can also lose an electron from the next-to-outermost energy level. In addition, transition elements can share electrons when they form bonds with other atoms. It is no wonder that transition elements form so many different compounds!

TRANSITION ELEMENTS	
Element	**Uses**
Iron (Fe)	Manufacturing; building materials; dietary supplement
Cobalt (Co)	Magnets; heat-resistant tools
Nickel (Ni)	Coins; batteries; jewelry; plating
Copper (Cu)	Electric wiring; plumbing; motors
Silver (Ag)	Jewelry; dental fillings; mirror backing; electric conductor
Gold (Au)	Jewelry; base for money systems; coins; dentistry
Zinc (Zn)	Paints; medicines; coat metals
Cadmium (Cd)	Plating; batteries; nuclear reactors
Mercury (Hg)	Liquid in thermometers, barometers, electric switches; dentistry; paints

Figure 5–20 *The transition elements have many common uses. Which transition element is liquid at room temperature?* 3

From Metals to Nonmetals

To the right of the transition elements are six families, five of which contain some metalloids. This means that certain members of these families show properties of metals as well as nonmetals. These four families are named after the first element in the family.

Family 13 is the **boron family.** Atoms of elements in this family have 3 valence electrons. Boron is a metalloid. The other elements, including aluminum, are metals.

Boron, which is hard and brittle, is never found uncombined in nature. It is usually found combined with oxygen. Compounds of boron are used to make heat-resistant glass, such as the test tubes used in your laboratory and the glass cookware used in your kitchen. Boron is also found in borax, a cleaning compound that may be familiar to you.

Aluminum is the most abundant metal and the third most abundant element in the Earth's crust. Aluminum is also found combined with oxygen in the ore bauxite. Aluminum is an extremely important

ANNOTATION KEY

Answers

1 Calcium. (Interpreting charts)

2 The mercury in a thermometer expands when the temperature goes up and contracts when it goes down. Mercury will remain liquid at temperatures encountered in an ordinary household. (Making inferences)

3 Mercury. (Interpreting charts)

Integration

1 Fine Arts

HISTORICAL NOTE

CHARLES HALL

Aluminum is plentiful and has many uses. It was not until the late 1800s, however, that aluminum could be obtained cheaply enough to be used. It was then that a young graduate student, 21-year-old Charles Hall, developed a way of dissolving aluminum oxide in cryolite, then using an electric current to extract pure aluminum. The Hall process paved the way for the cheap production of aluminum.

● ● ● ● Integration ● ● ● ●

Use the illustration of artists' pigments to integrate concepts from the fine arts into your science lesson.

GUIDED PRACTICE

Skills Development

Skill: Interpreting charts

Have students find Family 13 through Family 16 in the periodic table.

• **Are the elements in these families metals or nonmetals?** (Both. The families contain metals, metalloids, and nonmetals.)

• **Which of these elements do you recognize?** (Students will likely know many of the elements.)

CONTENT DEVELOPMENT

Explain that each of these four families is often referred to by the element at the top of each column.

• **Which element in the boron family is most familiar to you? What is this element used for?** (Students probably will say aluminum. It is used for cans, cooking utensils, window and door frames, and so on.)

Explain that in these families the elements change from metallic to nonmetallic. In each row, the nucleus is becoming more positive and therefore able to attract new electrons. Within each family, from bottom to top, the nucleus also gets less positive, and the atoms are getting smaller. In both cases, the elements are becoming less metallic.

ENRICHMENT

▶ *Activity Book*

Students who have a good understanding of the periodic table may enjoy working the puzzle in the Chapter 5 activity in the *Activity Book* called Interpreting the Periodic Table.

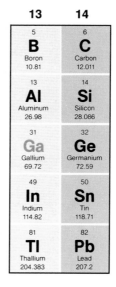

Figure 5–21 *Family 13 is also known as the boron family. Elements in Family 14 are also known as the carbon family.*

Figure 5–22 *Carbon is found in oil, gas, and other petroleum products. In an oil refinery, crude oil is processed into many different products. Silicon is one of the most abundant elements in the Earth's crust.* ❶

metal in industry. It is light, strong, and does not corrode. It is an excellent reflector of light and a good conductor of heat and electricity. Aluminum is used to make parts for cars, trains, and planes. It is also made into the pots and pans used in cooking. Because aluminum is so malleable, it can also be made into foil used to wrap food for storage.

The **carbon family** is Family 14. Atoms of the elements in this family have 4 valence electrons. Carbon is a nonmetal. But the next two elements, silicon and germanium, are metalloids. And tin and lead are metals.

Carbon atoms, with their 4 valence electrons, form an unbelievable number of different compounds—more than 5 million by some estimates! The element carbon is often called the "basis of life." Your body contains a wide variety of carbon compounds. Sugars and starches are two important examples. Fuels such as gasoline also contain carbon compounds. Carbon compounds are so numerous, in fact, that a whole branch of chemistry is devoted to their study. This branch is called organic chemistry.

Silicon is the second most abundant element in the Earth's crust. Silicon combined with oxygen to form sand is used to make glass and cement. Silicon is also used to make solar cells, which are able to convert the energy of sunlight into electricity. Solar cells are commonly found in roof panels and are also used on space satellites. One of the most important uses of silicon is probably quite familiar to you. Silicon chips are used for circuitry and memory in computers.

5–3 (continued)

CONTENT DEVELOPMENT

Explain to students that the name *carbon* comes from the Latin word for coal. All living things contain carbon. As decaying plant matter breaks down, the elements other than carbon are released as gases or liquids. So the decaying material comes to consist more and more of carbon. Wood is about 50 percent carbon; coal is more than 80 percent carbon.

When the atoms in carbon are arranged as crystals, carbon takes the form of graphite or diamonds.

• **Find carbon in the periodic table. Which element is just below it?** (Silicon.)

Explain that silicon has many of the same properties as carbon. Because of this, silicon atoms can sometimes replace carbon atoms in a compound.

● ● ● ● **Integration** ● ● ● ●

Use the discussion of the elements in the Earth's crust to integrate concepts of geology into your lesson.

ENRICHMENT

Have students use reference materials to explain the roles of carbon and silicon in forming fossils. (Sometimes dead organisms do not turn into coal. Instead, the carbon atoms are slowly replaced by silicon atoms, resulting in a stony replica of the original organism.)

CONTENT DEVELOPMENT

Have students find nitrogen in the periodic table. Explain that nitrogen is found

Figure 5–23 *Nitrogen is used to make explosives. This building is being demolished by a controlled explosion that causes the building to collapse.*

Germanium is a metalloid commonly used in transistors. Transistors are components of many electronic devices, including radios, televisions, and computer games. Tin is a metal that resists rusting and corrosion. The common "tin can" used as a container for your favorite soup is actually a steel can lined with a very thin layer of tin. The tin lining prevents the food in the can from coming into contact with the steel wall of the can.

Lead is another metal in the carbon family. In the past, lead was used to color paint. It was also an important additive in gasoline. However, because of the dangers associated with exposure to lead, it has been removed from paints and gasoline. And just so you do not become concerned about using an ordinary pencil, you should know that the "lead" in a lead pencil is not really lead but is a form of carbon known as graphite. A lead pencil is perfectly safe to use.

The **nitrogen family,** Family 15, is named after an element that makes up 78 percent of the air around you: nitrogen. The atoms of elements in this family have 5 valence electrons in their outermost energy level. These atoms tend to share electrons when they bond with other atoms.

Nitrogen is the most abundant element in the Earth's atmosphere. It is an exceptionally stable element and does not combine readily with other elements. Nitrogen is an important part of many fertilizers, which are substances used to enhance plant growth. Nitrogen is also used to produce explosives, medicines, and dyes. Ammonia, a common household cleaning agent, is a compound made of nitrogen and hydrogen.

Phosphorus is an active nonmetal that is not found free in nature. One of its main uses is in making the tips of matches. It is also used in flares. Arsenic is an important ingredient in many insecticides. Both antimony and bismuth are used in making alloys.

The elements making up Family 16 are called the **oxygen family.** Atoms of these elements have 6 valence electrons. Most elements in this family share electrons when forming compounds.

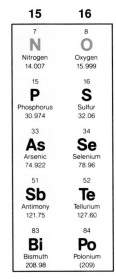

Figure 5–24 *Family 15 is the nitrogen family. Which element in this family shows the most metallic properties? Family 16 is the oxygen family. Which member of this family is a gas?* ❶

N ■ 127

ANNOTATION KEY

Answers

❶ Bismuth; oxygen. (Making inferences)

Integration

❶ Earth Science: Geology. See *Exploring Planet Earth*, Chapter 5.

BACKGROUND INFORMATION
THE CHALCOGENS

The elements of the oxygen family are sometimes called the chalcogens. The term comes from a Greek word meaning to give rise to ores. Ores are naturally occurring minerals that contain metals such as aluminum, iron, and copper. The ore is usually a compound of the desired metal with oxygen or sulfur.

BACKGROUND INFORMATION
ALLOTROPES

Two forms of an element that differ in their physical properties but give rise to identical chemical compounds are called allotropes. Two allotropic forms of carbon are diamond and graphite. Ozone is an allotropic form of oxygen.

---

in explosives, common household ammonia, and fertilizers.

• **Which element in the nitrogen family is a well-known poison?** (Arsenic.)

Students may be interested to know that arsenic itself is not particularly poisonous! The compound arsenic trioxide is the actual poison mentioned in detective stories.

Nitrogen does not easily combine with other elements because the nitrogen atom is held together with a triple bond. Plants capable of breaking this bond are called nitrogen fixers. Soybeans and alfalfa plants are host to bacteria in their roots. The bacteria are able to change the nitrogen to ammonia and help to form amino acids. It is interesting that an enzyme in these bacteria is able to do, under mild field conditions, what we must use temperatures of 300°C and extreme pressures to accomplish.

GUIDED PRACTICE
Skills Development
Skill: Relating facts

Divide the class into groups of two to four students. Have each group choose an element from the nitrogen or oxygen family that interests them. Tell them to make a report by answering the following questions: When, how, and by whom was the element discovered? What are its physical and chemical properties? How have people used this element?

Iodine deficiences can cause thyroid problems such as possible goiter formation. Common table salt is frequently "iodized" by adding a small amount, approximately 0.02 percent, of potassium iodide, a compound with a molecule containing 1 potassium atom and 1 iodine atom. In places where the soil has very little iodine, small quantities of iodides are sometimes added to drinking water.

Tincture of iodine is an antiseptic used to kill bacteria. A tincture is a solution of a chemical dissolved in alcohol.

Charcoal is formed by heating wood in the absence of air. When very finely powdered, charcoal has the ability to absorb many types of molecules and is sometimes called activated charcoal.

Gas masks can be made from activated charcoal. Air is breathed in through the charcoal, which allows the oxygen and nitrogen atoms to pass. Poison gases with large molecules remain behind, stuck to the small charcoal particles.

5-3 (continued)

CONTENT DEVELOPMENT

● ● ● ● Integration ● ● ● ●

Use the discussion of how plants and animals use oxygen to integrate concepts of life science into your lesson.

FOCUS/MOTIVATION

Explain to students that table salt is made up of sodium and chlorine. Sodium is a silvery, soft, highly reactive metal. Chlorine is a green poisonous gas. Yet when they react together, they form the stable white crystal salt.

CONTENT DEVELOPMENT

● **Which family in the periodic table contains chlorine?** (Family 17.)

HALOGENS	
Element	**Uses**
Fluorine (F)	Etching glass; refrigerants; nonstick utensils; preventing tooth decay
Chlorine (Cl)	Bleaching agent; disinfectant; water purifier
Bromine (Br)	Medicine; dyes; photography
Iodine (I)	Medicine; disinfectant; dietary supplement in salt
Astatine (At)	Rare element

Figure 5-25 *Because of their chemical reactivity, the halogens have many uses.*

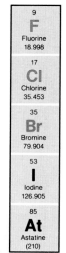

Figure 5-26
Family 17 is known as the halogen family.

Oxygen, the most abundant element in the Earth's crust and the second most abundant element in the atmosphere, is an extremely reactive element. It combines with almost every other element. You already know how important oxygen is to you—and to almost all other forms of life on Earth. Your body uses the oxygen you breathe to break down carbohydrates to produce energy. Plants also use oxygen to break down carbohydrates. In addition to combining with other elements, oxygen can also form molecules by bonding with itself. You might be familiar with the word ozone. Three atoms of oxygen bond to form a molecule of ozone, O_3. In the atmosphere, the ozone layer screens out harmful ultraviolet radiation from the sun, thus protecting life on Earth.

Sulfur, selenium, and tellurium are brittle solids at room temperature. They all combine with oxygen as well as with metals and with hydrogen. Sulfur is used to manufacture medicines, matches, gunpowder, and synthetic rubber. Selenium is used to color glass red and to make enamels. Tellurium is useful in making alloys. Polonium, another member of this family, is an extremely rare element.

The Halogens

The elements of Family 17 are fluorine, chlorine, bromine, iodine, and astatine. Together they are known as the **halogen family**. Halogens have 7 valence electrons, which explains why they are the most active nonmetals. Atoms of these elements need to gain only 1 electron to fill their outermost energy level. The great reactivity of the halogens explains why they are never found free in nature.

Halogens form compounds in which they share or gain 1 electron. They react with the alkali metals (Family 1) quite easily. One common compound formed when the alkali metal sodium gives up 1 electron to the halogen chlorine is called sodium chloride. You know this compound better as table salt. When halogens react with metals, they form compounds called salts. Perhaps you have heard of sodium fluoride, which is the salt used to fluoridate water and toothpaste, or of calcium chloride, which is used to melt snow and ice on streets and

● **Do you recognize any other elements in this family? What are these elements used for?** (Answers will vary. Students might say that fluorine is used to kill bacteria in water or that iodine is used to kill bacteria on cuts.)

All the elements in Family 17 form compounds similar to table salt. So the family is called the halogens, from a Greek word meaning giving rise to salt.

The halogen family presents interesting contrasts in physical properties. Fluorine and chlorine are gases, bromine is a liq-

uid, and iodine and astatine are found in solid form.

INDEPENDENT PRACTICE

▶ *Activity Book*

Students who need practice with Family 17 in the periodic table should be provided with the Chapter 5 activity in the *Activity Book* called Halogens.

sidewalks. Silver bromide, another halogen salt, is used in photographic film.

Fluorine is the most active halogen. Fluorine and chlorine, which is also highly active, are never found uncombined in nature. As you can see from the periodic table, fluorine and chlorine are gases. Bromine is one of the few liquid elements, while iodine and the metalloid astatine are solids.

The Noble Gases

Your tour across the periodic table ends with Family 18, the **noble gases.** All of the elements in this family are gases that are normally unreactive. But under special conditions, certain noble gases will combine chemically with other elements. Because they do not readily form compounds with other elements, the noble gases are also called the inert gases. The noble, or inert, gases include helium (He), neon (Ne), argon (Ar), krypton (Kr), xenon (Xe), and radon (Rn). Can you figure out why they are so unreactive? Atoms of noble gases already have complete outermost energy levels. They do not need to bond with other atoms. Among the noble gases, helium has 2 valence electrons; neon, argon, krypton, xenon, and radon each has 8 valence electrons.

All of the noble gases are found in small amounts in the Earth's atmosphere. Argon, the most common of the noble gases, makes up only about 1 percent of the atmosphere. Because they are so scarce and so unreactive, the noble gases were not discovered until the end of the nineteenth century. This was almost 50 years after Mendeleev's work.

Some common uses of the noble gases are probably quite familiar to you. No doubt you have seen a balloon filled with helium floating at the end of a string. The brightly colored signs above theaters, restaurants, and stores are filled with inert gases, often called "neon" lights. However, only the red lights are produced by neon. The other colors are produced by argon and several of the other noble gases. Some of the other uses of the noble gases may be less familiar to you. Radon is used to treat certain cancers. Argon and xenon are used in certain light bulbs and lamps.

18

2
He
Helium
4.003

10
Ne
Neon
20.179

18
Ar
Argon
39.948

36
Kr
Krypton
83.80

54
Xe
Xenon
131.29

86
Rn
Radon
(222)

Figure 5–27 *Family 18 is known as the noble gases.*

Figure 5–28 *Crystals of xenon tetrafluoride were first prepared in 1962. Before that time, it was believed that noble gases could not form compounds.*

ECOLOGY NOTE
RADON

Radon is a naturally occurring radioactive gas that seeps from certain kinds of underground rocks. When diluted with outside air, radon is harmless. But it can leak through a basement wall and accumulate in a house—especially one that is tightly closed—and thus create a significant health risk.

A simple testing procedure has been developed to tests homes for radon levels. Those interested in checking the radon level of their homes can get a list of companies that conduct radon testing from state environmental agencies.

FACTS AND FIGURES
ASTATINE

The last halogen, astatine, is used to produce radioactive substances. These substances are then used for food sterilization and in the treatment of certain diseases. Astatine is itself radioactive, with a half-life of only 8.3 hours. The name for astatine comes from the Greek word for unsteady.

GUIDED PRACTICE

Skills Development

Skills: Making observations, applying concepts, making inferences

At this point have students investigate various chlorides by completing the in-text Chapter 5 Laboratory Investigation: Flame Tests.

CONTENT DEVELOPMENT

The elements in Family 18 do not easily form compounds with other elements. Because of this, they are called the inert gases or the noble gases.

One way to explain the inactivity of this family is to show diagrams of the valence electrons in the outermost energy levels. Each element has an already-filled valence level. Because the valence level is filled and therefore stable, these atoms would not gain stability in combining with other elements.

ENRICHMENT

In 1962, Neils Bartlett produced the first known compound using a noble gas. The compound did not involve radon because of the difficulty of working with radioactive elements.

• **Which of the noble gases seems most likely to be the one involved in Bartlett's compound? Explain your answer.** (Xenon, because it has the greatest atomic mass. As a very large atom, it would be the most likely to lose its electrons.)

PROBLEM SOLVING

COMPLETING THE SQUARES

Students may approximate the atomic mass of oxygen by doubling the number of protons in the nucleus. And the number of protons is the same as the atomic number. (The symbol for carbon is C; its atomic number is 6. More than 70 percent of the air is nitrogen; its symbol is N. The element with the symbol O is oxygen; it has 8 protons, an atomic mass of about 16, and 8 electrons. The symbol for fluorine is F; its atomic number is 9. An inert gas used for signs is neon; its symbol is Ne.)

Integration: Use the Problem Solving feature to integrate critical thinking and mathematics into your lesson.

FIND OUT BY DOING

Homely Halogens

Fluorine, chlorine, bromine, and iodine are halogens found in many household substances. Investigate their uses by locating various substances in your environment that contain halogens. Make a chart of your findings. Include examples of the substances if possible.

Rare-Earth Elements

Even though you have completed your tour across the periodic table, you probably have at least one question lurking in the back of your mind. Why are there two rows of elements standing alone at the bottom of the periodic table? The elements in these two rows are called the **rare-earth** elements. The rare-earth elements have properties that are similar to one another. They have been separated out and displayed under the main table to make the table shorter and easier to read.

The first row, called the **lanthanoid series,** is made up of soft, malleable metals that have a high luster and conductivity. The lanthanoids are used in industry to make various alloys and high-quality glass.

The elements in the second row make up the **actinoid series.** All the actinoids are radioactive. (Changes in the nucleus of radioactive atoms cause particles and energy to be given off.) With the exception of the first three elements, all the actinoids are synthetic, or made in the laboratory. The best known actinoid is uranium, which is used as a fuel in nuclear-powered electric generators. You won't be surprised to learn that elements 104 to 109 in period 7 are also synthetic and radioactive.

5–3 Section Review

1. What is the key to the placement of an element in the periodic table?
2. Which two families contain the most active metals?
3. To which family do the most active nonmetals belong?
4. Why are the elements in Family 18 called inert gases?

Critical Thinking—*Applying Concepts*
5. How can the arrangement of elements in the periodic table be used to predict how they will react with other elements to form compounds?

5–3 (continued)

INDEPENDENT PRACTICE

Section Review 5–3

1. Elements in the periodic table are arranged in increasing order by their atomic numbers. Elements in the same column have the same number of valence electrons.
2. Family 1 (the alkali metals) and Family 2 (the alkaline earth metals) contain the most active metals.

3. Family 17 (the halogens) contains the most active nonmetals.
4. They exist as gases at normal temperatures and pressures and do not combine easily with other elements.
5. The position of an element in the periodic table indicates the number of electrons in its outermost energy level. The most active metals are in Family 1; the most active nonmetals are in Family 17. As you move inward on the table, the elements are less active and form compounds less readily.

REINFORCEMENT/RETEACHING

Review students' responses to the Section Review questions. Reteach any material that is still unclear, based on their responses.

CLOSURE

▶ *Review and Reinforcement Guide*

Have students complete Section 5–3 in their *Review and Reinforcement Guide.*

PROBLEM ??? Solving

Completing the Squares

Look at the data for the five elements below. Fill in the missing data. Then construct a square for each element as it would appear in a modern periodic table. In some cases you will have to perform calculations to fill in the missing data. Do not use a completed periodic table in this activity. It is much more fun to do the calculations yourself. How would you use this information in a laboratory?

Data

- Carbon (symbol ?); atomic mass, 12.01; number of electrons, 6; (atomic number ?)
- More than 70 percent of the air (name ?); (symbol ?); atomic number, 7; atomic mass, 14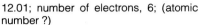
- (Name ?); O; (number of protons ?); (atomic mass ?); (number of electrons ?)
- Fluorine (atomic symbol ?); number of protons, 9; atomic mass, 18.99; (atomic number ?)
- Inert "sign" gas (name ?); (atomic symbol ?); number of electrons, 10; atomic mass, 20.17

atomic number
symbol
name
atomic mass

5–4 Periodic Properties of the Elements

You have learned several ways in which the periodic table provides important information about the elements. Elements in the same family, or vertical column, have similar properties. Elements at the left of the table are metals. Elements at the right are nonmetals. Metalloids, which show properties of both metals and nonmetals, are located on either side of the dark zigzag line.

Additional information about the elements can be obtained from their location in a period, or

Guide for Reading

Focus on this question as you read.

▶ *What periodic trends can be identified in the elements in the periodic table?*

5–4 Periodic Properties of the Elements

MULTICULTURAL OPPORTUNITY 5–4

Have students create a wall-sized periodic table using the elemental models that they created in Chapter 4. Once they have built this large-scale model, they should be able to easily see the trends in valence electrons.

ESL STRATEGY 5–4

Have students refer to the periodic table in their textbooks as they answer the following questions. As students report their answers, have one student act as a coach, approving or correcting answers.
1. What do elements in the same family have in common? (The number of valence electrons.)
2. On which side of the table are the metals located? Nonmetals? (Left; right.)
3. Which group of elements is located on either side of the dark zigzag line? (Metalloids.)
4. What is the key to an element's placement in the table? (Its atomic number.)

ANNOTATION KEY

Integration
❶ Mathematics

TEACHING STRATEGY 5–4

FOCUS/MOTIVATION

For each group of students, prepare a deck of cards with three cards removed from each suit.
• **Can you predict which cards are missing from your deck?** (Students should be able to identify the missing cards because they are familiar with the "periods" that are present in a deck of cards.)

• **How did the empty spaces in Mendeleev's original periodic table help to predict new elements?** (The empty spaces suggested elements with certain properties that had not yet been discovered.)

CONTENT DEVELOPMENT

The number 8 is a key number for the periodic table. It is the maximum number of electrons in the outermost energy level of the atom of an element.

The valence number, on the other hand, shows the combining power of an element. An element with a valence of 1 will gain, lose, or share 1 electron in a chemical combination.
• **Which family has a valence of 1 because the elements will lose 1 electron?** (Family 1.)
• **Which family has a valence of 1 because the elements will gain 1 electron?** (Family 17.)

▶ *Multimedia* ◀
An alternative way to begin the lesson is to have students use the video called Periodic Table and Periodicity. In this video students examine the periodic nature of the periodic table.

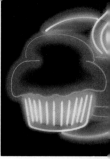

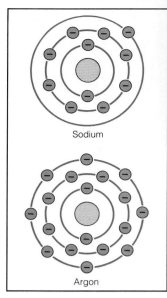

Sodium

Argon

Figure 5–29 *Sodium, an extremely reactive metal, is used in its vapor phase in street lights. Sodium vapor lights provide bright-yellow light (top center). Argon, an extremely unreactive gas, is used to make glowing works of art (top right). How does the electron arrangement of each element account for its reactivity?* ❹

5–4 (continued)

INDEPENDENT PRACTICE

▶ *Activity Book*

Students who need practice in using the periodic table will benefit from the activity called Identifying Unknown Elements in the *Activity Book*.

ENRICHMENT

▶ *Activity Book*

Academic students will enjoy the puzzlelike nature of the activity called Element Maze in the *Activity Book*.

GUIDED PRACTICE

Skills Development

Skill: Interpreting diagrams

Have students examine Figure 5–29. Explain that the diagrams show the electrons in the various energy levels for each element. The first energy level contains up to 2 electrons; all other energy levels contain up to 8 electrons.

• **How are the diagrams for sodium and argon alike?** (The first two energy levels are filled.)

• **How are the diagrams different?** (Sodium has just 1 electron in the third energy level. For argon, the third level is full—it has all 8 electrons.)

ENRICHMENT

Have students work in small groups to answer these questions:

• **Why was hydrogen placed in the alkali family when it is not a true metal?** (It has only 1 electron in its outermost energy level and is very reactive with other elements.)

• **Why was helium, with 2 valence electrons, placed in the noble gases rather than in the alkaline earth metals?** (Even though helium has only 2 valence electrons, these valence electrons are in the first energy level, which holds only 2 electrons. Therefore, the outermost electron shell is filled in helium, and its properties are similar to those of the other noble gases.)

horizontal row. **Certain properties of elements vary in regular ways from left to right across a period. These properties include electron arrangement, reactivity, atomic size, and metallic properties.**

The valence number of an element is related to the electrons in the outermost energy level of an atom of that element. It is these electrons that are involved in the chemical combining of elements to form compounds.

Remember the pattern of valence numbers discovered by Mendeleev: Starting at the left of each period, the pattern of valence numbers is 1 2 3 4 3 2 1 0. An element with a valence of 1 will gain, lose, or share 1 electron in a chemical combination. An element with a valence of 4 will gain, lose, or share 4 electrons. What will happen if an element has a valence of zero? How reactive is such an element? ❶

Elements at the left in a period tend to lose electrons easily when they combine with other elements. You know that the elements at the left of the table are metals. So an important property of metals is that they lose electrons in a chemical combination. Elements at the right in a period tend to gain electrons easily when they combine with other elements. What kinds of elements are these? ❷

The amount of energy needed to remove an electron from an atom shows a periodic increase from left to right across a period. Since atoms of elements at the left in a period tend to lose electrons, removing an electron from such an atom requires a small amount of energy. Removing an electron from an element at the right in a period requires a great amount of energy. Why? ❸

Another property of elements that varies periodically is atomic size. From left to right across a period, atomic size tends to decrease. The decrease can

INDEPENDENT PRACTICE

▶ *Activity Book*

Students who need further practice with the concepts of this chapter should be provided with the Chapter 5 activities in the *Activity Book* called Element Code and Identifying Unknown Elements.

Figure 5–30 *Fireworks! Colors and noises that astound and amaze! Such brilliant bursts are the results of explosive chemical reactions. Not all chemical reactions are explosive, however. But all chemical reactions do depend on the properties of the elements involved—properties that show a characteristic periodicity.*

be explained in terms of electron arrangement. As the atomic number increases across a period, 1 electron is added to each successive element. But this electron is still in the same energy level. The increase in the number of electrons in the energy level and the number of protons in the nucleus produce a stronger attraction between these oppositely charged particles. The electrons are pulled closer to the nucleus. The size of the atom decreases. Now explain why atomic size increases from top to bottom in a family.

Metallic properties of the elements are also periodic. From left to right across a period, elements become less metallic in nature.

5–4 Section Review

1. What properties are periodic in nature?
2. What is the pattern of valences as you move from left to right across a period?
3. How does atomic size change across a period?

Critical Thinking—*Relating Concepts*

4. A scientist claims that she has discovered a new element that should be inserted between nitrogen and oxygen in the periodic table. Why is it most likely that this scientist has made a mistake? (*Hint:* How does the number of electrons change as you move from left to right across a period?)

ties, tendency to lose or gain an electron, energy required to remove an electron.
2. 1 2 3 4 3 2 1 0
3. Atomic size decreases from left to right across a period.
4. Nitrogen has an atomic number of 7 and 5 valence electrons in its outermost energy level. Oxygen has an atomic number of 8 and 6 electrons in the outermost level. There is no gap in the patterns between nitrogen and oxygen, so it is unlikely that a new element would belong between them.

GUIDED PRACTICE

▶ *Laboratory Manual*

Skills Development

Skills: Making observations, applying concepts, making inferences

At this point you may want to have students complete the Chapter 5 Laboratory Investigation in the *Laboratory Manual* called Investigating the Activity Series of the Metals. In this investigation students will explore another way of arranging the elements.

ENRICHMENT

▶ *Activity Book*

Students who have mastered the concepts in this chapter will be challenged by the Chapter 5 activities in the *Activity Book* called Valence Clues and Element Maze.

INDEPENDENT PRACTICE

Section Review 5–4

1. Valence, atomic size, metallic proper-

REINFORCEMENT/RETEACHING

Review students' responses to the Section Review questions. Reteach any material that is still unclear, based on their responses.

CLOSURE

▶ *Review and Reinforcement Guide*

Have students complete Section 5–4 in their *Review and Reinforcement Guide.*

Remind students that mercury is a metal that is liquid at room temperature. It is also a very heavy element, twice as heavy as iron and a third heavier than lead. Like lead compounds, most compounds containing mercury are poisonous.

In light of the negative effects of mercury on the food chain, it is perhaps ironic that, in Greek mythology, Mercury was the messenger of the gods. (Some of the meanings of the adjective *mercurial* are eloquent, clever, thieving, volatile.) The "message" being delivered today by the element mercury is a serious warning about the dangers of chemical pollution in the environment.

In discussing the Connections feature, help students associate the chemical properties of the elements with the steps needed to prevent environmental pollution. For example, the periodic table might be used to identify other elements that are potentially harmful in the food chain.

If you are teaching thematically, you may want to use the Connections feature to reinforce the themes of systems and interactions or unity and diversity.

Integration: Use the Connections feature to integrate ecology with the concepts of chemistry covered in this chapter.

CONNECTIONS

The Chains That Bind ❶

Fly from New York to Japan and after hours in the air over land and water, you become convinced of the enormous size of Planet Earth. But in many ways—some more obvious than others—humans are becoming aware of the incredibly small size of the Earth. Although this may seem like a contradiction, in some important ways it is a significant—and alarming—fact.

By now everyone is aware of the dangers of polluting the *environment*. But in the not-too-distant past, such was not the case. The economic growth of major industrial countries was based in large part on the erroneous belief that the enormous size of the Earth made it permissible to dump hazardous substances into the environment. Today we know that, in terms of pollution, the Earth is small. The effects of dumping some hazardous chemicals reach far from their point of introduction into the environment.

You are probably familiar with the element mercury. Mercury is an important part of

many industrial processes. For example, it is used in the manufacture of paper and paints. Industrial processes often need a good source of water—especially for washing away the waste byproducts of the manufacturing process. So for a long time, waste mercury was dumped into rivers and streams. After all, the logic was, the water would carry the mercury far away until it eventually reached the vastness of the oceans. There it would be diluted to levels that were no longer dangerous to life.

One major flaw in this logic became evident over time, however. Mercury was found in ever-increasing amounts in the body tissues of certain fishes and other animals. How

could the level of mercury reach dangerous proportions in certain organisms? The answer was found by biologists when they examined food chains. A food chain describes a series of events in which food, and therefore energy, is transferred from one organism to another. The first organisms in a food chain are small organisms that are able to produce their own food using simple substances. These organisms are often microscopic and make food by using the energy of the sun or the energy stored in chemicals. Some of these organisms also ingest small amounts of chemicals such as mercury, which is stored in their bodies. In turn, these small organisms are eaten by larger ones—small fishes, for example. And these small

fishes store the mercury in their tissues, only in slightly larger amounts. The storage of these chemicals in ever-increasing amounts in the living tissues of organisms in a food chain is called *biological magnification*. By the time mercury has moved through a food chain to reach tuna, birds, cattle, and other larger animals, the amount of stored mercury may have reached levels high enough to threaten health and even endanger survival.

When it comes to certain things—the pollution of water by mercury, for example—the Earth is actually a small place. And the food chains that link one organism to another—the ties that bind—may hold so tightly that organisms at one link of the chain cannot survive.

INTEGRATION
LANGUAGE ARTS

Have students choose two people from the list below. Using reference materials from the library, students should prepare short biographies of the two people, with particular emphasis on their contributions to modern chemistry. Finally, students should discuss which of the two made a greater contribution and why.

Bohr, Niels	Lavoisier, Antoine
Boyle, Robert	Lawrence, Ernest
Cavendish, Henry	Mendeleev, Dmitri
Curie, Marie	Moseley, Henry
Dalton, John	Pasteur, Louis
Davy, Humphry	Priestley, Joseph
Fermi, Enrico	Scheele, Carl
Henry, Joseph	Whöler, Friedrich

BACKGROUND INFORMATION
THE TRANSITION METALS

The pattern of valence numbers across a period, 1 2 3 4 3 2 1 0, does not include the transition metals. These metals tend to behave somewhat differently because their inner energy levels are not completely filled. Thus transition metals are not as active as one might expect from their outermost energy level structures, and they often exhibit two or more valence numbers in chemical combinations.

Laboratory Investigation

FLAME TESTS

BEFORE THE LAB

1. Gather all materials at least one day in advance. You should gather enough equipment to meet all your class needs, assuming six students per group.
2. Prepare an unknown solution, using any element you have available that will readily form a chloride.

PRE-LAB DISCUSSION

Write the symbols for these seven compounds on the chalkboard: LiCl, CaCl₂, KCl, CuCl₂, SrCl₂, NaCl, BaCl₂.

- **What do the seven compounds have in common?** (They all contain the symbols Cl.)
- **What element is represented by the symbol Cl? To what family does this element belong?** (Chlorine; the halogens.)

Explain that the second word in the name of each compound is *chloride*. This shows that chlorine is one of the elements in the compound.

- **For each compound, what element is combined with chlorine?** (Lithium, calcium, potassium, copper, strontium, sodium, barium.)
- **Why do some of the compounds have a small number 2 after the symbol for chlorine?** (To show that a molecule of the compound has 2 chlorine atoms rather than 1.)

Explain that students will use a flame test to find the characteristic color associated with the metal combined with chlorine in each of the compounds. They will then investigate an unknown chloride.

Discuss with students whether they think the color produced in a flame test is a good indicator of the substances being used. Point out that it is, in fact, a good indicator but that it cannot be used to positively identify a particular substance.

You may want to mention that if the light from the flame were passed through a spectroscope, the characteristic spectral lines of the substance would appear. These spectral lines are like the fingerprints of each substance and can be used to positively identify the elements in any particular compound.

Laboratory Investigation

Flame Tests

Problem

How can elements be identified by using a flame test?

Materials *(per group)*

```
nichrome or platinum wire
cork
Bunsen burner
hydrochloric acid (dilute)
distilled water
8 test tubes
test tube rack
8 chloride test solutions
safety goggles
```

Procedure

1. Label each of the test tubes with one of the following compounds: LiCl, CaCl₂, KCl, CuCl₂, SrCl₂, NaCl, BaCl₂, unknown.
2. Pour 5 mL of each test solution in the correctly labeled test tube. Be sure to put the correct solution in each labeled test tube.
3. Push one end of a piece of nichrome or platinum wire into a cork. Then bend the other end of the wire into a tiny loop.
4. Put on your safety goggles. Clean the wire by dipping it into the dilute hydrochloric acid and then into the distilled water. You must clean the wire after you make each test. Holding the cork, heat the wire in the blue flame of the Bunsen burner until the wire glows and no longer colors the burner flame.
5. Dip the clean wire into the first test solution. Hold the wire at the tip of the inner cone of the burner flame. Record the color given to the flame in a data table similar to the one shown here.
6. Clean the wire by repeating step 4.

7. Repeat step 5 for the other six known test solutions. Remember to clean the wire after you test each solution.
8. Obtain an unknown solution from your teacher. After you clean the wire, repeat the flame test for this compound.

Compound		Color of Flame
Lithium chloride	LiCl	
Calcium chloride	CaCl₂	

Observations

1. What flame colors are produced by each compound?
2. What flame color is produced by the unknown compound?

Analysis and Conclusions

1. Is the flame test a test for the metal or for the chloride in each compound? Explain your answer.
2. Why is it necessary to clean the wire before you test each solution?
3. What metal is present in the unknown solution? How do you know?
4. How can you use a flame test to identify a metal?
5. What do you think would happen if the unknown substance contained a mixture of two compounds? Could each metal be identified?
6. **On Your Own** Suppose you are working in a police crime laboratory and are trying to identify a poison that was used in a crime. How could a knowledge of flame tests help you?

TEACHING STRATEGY

1. You may wish to tell students that nichrome is an alloy composed of nickel and chromium. Nichrome is often used in laboratory investigations because it can withstand high temperatures and is a poor conductor of electricity.
2. It is essential that students carefully clean their nichrome wire loop prior to each test.

Study Guide

Summarizing Key Concepts

5–1 Arranging the Elements

▲ The elements in Mendeleev's periodic table are arranged in order of increasing atomic mass.

▲ Mendeleev discovered that the properties of the elements recurred at regular intervals.

▲ Mendeleev left spaces for elements not yet discovered and predicted the properties of these missing elements based on their position in the periodic table.

▲ The modern periodic table is based on the periodic law, which states that the physical and chemical properties of the elements are periodic functions of their atomic numbers.

5–2 Design of the Periodic Table

▲ Horizontal rows of elements are called periods.

▲ Vertical columns of elements are called groups or families.

▲ Elements in the same family have similar properties.

▲ Each square in the periodic table gives the element's name, chemical symbol, atomic number, and atomic mass.

▲ According to their properties, the elements are classified as metals, nonmetals, and metalloids.

5–3 Chemical Families

▲ The number of valence electrons in an atom of an element is the key to its placement in a family in the periodic table.

5–4 Periodic Properties of the Elements

▲ Periodic properties of the elements include electron arrangement, reactivity, atomic size, and metallic properties.

Reviewing Key Terms

Define each term in a complete sentence.

5–1 Arranging the Elements
 periodic law

5–2 Design of the Periodic Table
 group
 family
 period
 metal
 luster
 ductile
 malleable
 corrosion
 nonmetal
 metalloid

5–3 Chemical Families
 alkali metal
 alkaline earth metal
 transition metal
 boron family
 carbon family
 nitrogen family
 oxygen family
 halogen family
 noble gas
 rare-earth element
 lanthanoid series
 actinoid series

ANALYSIS AND CONCLUSIONS

1. The metal, because each compound contained a chloride. If the test showed the presence of chlorine, the color would be the same in all the tests.

2. To remove any substances from prior flame tests that might provide a false color.

3. Answers will vary depending on the unknown chloride chosen.

4. By its characteristic color.

5. The color would be a mixture of the colors produced by each metal. No. You could not identify the two metals by a flame test alone.

6. Flame tests, as well as other chemical procedures, can be used to identify the presence of poisonous elements in food or on clothing.

GOING FURTHER: ENRICHMENT

Part 1

Provide other unknown samples of various chloride compounds and have students perform flame tests on these samples.

Part 2

If spectroscopes are available, have students observe the characteristic spectral lines produced by each chloride compound during the flame test. Have them sketch what they see.

• **How might scientists use this method to determine the composition of distant objects such as the sun?** (By comparing the spectral lines from the sun to known spectral lines of elements on Earth, scientists can determine the composition of the sun or other stars.)

DISCOVERY STRATEGIES

Discuss how the investigation relates to the chapter ideas by asking open questions similar to the following:

• **What do you know about chlorine from its position in the periodic table?** (It is a nonmetal. As a member of Family 17, it is highly active and forms many compounds.)

• **A flame test is qualitative rather than quantitative. What do you think is the difference between the two types of tests?** (A qualitative test indicates the presence of an element, but not the amount of the element. A quantitative test would show the amount of an element in a compound.)

• **Under what circumstances would chemists need a quantitative test? A qualitative test?** (Accept all logical responses.)

OBSERVATIONS

1. LiCl: crimson; $CaCl_2$: yellow-red; KCl: violet; $CuCl_2$: blue-green; $SrCl_2$: red; NaCl: yellow; $BaCl_2$: green-yellow.

2. Answers will depend on your choice of the unknown chloride.

Chapter Review

Chapter Review

ALTERNATIVE ASSESSMENT

The *Prentice Hall Science* program includes a variety of testing components and methodologies. Aside from the Chapter Review questions, you may opt to use the Chapter Test or the Computer Test Bank Test in your *Test Book* for assessment of important facts and concepts. In addition, Performance-Based Tests are included in your *Test Book*. These Performance-Based Tests are designed to test science process skills, rather than factual content recall. Since they are not content dependent, Performance-Based Tests can be distributed after students complete a chapter or after they complete the entire textbook.

CONTENT REVIEW

Muiltiple Choice

1. c
2. d
3. b
4. b
5. a
6. d
7. b
8. a
9. b
10. d

True or False

1. T
2. F, ductile property
3. F, alkali
4. T
5. T
6. F, gain
7. F, families or groups

Concept Mapping

Row 1: Elements
Row 2: Moseley
Row 3: Valence numbers, Atomic mass

CONCEPT MASTERY

1. Mendeleev was able to tell that there were elements yet to be discovered because the arrangement of elements in his periodic table left gaps in certain places. The gaps were based on properties of the elements above and below the spaces in his table.
2. Metals are good conductors of heat and electricity. They are shiny, and they

Content Review

Multiple Choice

Choose the letter of the answer that best completes each statement.

1. The periodic law states that the properties of elements are periodic functions of their
   a. mass.
   b. symbol.
   c. atomic number.
   d. valence.
2. Which of the following is a noble gas?
   a. sodium
   b. gold
   c. chlorine
   d. neon
3. When a metal combines with a halogen, the kind of compound formed is called a (an)
   a. organic compound.
   b. salt.
   c. actinoid.
   d. oxide.
4. If a metal can be hammered or rolled into thin sheets the metal is said to be
   a. ductile.
   b. malleable.
   c. brittle.
   d. active.
5. In the periodic table, the metallic character of the elements increases as you move in a period from
   a. right to left.
   b. top to bottom.
   c. left to right.
   d. bottom to top.
6. Which of the following is a halogen?
   a. sodium
   b. silver
   c. carbon
   d. iodine
7. Moseley was able to determine each element's
   a. atomic mass.
   b. atomic number.
   c. symbol.
   d. brittleness.
8. Each period of the table begins on the left with a
   a. highly active metal.
   b. metalloid.
   c. rare-earth element.
   d. nonmetal.
9. Which element is called the "basis of life"?
   a. neon
   b. carbon
   c. sodium
   d. oxygen
10. A brittle element that is not a good conductor of heat and electricity is
    a. inert.
    b. a metal.
    c. ductile.
    d. a nonmetal.

True or False

If the statement is true, write "true." If it is false, change the underlined word or words to make the statement true.

1. Mendeleev noticed a definite pattern in the <u>valence numbers</u> of the elements.
2. The property of a metal that means it can be drawn into thin wire is called <u>luster</u>.
3. Sodium belongs to the <u>transition</u> metals.
4. <u>Nonmetals</u> are usually poor conductors of electricity.
5. The most striking property of the noble gases is their extreme <u>inactivity</u>.
6. In forming compounds, nonmetals tend to <u>lose</u> electrons.
7. Vertical columns of elements in the periodic table are called <u>periods</u>.

Concept Mapping

Complete the following concept map for Section 5–1. Refer to pages N6–N7 to construct a concept map for the entire chapter.

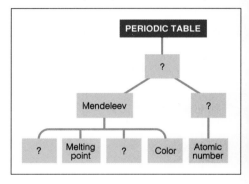

can be drawn out into thin wires and hammered into different shapes. Metals usually have high melting points. Metals give up their electrons when they form compounds. Nonmetals are poor conductors of heat and electricity. They are usually brittle solids that break rather than bend. Low melting points are common to nonmetals. Nonmetals share or gain electrons when they bond. Metalloids have properties of metals and nonmetals. Some metalloids are shiny, like metals. They conduct electricity better than nonmetals, but not as well as metals. Examples of each type of element will vary.

3. Metals with valences of 1 (the alkali metals in Family 1) need to lose only 1 electron to form a stable electron configuration. This requires a relatively small amount of energy, so these metals combine easily with other elements. Nonmetals with valences of 1 (the halogens in Family 17) have 7 electrons in their outermost energy levels and need gain only 1 electron to become stable.

Concept Mastery

Discuss each of the following in a brief paragraph.

1. How was Mendeleev able to tell that there were elements not yet discovered?
2. Compare metals, nonmetals, and metalloids. Give an example of each.
3. Why are elements with 1 valence electron the most active metals or nonmetals?
4. What happens to an atom's size as you move from left to right across a period? From top to bottom in a family?
5. What does the term periodic mean? Give two examples of daily periodic occurrences in your life.

Critical Thinking and Problem Solving

Use the skills you have developed in this chapter to answer each of the following.

1. **Applying definitions** Metals are ductile. In what three ways has this property of metals affected your daily life?
2. **Interpreting charts** Look at these three squares from the periodic table. What kinds of information can you gather from these squares? How would you use this information in a laboratory?

7	8	9
N	**O**	**F**
Nitrogen	Oxygen	Fluorine
14.007	15.999	18.998

3. **Relating concepts** Use the periodic table to help predict what will happen when the elements in each of the following pairs are brought together in a chemical reaction:
   a. barium and oxygen
   b. lithium and argon
   c. potassium and iodine
   d. sodium and bromine
4. **Applying concepts** Determine the identity of the following elements:
   a. This nonmetal has 4 valence electrons, properties similar to carbon, and an atomic mass slightly less than phosphorus.

   b. This element has 5 valence electrons, shows properties of metals and nonmetals, and has 33 protons in the nucleus of each atom.
   c. This highly active metal is a liquid. It has 1 valence electron.
5. **Making diagrams** Draw a diagram to show the arrangement of electrons in the outermost energy level of an atom in each family in the periodic table.
6. **Classifying elements** Classify each of the following elements as very active, moderately active, fairly inactive, or inert: magnesium, mercury, fluorine, krypton, helium, gold, potassium, calcium, bromine.
7. **Using the writing process** Suppose Mendeleev was alive today and his development of the periodic table occurred yesterday. Plan and write a script for a "media event" that would bring Mendeleev's work to the attention of the public. For example, you might want to produce a television interview with Mendeleev. Or you might want to write a newspaper article.

---

3. a. BaO.
   b. No reaction.
   c. KI.
   d. NaBr.
4. a. Silicon.
   b. Arsenic.
   c. Cesium.
5. The number of electrons in the outermost energy level should be 1 for alkali metals, 2 for alkaline earth metals, 3 for the boron family, 4 for the carbon family, 5 for the nitrogen family, 6 for the oxygen family, 7 for the halogens, and 8 for the noble gases.
6. Very active: fluorine, potassium, bromine; moderately active: magnesium, calcium; fairly inactive: mercury, gold; inert: krypton, helium.
7. Before drafting their scripts, students might do library research on Mendeleev and the events surrounding the development of the periodic table. For example, a German scientist, Dr. Lothar Meyer, was working on a similar idea at about the same time. He also realized that the masses of the elements were a key factor. Because Mendeleev published his results before Meyer, historians give Mendeleev full credit for the table.

KEEPING A PORTFOLIO

You might want to assign some of the Concept Mastery and Critical Thinking and Problem Solving questions as homework and have students include their responses to unassigned questions in their portfolio. Students should be encouraged to include both the question and the answer in their portfolio.

ISSUES IN SCIENCE

The following issue can be used as a springboard for discussion or given as a writing assignment:

Many scientists argue that one important reason for space research is that elements that are scarce on Earth may be plentiful on other bodies in space such as planets and asteroids. Other scientists feel we have all the resources of important elements we need right here on Earth. They feel the money spent on space research could be better spent searching for new deposits of vital elements. What is your opinion?

---

4. Moving from left to right across a period, atomic size tends to decrease. Moving from top to bottom in a family, atomic size tends to increase.
5. Periodic means repeating at regular intervals. Examples of periodic occurrences will vary.

CRITICAL THINKING AND PROBLEM SOLVING

1. Possible answers include the use of wires to carry electricity, as filaments in light bulbs, as parts of various machinery. Heavy wires are also used to support structures and as part of lifting devices.
2. The squares show the atomic numbers and atomic masses. In a laboratory, the atomic numbers would help locate each element in a periodic table and, by indicating the number of valence electrons, suggest the combining power of that element. The atomic masses might help in determining whether an element were part of an unknown substance.

SHIRLEY ANN JACKSON: HELPING OTHERS THROUGH SCIENCE

Background Information

According to the Information Division at Bell Laboratories, Dr. Shirley Ann Jackson "is as intriguing and dynamic as the microscopic particles she studies." In addition to her work at Fermilab and Bell Laboratories, Dr. Jackson served as a visiting scientist in the theoretical division at CERN (European Organization for Nuclear Research) in Geneva, Switzerland. Dr. Jackson has written numerous articles for leading physics journals and is a frequent speaker at scientific meetings.

Although Dr. Jackson was accepted to do graduate work at Harvard, Brown, and the University of Chicago, she chose to remain at MIT, where she had completed her undergraduate studies, because she wanted to encourage the enrollment of more African-American students there. She continues to maintain a connection with MIT as a member of the board of trustees. Dr. Jackson is also involved in organizations dedicated to the cause of helping women gain education and employment in the sciences.

SHIRLEY ANN JACKSON: Helping Others Through SCIENCE

▲ **Shirley Ann Jackson, in her office at Bell Laboratories, is presently doing research in the field of optoelectronic materials used in communication devices.**

Imagine what it would be like to catch a glimpse of the universe as it was forming—to look back in time nearly 20 billion years! Of course, no one can really see the beginning of time. But physicists such as Shirley Ann Jackson believe that learning about the universe as it was in the past will help us understand the universe as it is now and as it will be in the future.

By unraveling some of the mysteries of the universe, Dr. Jackson hopes to fulfill a basic ambition: to enrich the lives of others and to make the world a better place in which to live. This contribution, Dr. Jackson believes, can be achieved through science.

Jackson was born and raised in Washington, DC. After graduating from high school as valedictorian, she attended Massachusetts Institute of Technology, MIT. There, her role as a leader in physics began to take root. Jackson became the first

---

TEACHING STRATEGY: ADVENTURE

FOCUS/MOTIVATION

Bring in photographs of telephones, radios, television sets, and computers. Display the photographs and explain that much of the research that makes the production of devices such as these possible is done at a place called Bell Laboratories in Murray Hill, NJ. Point out that in this Adventure lesson, students will read about a prominent physicist at Bell Laboratories, Dr. Shirley Ann Jackson.

CONTENT DEVELOPMENT

Have students read the article about Dr. Jackson. Point out that Dr. Jackson is an unusual person. As an African American and as a woman, Dr. Jackson probably had to overcome certain obstacles in order to obtain her goal.

Explain to students that the area of physics that Dr. Jackson is currently involved in is called solid-state or condensed-

African-American woman to earn a doctorate degree from MIT. She is also the first African-American woman to earn a PhD in physics in the United States.

After graduate school, Jackson began work as a research associate in high-energy physics at the Fermi National Accelerator Laboratory in Batavia, Illinois. This branch of physics studies the characteristics of subatomic particles—such as protons and electrons—as they interact at high energies.

Using devices at Fermilab called particle accelerators, physicists accelerate subatomic particles to speeds that approach the speed of light. The particles collide and produce new subatomic particles. By analyzing these subatomic particles, physicists are able to learn more about the structure of atoms and the nature of matter.

The experiments in which Jackson participated at Fermilab helped to prove the existence of certain subatomic particles whose identity had only been theorized. This information is important in understanding the nuclear reactions that are taking place at the center of the sun and other stars.

Jackson's research is not limited to the world of subatomic particles alone. Her work

also includes the study of semiconductors—materials that conduct electricity better than insulators but not as well as metal conductors. Semiconductors have made possible the development of transistor radios, televisions, and computers—inventions that have dramatically changed the ways we live.

Jackson's current work in physics at Bell Laboratories in Murray Hill, New Jersey, has brought her from the beginnings of the universe to the future of communication. This talented physicist has been doing research in the area of optoelectronic materials. This branch of electronics—which deals with solid-state devices that produce, regulate, transmit, and detect electromagnetic radiation—is changing the way telephones, computers, radios, and televisions are made and used.

Looking back on her past, Jackson feels fortunate to have been given so many opportunities at such a young age. And she is optimistic about the future. "Research is exciting," she says. Motivated by her research, Shirley Ann Jackson is happy to be performing a service to the public in the way she knows best—as a dedicated and determined scientist.

▼ **This particle-accelerator generator at Fermilab is familiar equipment to Shirley Ann Jackson.**

GAZETTE ■ 141

Additional Questions and Topic Suggestions

1. What aspects of the scientific method are illustrated by Dr. Jackson's work at Fermilab? (Scientists had predicted the existence of certain subatomic particles. Dr. Jackson gathered information to test this idea by carrying out experiments. When the results of these experiments were analyzed, she concluded that these particles do indeed exist.)
2. According to the article, what is Dr. Jackson's chief motivation as a scientist? Does your own attitude toward science fit in with her viewpoint? (To help other people through science; answers will vary.)
3. In what ways is Dr. Jackson's story encouraging to women? To members of minorities? (First African-American woman to receive doctorate from MIT; answers will vary.)

Critical Thinking Questions

1. Pure research involves the gathering of knowledge for its own sake. Applied research has practical goals in mind, often related to technology or medicine. Based on the article, which of these areas has Dr. Jackson been involved in? Explain your answer. (Both areas: work at Fermilab was probably pure research, but work at Bell Labs is applied to communications technology.)
2. Can you think of reasons why studying subatomic particles might lead to an understanding of the past and future of the universe? (One possible answer is that because atoms are the basis of all matter, they may hold the key to the changes that have taken and will take place in the universe.)

state physics. Solid-state physics is concerned with the physical properties of crystalline solids. Many students have probably heard the expression solid-state applied to various types of electronics equipment. This label refers to items based on or composed of transistors or related semiconductor devices.

ENRICHMENT

Have interested students choose one type of electronic equipment and investigate how applied research in physics

made the production of this equipment possible. Have them report their findings to the class. Encourage the use of visuals to help support their explanations.

INDEPENDENT PRACTICE

▶ *Activity Book*
After students have read the Science Gazette article, you may want to hand out the reading skills worksheet based on the article in your *Activity Book.*

SCIENCE GAZETTE

ISSUES IN SCIENCE

ACID RAIN: IT WON'T GO AWAY

Background Information

Acid rain is caused by the release of two types of chemical pollutants into the atmosphere. These pollutants are sulfur dioxide and oxides of nitrogen. When the pollutants react with moisture in the atmosphere, sulfuric and nitric acids form, and these acids fall as acid rain.

Some sulfur dioxide is released into the atmosphere by natural processes such as volcanic eruptions, forest fires, and the decay of organic matter. About half of the sulfur dioxide currently in the atmosphere is produced naturally. The other half comes from industrial pollutants.

The main source of sulfur dioxide from industry is the burning of fossil fuels. There are several ways that the amount of air pollution caused by sulfur dioxide could be reduced. One of these is the washing of coal: High-sulfur coal is crushed and then washed through an electrostatic water process. Sulfur can be removed from oil by distillation. Gaseous pollutants can be reduced if the temperature at which fuels are burned is lowered. Yet another way to reduce pollution is to place filters on industrial smokestacks and catalytic converters on motor vehicles.

What is really needed in the United States is a program for emissions control.

ACID RAIN:
It Won't Go Away

igh in the Adirondack Mountains of northern New York State, a crystal-blue lake shimmers in the sun. Cradled by green slopes, the lake once held huge trout, which drew anglers from all over the country. But now the lake has no fish. Why? For years the lake has been pelted by polluted rain that is almost as acid as vinegar.

▲ Although many lakes look clean and beautiful, their waters will no longer support life. Unable to live in highly acidic water, dead fish wash up on shore.

142 ■ GAZETTE

TEACHING STRATEGY: ISSUE

FOCUS/MOTIVATION

Set up a simple distillation apparatus. Review the principles of evaporation and condensation. Have students identify the point in the apparatus at which condensation occurs.

• **Suppose that certain chemicals were mixed with the air at the point at which condensation occurs. What do you think might happen as the water condenses?** (Accept all answers. Possible answers include the chemicals might dissolve in the water and the chemicals might react with the water.)

CONTENT DEVELOPMENT

Use the previous demonstration to illustrate how acid rain forms. Explain that certain chemicals such as sulfur dioxide and nitric oxide react with water to form acids. When these chemicals are in the atmosphere, they combine with condensed water vapor to form acid rain.

Emphasize that the main source of sulfur and nitrogen-oxide pollutants is the burning of fossil fuels by industry. Sulfur in coal or oil mixes with oxygen in the air

to produce sulfur dioxide. The nitrogen in the air and in the fuels themselves join to form nitrogen oxides.

Point out that acid rain is an example of how air pollution begets water and land pollution. As acid rain falls to the Earth, lakes, rivers, and streams become more acidic. Soil, which soaks up rainwater, also becomes more acidic. Living things, including fish, plants, and trees, cannot exist when the acidity of their environment becomes too high.

◄ **Tall smokestacks spew clouds of chemicals high into the air. The chemicals can mix with rain, resulting in acid rain.**

Unable to survive the high acid content of the water, the fish died.

The tragedy of acid rain has not struck just this one lake in the Adirondacks. At least 180 trout ponds and lakes in these mountains no longer support fish, according to the National Wildlife Federation. What is more, acid rain is not confined to the Adirondacks.

Acid rain has fallen from coast to coast. Rainfall in general seems to have become more acidic. This has led conservation groups such as the National Wildlife Federation to issue warnings about acid rain's danger to the environment. "Acid rain is a growing threat," says the federation. The wildlife federation estimates that "acid rain may be slowly poisoning 160,000 kilometers of streams and 20,000 lakes" across the United States, mostly in the eastern half of the country. Acid rain also kills trees and wears down bricks, concrete, and statues made of stone and metal. It may even affect our drinking water.

HOW BAD IS IT?

Acid rain is a fact. But not all scientists agree on how widespread or how dangerous it is. "There is no question that the northeastern United States is experiencing acid rains,"

admits F. D. Bess, an environmental engineer for the Union Carbide Corporation. But he adds that the amount of increase in rain's acidity and the regions it affects are uncertain. And the American Chemical Society has said that earlier measurements of the amount of acid in rain may have been wrong. So it may be difficult to compare the acidity of rain today with, for instance, rain in the 1950s.

Some biologists representing fishing groups say that the danger may not be as great as many conservationists believe. "We are concerned but not going as far out as other environmental groups," says Bob Martin, a biologist for the Sports Fishing Institute. And scientists who work for industries blamed for acid rain argue that before industry can be condemned, many more facts about acid rain must be learned.

Conservationists and industry scientists alike agree that much about acid rain is a mystery. Acid rain (the term includes snow, fog, and other moisture from above) is formed from two types of chemical pollutants: sulfur dioxide and oxides of nitrogen. These pollutants react with moisture in the atmosphere to form sulfuric acid and nitric acid. Then when the moisture falls, it is acidic.

WHERE DOES IT COME FROM?

The chemicals that cause acid rain can also enter the atmosphere naturally—from volcanoes and forest fires, for instance. According to the American Chemical Society, "natural emissions of sulfur into the atmosphere are thought to be greater than industrial sources." Actually, "pure" rain is naturally a bit acidic. But pollutants also come from automobile engines and from industrial factories that burn coal and other fossil fuels. These factories, in the eyes of many conservationists, are the real culprits.

One of the most important sources of acid rain in the Northeast, according to the

GAZETTE ■ 143

Yet, according to columnist Tom Wicker of *The New York Times,* the United States currently is paralyzed by a debate over who is responsible and who should pay for such controls. Tracing the specific sources of acid rain in an area is difficult. If, for example, the industries in the Ohio Valley are singled out for causing acid rain the the Northeast, they immediately point their fingers to industries in the Midwest and claim that winds blow as much sulfur dioxide from these factories as from their own. Debate also rages about who is responsible for the cleanup. Should industry pay or should the government? If the government pays, should every state bear an equal share of the cost or should only those states that are affected by acid rain pay? If industry pays, should all industries bear the cost or only those industries responsible for causing acid rain?

Additional Questions and Topic Suggestions

1. Find out how air pollution contributed to the severe weathering of the Statue of Liberty, which was recently restored.
2. What are the most promising solutions for reducing acid rain? (Developing alternative energy sources such as solar energy, geothermal energy, nuclear energy, and tidal energy.)

GUIDED PRACTICE

Skills Development

Skill: Developing a model

Divide the class into teams of four to six students. Provide each team with a small beaker, a limestone rock, and some vinegar. Have students place the limestone in the vinegar and observe the results.
• **What happened?** (Accept all logical answers. Students should observe that the limestone fizzed and bubbled.)

• **What do you predict might happen by tomorrow or next week if the rock remains in the vinegar?** (Accept all logical answers.)

Point out that concrete, marble, and many building materials are made of limestone.
• **What damage might acid rain cause to highways, monuments, and buildings made of limestone?** (Accept all logical answers. The damage is likely to be considerable over long periods of time.)

Point out that even low levels of naturally occurring acids in rainwater can cause rocks to weather into pebbles, sand, and clay. Weathering from rainwater is greatly increased when pollutants in the air increase the water's acidity.

Critical Thinking Questions

1. How can a rural area with no industrial facilities suffer from the consequences of acid rain? (Pollutants from industrial areas quite far away can be carried by wind currents to a rural area.)

2. Some cities regulate the number of automobiles that can come into the city in an attempt to reduce air pollution. Do you think this is an invasion of private rights? Why or why not? (Accept all answers.)

3. Ethanol and gasohol produce fewer acid-forming pollutants than gasoline does. Should the government force auto manufacturers to make engines that burn only alcohol? Why or why not? (Accept all answers.)

Class Debate

Have students debate the following question: Should the cost of developing and implementing ways to control acid rain be charged to industrial producers of the pollutants?

Have students research the question and then form teams to represent each side of the issue.

National Wildlife Federation and other conservation groups, is the Ohio Valley industries. Especially cited are those industries with smokestacks that reach high into the air. Conservationists claim that winds blowing east from the Ohio Valley carry pollutants to places such as the Adirondacks, where they fall as acid rain. But many scientists who have studied the problem say that tracing acid rain to its source is still difficult.

Kenneth A. Rahn, a University of Rhode Island scientist, has been developing a method to trace chemical pollutants. He has found, for example, that some of the acid rain falling on the Adirondack lakes may come from Canada and not from the Ohio Valley. Meanwhile, Canadians have claimed that acid rain from American industries is polluting their lakes. The Canadians have demanded that the United States government do something about it.

Spokespeople for the Ohio Valley region have also blamed other sources for the problem. In 1980, an environmental official from Pennsylvania, William B. Middendorf, told Congress that the acid rain falling on the parts of the Ohio Valley that are in his state may be caused by pollutants from the Midwest. If this is true, then the Ohio Valley may not be the only major source of the rain that is killing Adirondack trout.

IS THERE A SOLUTION?

The effects of acid rain depend on the location of the lake. Even if acid rain is a widespread problem, not all lakes are affected by it in the same way. Many Adirondack lakes lie on steep slopes and are surrounded by thin soil. Rainwater passes through the soil quickly. Minerals in the soil, such as limestone, that could remove acids do not have time to work. Some Adirondack lakes lie on granite, which does not permit water to seep through into the soil. So the acids build up in the lakes. In lakes lying on limestone, however, acids are neutralized.

Ironically, other types of pollution can work against the effects of acid rain. Sewage,

▲ Acid rain eats away at stone and metal statues and monuments. Acid rain is probably one of the factors that has caused this statue to decay.

for example, often contains chemicals that undo the effects of acids. So lakes that are in the wilderness away from people may be more threatened by acid rain than lakes in cities.

In the long run, a solution must be found to the problem of acid rain. The National Academy of Sciences suggests that industry reduce by 12 million tons the amount of chemical pollutants being released into the air. One way to do this is to install devices called "scrubbers" in smokestacks. The scrubbers clean emissions before they are released into the air. Another solution is to use low-sulfur coal, which creates less pollution than other types of coal. But that would be expensive and would possibly cost some coal miners their jobs.

Someone will have to pay for solving the acid rain problem. Should it be industry? Should the government—that is, the taxpayers—pay the bill? If the pollution does come from the Ohio Valley, should that part of the country pay? Or should the Northeast help? Acid rain and the questions it raises will be around for a long time.

ISSUE (continued)

INDEPENDENT PRACTICE

▶ *Activity Book*

After students have read the Science Gazette article, you may want to hand out the reading skills worksheet based on the article in your *Activity Book*.

FACTORIES BEYOND EARTH

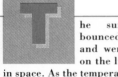

The sun's intense rays bounced off giant mirrors and were instantly focused on the lump of iron hanging in space. As the temperature of the iron rose, it began to melt. Quickly, two white-suited astronauts floating out of range of the hot rays added a little carbon and aluminum to the molten iron.

"Maybe we should add some nickel from that last asteroid the space miners brought back," one of the astronauts radioed to her co-worker. "We want that steel we're making to be tough and acid-resistant."

"I'll call the customer on my long-range radio and let you know," the other astronaut replied. "Just let the steel hang there in a molten lump until I get the answer."

Meanwhile, inside a nearby space factory, a chemist was busy growing crystals for electronic circuits. "I wonder what it was like to grow crystals like these on Earth,

---

FUTURES IN SCIENCE
FACTORIES BEYOND EARTH

Background Information

The idea of processing materials in space opens up many possibilities for creating products that cannot be made on Earth. For example, auto manufacturers have acknowledged that engines made of a lead-aluminum alloy would be cheaper and would last longer than present engines, which are made of alloys of aluminum and tin. It is not possible, however, to make a lead-aluminum alloy on Earth. The reason for this is that lead is more than four times as dense as aluminum. When the two metals are mixed together in the molten state (which is how metal alloys are made), the heavy lead quickly separates from the aluminum and sinks to the bottom of the mixture. When cooled, the mixture is not uniform and smooth as it should be but is instead lumpy and useless.

Lead and aluminum would still have the same densities in space because mass and volume do not change. What would change, however, would be weight—in an environment of zero gravity, lead would not be heavier than aluminum because both would be weightless. Thus, there would be no separation of materials when liquid aluminum and lead are mixed together, and the desired alloy could be produced easily.

Scientists estimate that there are about 400 potentially useful alloys that cannot be made on Earth because of gravity. Many other manufacturing processes are also hampered by gravity. Liquid mixtures of many types, such as those that make up protective coatings for jet engines, would be smoother and more uniform in a weightless environment. Crystals grown in liquid environments form more perfectly without the effects of gravity. Perhaps most important, biological materials and medicines could be produced more rapidly and in much purer form in zero gravity.

TEACHING STRATEGY: FUTURE

FOCUS/MOTIVATION

Fill a large cardboard carton with books. Make a box heavy enough so that it is difficult for one person to lift. Display the box and its contents. Carry the box across the classroom. Ask the class the following questions:

• **What did you observe as I attempted to carry the box across the room?** (It was very heavy. It was hard to lift and carry.)

• **Was it possible to lift and carry the box very rapidly? Why?** (No. It was too heavy.) Next, remove all the books from the carton and ask a student volunteer to carry the box across the room.

• **What did you observe as (name) attempted to carry the box?** (It was very light. It was easy to carry.)

• **Could the box be carried rapidly across the room?** (Yes.)

Additional Questions and Topic Sggestions

1. Discuss some potential hazards that a weightless environment might pose for humans. (Answers may vary. Possible answers include the altering of certain physiological functions that depend on gravity and the psychological difficulties associated with a weightless state.)

2. In addition to materials processing, scientists are considering the possibility of carrying out medical procedures, such as operations, in space. Find out more about this topic and report your findings to the class.

3. Create a classified advertisement for factory workers in space that might appear in a twenty-first-century newspaper.

Critical Thinking Questions

1. How is the use of solar energy described in this article? (Solar energy reflected by mirrors is used to produce temperatures high enough to melt iron.)

2. Can you think of other products that could be manufactured in space, in addition to those mentioned in this article? (Accept all logical answers.)

3. What are some economic advantages and disadvantages of processing materials in space? (At the present time, the greatest disadvantage is the cost of getting people and materials into space. The economic advantages include the use of "free" solar energy and the many tasks that can be accomplished more easily, and thus more cheaply, in a weightless environment.)

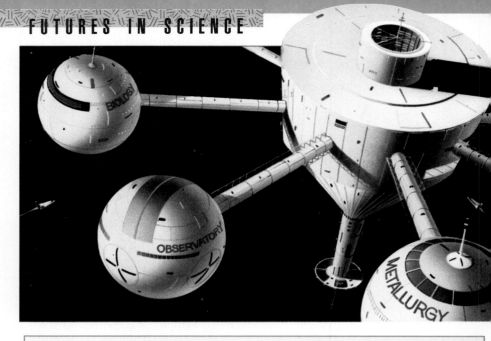

FUTURES IN SCIENCE

where gravity kept them from forming the perfect shape they form here in space," he thought to himself. "I guess chemists had problems in the days when there were no gravity-free laboratories or processing plants. The crystals I'm growing will be used to make the very best computers in the solar system."

Down the hall from the chemist, a biology professor was telling her medical students about the advantages of making medicines in space. "We know from an experiment performed in space way back in 1975 that kidney cells produce much more of a special chemical when they are grown in space than when they are grown on Earth," she explained. "We have recently discovered that, like kidney cells, human pancreas cells will produce more of their special chemical, insulin, when they are grown in space labs. We are also growing bacteria in space that can produce human insulin. Bacteria grow faster in space than on Earth. Growing more human insulin at a faster rate is a big help to people who have diabetes.

"We're also making purer vaccines and medicines here in space than we ever made on Earth," the professor continued.

"Why is that?" asked a student.

"Because we don't need to use containers to hold the materials we're mixing," she responded. "Without gravity, they hold together all by themselves. And because we can eliminate containers, we avoid contaminating the materials we're working with. On Earth, microscopic pieces of containers unavoidably got mixed in with the products. There was no such thing as a really pure product on Earth—whether it was a medicine, cosmetic. metal, or glass."

SPACE METALS

In another space factory a few thousand kilometers away, astronauts were setting up a seemingly strange experiment with metals. "Just let those metals sit outside on the dark side of the factory for a few minutes. They will cool off quickly in dark space because they are shielded from the sun there. Then we'll see what happens to the metals as they

CONTENT DEVELOPMENT

Use the previous activity to illustrate the difference that weight can make in performing a task. In the first case, the box was so heavy that it could be moved only slowly and with much effort. In the second case, the box was so light that one person could move it rapidly and with ease.

• **Suppose you had a box full of books in outer space, where gravity is zero. Would the box be easy or hard to lift and carry? Why?** (Easy. It would have no weight.)

Explain that this is one of the advantages of manufacturing in space. Lack of gravity makes many tasks easier. Go on to explain that another advantage of manufacturing in space is that differences in weight do not matter because everything has a weight of zero. This means, for example, that a block of lead and a block of aluminum the same size would both "weigh" the same—nothing.

Emphasize that weightlessness is very useful in manufacturing alloys, which are made by mixing two or more metals in the liquid state. If metals of different densities are mixed on Earth, the heavier metal quickly sinks to the bottom of the mixture. This makes it nearly impossible to make a smooth, uniform alloy. In outer space, however, neither metal would outweigh the other, and the mixture would produce the desired alloy.

REINFORCEMENT/RETEACHING

Review some of the advantages of outer space as an environment for manufacturing and scientific research. These inget colder and colder," the chief scientist told the astronauts. "We want to see how these new mixtures of metals, or alloys, stand up to the cold of dark space. Will they stay tough yet flexible out in space, or will they become brittle and shatter if something hits them? Will dust-sized micrometeorites damage them? Or would the object have to be baseball-sized, car-sized, or even larger? Which metals will 'survive' when they are half in sunlight and half in shadow?"

"These alloys could never have been made on Earth," observed one of the astronauts.

"That's right," responded the scientist. "They can be produced only in zero gravity. But there are many questions to be answered about these metals before we can use them in building space colonies."

In another part of the factory, workers were making superlight, high-strength alloys for use both on Earth and in space. Some of these metals would be used as thin, protective coatings on everything from space shuttles to earthbound craft.

HOLD THAT VIRUS!

In a space laboratory beyond the moon, medical researchers were performing experiments in genetic engineering. They were trying to find cures for age-old diseases by attempt-

ing to "redesign" viruses and bacteria.

"We would never have been able to do this kind of research on Earth," one of the older scientists said to a new lab assistant. "It's much too risky. On Earth, if some of the altered bacteria or viruses 'escaped' from the lab, we might be in big trouble. And if we didn't know how to control them, we might find ourselves in the middle of a major epidemic. Here a million and a half kilometers from Earth, we can work with more safety controls than we ever could have on Earth. Our research can go on without endangering people in other space colonies or on Earth."

DOWN-TO-EARTH QUESTIONS

What else will we be able to make in the airlessness of space? In zero gravity? In the heat of direct, focused sunlight? In the supercold regions shaded from the sun? What will we build with our perfectly shaped crystals, our pure chemicals, and our metal alloys that cannot be produced on Earth? What medical breakthroughs will we make in space? What dangerous but vital research can we perform in space while Earth is protected from its risks?

Will you be one of the space researchers who will answer these questions?

▼ In preparation for future space missions, in which they will build orbiting factories, astronauts practice in an underwater weightless environment.

clude zero gravity, airlessness (vacuum), direct sunlight and unlimited solar energy, and dark supercold regions.

Also review the processes that can be carried out effectively in space. These include growing crystals in perfect shapes, increasing the production of certain chemicals by living cells, producing purer vaccines and medicines, and making metal alloys that cannot be made on Earth.

INDEPENDENT PRACTICE

▶ *Activity Book*

After students have read the Science Gazette article, you may want to hand out the reading skills worksheet based on the article in your *Activity Book*.

For Further Reading

If you have been intrigued by the concepts examined in this chapter, you may also be interested in the ways fellow thinkers—novelists, poets, essayists, as well as scientists—have imaginatively explored the same ideas.

Chapter 1: General Properties of Matter

Dahl, Roald. *Charlie and the Chocolate Factory.* New York: Penguin.

Lipsyte, Robert. *One Fat Summer.* New York: Bantam.

Verne, Jules. *Around the World in Eighty Days.* New York: Bantam.

———. *Twenty Thousand Leagues Under the Sea.* New York: Pendulum Press.

Chapter 2: Physical and Chemical Changes

Crichton, Michael. *The Andromeda Strain.* New York: Knopf.

Hawthorne, Nathaniel. "The Birthmark," in *Tales and Sketches.* New York: Viking Press.

McKillip, Patricia. *The Changeling Sea.* New York: Ballantine.

O'Dell, Scott. *Black Pearl.* New York: Dell.

Chapter 3: Mixtures, Elements, and Compounds

Hamilton, Virginia. *Arilla Sun Down.* New York: Greenwillow.

Mahy, Margaret. *The Catalogue of the Universe.* New York: Macmillan.

Plotz, Helen. *Imagination's Other Place: Poems of Science and Math.* New York: Crowell.

Shelley, Mary Wollstonecraft. *Frankenstein.* New York: Bantam.

Chapter 4: Atoms: Building Blocks of Matter

Asimov, Isaac. *How Did We Find Out About Atoms?* New York: Walker & Co.

Feynman, Richard. *Surely You're Joking, Mr. Feynman! Adventures of a Curious Character.* New York: Bantam.

Larsen, Rebecca. *Oppenheimer and the Atomic Bomb.* New York: Watts.

Keller, Mollie. *Marie Curie.* New York: Watts.

Chapter 5: Classification of Elements: The Periodic Table

Konigsburg, E. L. *Father's Arcane Daughter.* New York: Atheneum.

Levi, Primo. *The Periodic Table.* New York: Schocken.

Lowell, Amy. "Patterns" in *Selected Poems of Amy Lowell.* Cambridge. MA: Riverside Press.

Paton Walsh, Jill. *A Parcel of Patterns.* New York: Farrar, Straus & Giroux, Inc.

Appendix A

The metric system of measurement is used by scientists throughout the world. It is based on units of ten. Each unit is ten times larger or ten times smaller than the next unit. The most commonly used units of the metric system are given below. After you have finished reading about the metric system, try to put it to use. How tall are you in metrics? What is your mass? What is your normal body temperature in degrees Celsius?

Commonly Used Metric Units

Length   The distance from one point to another

meter (m)   A meter is slightly longer than a yard.
1 meter = 1000 millimeters (mm)
1 meter = 100 centimeters (cm)
1000 meters = 1 kilometer (km)

Volume   The amount of space an object takes up

liter (L)   A liter is slightly more than a quart.
1 liter = 1000 milliliters (mL)

Mass   The amount of matter in an object

gram (g)   A gram has a mass equal to about one paper clip.
1000 grams = 1 kilogram (kg)

Temperature   The measure of hotness or coldness

degrees   0°C = freezing point of water
Celsius (°C)   100°C = boiling point of water

Metric–English Equivalents

2.54 centimeters (cm) = 1 inch (in.)
1 meter (m) = 39.37 inches (in.)
1 kilometer (km) = 0.62 miles (mi)
1 liter (L) = 1.06 quarts (qt)
250 milliliters (mL) = 1 cup (c)
1 kilogram (kg) = 2.2 pounds (lb)
28.3 grams (g) = 1 ounce (oz)
°C = 5/9 × (°F – 32)

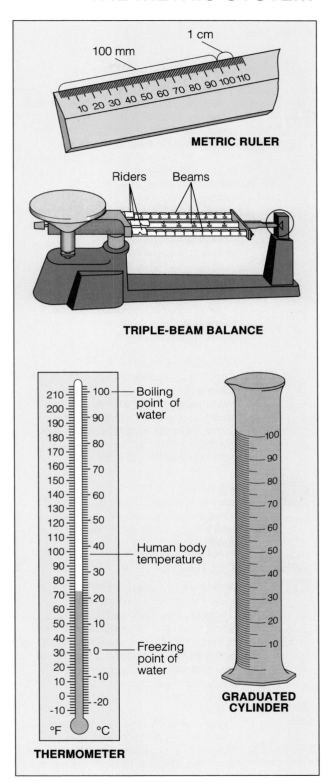

METRIC RULER

Riders   Beams

TRIPLE-BEAM BALANCE

Boiling point of water

Human body temperature

Freezing point of water

THERMOMETER

GRADUATED CYLINDER

Glassware Safety

1. Whenever you see this symbol, you will know that you are working with glassware that can easily be broken. Take particular care to handle such glassware safely. And never use broken or chipped glassware.
2. Never heat glassware that is not thoroughly dry. Never pick up any glassware unless you are sure it is not hot. If it is hot, use heat-resistant gloves.
3. Always clean glassware thoroughly before putting it away.

Fire Safety

1. Whenever you see this symbol, you will know that you are working with fire. Never use any source of fire without wearing safety goggles.
2. Never heat anything—particularly chemicals—unless instructed to do so.
3. Never heat anything in a closed container.
4. Never reach across a flame.
5. Always use a clamp, tongs, or heat-resistant gloves to handle hot objects.
6. Always maintain a clean work area, particularly when using a flame.

Heat Safety

Whenever you see this symbol, you will know that you should put on heat-resistant gloves to avoid burning your hands.

Chemical Safety

1. Whenever you see this symbol, you will know that you are working with chemicals that could be hazardous.
2. Never smell any chemical directly from its container. Always use your hand to waft some of the odors from the top of the container toward your nose—and only when instructed to do so.
3. Never mix chemicals unless instructed to do so.
4. Never touch or taste any chemical unless instructed to do so.
5. Keep all lids closed when chemicals are not in use. Dispose of all chemicals as instructed by your teacher.

6. Immediately rinse with water any chemicals, particularly acids, that get on your skin and clothes. Then notify your teacher.

Eye and Face Safety

1. Whenever you see this symbol, you will know that you are performing an experiment in which you must take precautions to protect your eyes and face by wearing safety goggles.
2. When you are heating a test tube or bottle, always point it away from you and others. Chemicals can splash or boil out of a heated test tube.

Sharp Instrument Safety

1. Whenever you see this symbol, you will know that you are working with a sharp instrument.
2. Always use single-edged razors; double-edged razors are too dangerous.
3. Handle any sharp instrument with extreme care. Never cut any material toward you; always cut away from you.
4. Immediately notify your teacher if your skin is cut.

Electrical Safety

1. Whenever you see this symbol, you will know that you are using electricity in the laboratory.
2. Never use long extension cords to plug in any electrical device. Do not plug too many appliances into one socket or you may overload the socket and cause a fire.
3. Never touch an electrical appliance or outlet with wet hands.

Animal Safety

1. Whenever you see this symbol, you will know that you are working with live animals.
2. Do not cause pain, discomfort, or injury to an animal.
3. Follow your teacher's directions when handling animals. Wash your hands thoroughly after handling animals or their cages.

One of the first things a scientist learns is that working in the laboratory can be an exciting experience. But the laboratory can also be quite dangerous if proper safety rules are not followed at all times. To prepare yourself for a safe year in the laboratory, read over the following safety rules. Then read them a second time. Make sure you understand each rule. If you do not, ask your teacher to explain any rules you are unsure of.

Dress Code

1. Many materials in the laboratory can cause eye injury. To protect yourself from possible injury, wear safety goggles whenever you are working with chemicals, burners, or any substance that might get into your eyes. Never wear contact lenses in the laboratory.

2. Wear a laboratory apron or coat whenever you are working with chemicals or heated substances.

3. Tie back long hair to keep it away from any chemicals, burners and candles, or other laboratory equipment.

4. Remove or tie back any article of clothing or jewelry that can hang down and touch chemicals and flames.

General Safety Rules

5. Read all directions for an experiment several times. Follow the directions exactly as they are written. If you are in doubt about any part of the experiment, ask your teacher for assistance.

6. Never perform activities that are not authorized by your teacher. Obtain permission before "experimenting" on your own.

7. Never handle any equipment unless you have specific permission.

8. Take extreme care not to spill any material in the laboratory. If a spill occurs, immediately ask your teacher about the proper cleanup procedure. Never simply pour chemicals or other substances into the sink or trash container.

9. Never eat in the laboratory.

10. Wash your hands before and after each experiment.

First Aid

11. Immediately report all accidents, no matter how minor, to your teacher.

12. Learn what to do in case of specific accidents, such as getting acid in your eyes or on your skin. (Rinse acids from your body with lots of water.)

13. Become aware of the location of the first-aid kit. But your teacher should administer any required first aid due to injury. Or your teacher may send you to the school nurse or call a physician.

14. Know where and how to report an accident or fire. Find out the location of the fire extinguisher, phone, and fire alarm. Keep a list of important phone numbers—such as the fire department and the school nurse—near the phone. Immediately report any fires to your teacher.

Heating and Fire Safety

15. Again, never use a heat source, such as a candle or burner, without wearing safety goggles.

16. Never heat a chemical you are not instructed to heat. A chemical that is harmless when cool may be dangerous when heated.

17. Maintain a clean work area and keep all materials away from flames.

18. Never reach across a flame.

19. Make sure you know how to light a Bunsen burner. (Your teacher will demonstrate the proper procedure for lighting a burner.) If the flame leaps out of a burner toward you, immediately turn off the gas. Do not touch the burner. It may be hot. And never leave a lighted burner unattended!

20. When heating a test tube or bottle, always point it away from you and others. Chemicals can splash or boil out of a heated test tube.

21. Never heat a liquid in a closed container. The expanding gases produced may blow the container apart, injuring you or others.

22. Before picking up a container that has been heated, first hold the back of your hand near it. If you can feel the heat on the back of your hand, the container may be too hot to handle. Use a clamp or tongs when handling hot containers.

Using Chemicals Safely

23. Never mix chemicals for the "fun of it." You might produce a dangerous, possibly explosive substance.

24. Never touch, taste, or smell a chemical unless you are instructed by your teacher to do so. Many chemicals are poisonous. If you are instructed to note the fumes in an experiment, gently wave your hand over the opening of a container and direct the fumes toward your nose. Do not inhale the fumes directly from the container.

25. Use only those chemicals needed in the activity. Keep all lids closed when a chemical is not being used. Notify your teacher whenever chemicals are spilled.

26. Dispose of all chemicals as instructed by your teacher. To avoid contamination, never return chemicals to their original containers.

27. Be extra careful when working with acids or bases. Pour such chemicals over the sink, not over your workbench.

28. When diluting an acid, pour the acid into water. Never pour water into an acid.

29. Immediately rinse with water any acids that get on your skin or clothing. Then notify your teacher of any acid spill.

Using Glassware Safely

30. Never force glass tubing into a rubber stopper. A turning motion and lubricant will be helpful when inserting glass tubing into rubber stoppers or rubber tubing. Your teacher will demonstrate the proper way to insert glass tubing.

31. Never heat glassware that is not thoroughly dry. Use a wire screen to protect glassware from any flame.

32. Keep in mind that hot glassware will not appear hot. Never pick up glassware without first checking to see if it is hot. See #22.

33. If you are instructed to cut glass tubing, fire-polish the ends immediately to remove sharp edges.

34. Never use broken or chipped glassware. If glassware breaks, notify your teacher and dispose of the glassware in the proper trash container.

35. Never eat or drink from laboratory glassware. Thoroughly clean glassware before putting it away.

Using Sharp Instruments

36. Handle scalpels or razor blades with extreme care. Never cut material toward you; cut away from you.

37. Immediately notify your teacher if you cut your skin when working in the laboratory.

Animal Safety

38. No experiments that will cause pain, discomfort, or harm to mammals, birds, reptiles, fishes, and amphibians should be done in the classroom or at home.

39. Animals should be handled only if necessary. If an animal is excited or frightened, pregnant, feeding, or with its young, special handling is required.

40. Your teacher will instruct you as to how to handle each animal species that may be brought into the classroom.

41. Clean your hands thoroughly after handling animals or the cage containing animals.

End-of-Experiment Rules

42. After an experiment has been completed, clean up your work area and return all equipment to its proper place.

43. Wash your hands after every experiment.

44. Turn off all burners before leaving the laboratory. Check that the gas line leading to the burner is off as well.

THE CHEMICAL ELEMENTS

NAME	SYMBOL	ATOMIC NUMBER	ATOMIC MASS†	NAME	SYMBOL	ATOMIC NUMBER	ATOMIC MASS†
Actinium	Ac	89	(227)	Neodymium	Nd	60	144.2
Aluminum	Al	13	27.0	Neon	Ne	10	20.2
Americium	Am	95	(243)	Neptunium	Np	93	(237)
Antimony	Sb	51	121.8	Nickel	Ni	28	58.7
Argon	Ar	18	39.9	Niobium	Nb	41	92.9
Arsenic	As	33	74.9	Nitrogen	N	7	14.01
Astatine	At	85	(210)	Nobelium	No	102	(255)
Barium	Ba	56	137.3	Osmium	Os	76	190.2
Berkelium	Bk	97	(247)	Oxygen	O	8	16.00
Beryllium	Be	4	9.01	Palladium	Pd	46	106.4
Bismuth	Bi	83	209.0	Phosphorus	P	15	31.0
Boron	B	5	10.8	Platinum	Pt	78	195.1
Bromine	Br	35	79.9	Plutonium	Pu	94	(244)
Cadmium	Cd	48	112.4	Polonium	Po	84	(210)
Calcium	Ca	20	40.1	Potassium	K	19	39.1
Californium	Cf	98	(251)	Praseodymium	Pr	59	140.9
Carbon	C	6	12.01	Promethium	Pm	61	(145)
Cerium	Ce	58	140.1	Protactinium	Pa	91	(231)
Cesium	Cs	55	132.9	Radium	Ra	88	(226)
Chlorine	Cl	17	35.5	Radon	Rn	86	(222)
Chromium	Cr	24	52.0	Rhenium	Re	75	186.2
Cobalt	Co	27	58.9	Rhodium	Rh	45	102.9
Copper	Cu	29	63.5	Rubidium	Rb	37	85.5
Curium	Cm	96	(247)	Ruthenium	Ru	44	101.1
Dysprosium	Dy	66	162.5	Samarium	Sm	62	150.4
Einsteinium	Es	99	(254)	Scandium	Sc	21	45.0
Erbium	Er	68	167.3	Selenium	Se	34	79.0
Europium	Eu	63	152.0	Silicon	Si	14	28.1
Fermium	Fm	100	(257)	Silver	Ag	47	107.9
Fluorine	F	9	19.0	Sodium	Na	11	23.0
Francium	Fr	87	(223)	Strontium	Sr	38	87.6
Gadolinium	Gd	64	157.2	Sulfur	S	16	32.1
Gallium	Ga	31	69.7	Tantalum	Ta	73	180.9
Germanium	Ge	32	72.6	Technetium	Tc	43	(97)
Gold	Au	79	197.0	Tellurium	Te	52	127.6
Hafnium	Hf	72	178.5	Terbium	Tb	65	158.9
Helium	He	2	4.00	Thallium	Tl	81	204.4
Holmium	Ho	67	164.9	Thorium	Th	90	232.0
Hydrogen	H	1	1.008	Thulium	Tm	69	168.9
Indium	In	49	114.8	Tin	Sn	50	118.7
Iodine	I	53	126.9	Titanium	Ti	22	47.9
Iridium	Ir	77	192.2	Tungsten	W	74	183.9
Iron	Fe	26	55.8	Unnilennium	Une	109	(266?)
Krypton	Kr	36	83.8	Unnilhexium	Unh	106	(263)
Lanthanum	La	57	138.9	Unniloctium	Uno	108	(265)
Lawrencium	Lr	103	(256)	Unnilpentium	Unp	105	(262)
Lead	Pb	82	207.2	Unnilquadium	Unq	104	(261)
Lithium	Li	3	6.94	Unnilseptium	Uns	107	(262)
Lutetium	Lu	71	175.0	Uranium	U	92	238.0
Magnesium	Mg	12	24.3	Vanadium	V	23	50.9
Manganese	Mn	25	54.9	Xenon	Xe	54	131.3
Mendelevium	Md	101	(258)	Ytterbium	Yb	70	173.0
Mercury	Hg	80	200.6	Yttrium	Y	39	88.9
Molybdenum	Mo	42	95.9	Zinc	Zn	30	65.4
				Zirconium	Zr	40	91.2

†Numbers in parentheses give the mass number of the most stable isotope.

Appendix E

Key

6	Atomic number
C	Element's symbol
Carbon	Element's name
12.011	Atomic mass

Transition Metals

1	2	3	4	5	6	7	8	9
1 1 **H** Hydrogen 1.00794								
2 3 **Li** Lithium 6.941	4 **Be** Beryllium 9.0122							
3 11 **Na** Sodium 22.990	12 **Mg** Magnesium 24.305	3	4	5	6	7	8	9
4 19 **K** Potassium 39.098	20 **Ca** Calcium 40.08	21 **Sc** Scandium 44.956	22 **Ti** Titanium 47.88	23 **V** Vanadium 50.94	24 **Cr** Chromium 51.996	25 **Mn** Manganese 54.938	26 **Fe** Iron 55.847	27 **Co** Cobalt 58.9332
5 37 **Rb** Rubidium 85.468	38 **Sr** Strontium 87.62	39 **Y** Yttrium 88.9059	40 **Zr** Zirconium 91.224	41 **Nb** Niobium 92.91	42 **Mo** Molybdenum 95.94	43 **Tc** Technetium (98)	44 **Ru** Ruthenium 101.07	45 **Rh** Rhodium 102.906
6 55 **Cs** Cesium 132.91	56 **Ba** Barium 137.33	57 to 71	72 **Hf** Hafnium 178.49	73 **Ta** Tantalum 180.95	74 **W** Tungsten 183.85	75 **Re** Rhenium 186.207	76 **Os** Osmium 190.2	77 **Ir** Iridium 192.22
7 87 **Fr** Francium (223)	88 **Ra** Radium 226.025	89 to 103	104 **Unq** Unnilquadium (261)	105 **Unp** Unnilpentium (262)	106 **Unh** Unnilhexium (263)	107 **Uns** Unnilseptium (262)	108 **Uno** Unniloctium (265)	109 **Une** Unnilennium (266)

Rare-Earth Elements

Lanthanoid Series

57 **La** Lanthanum 138.906	58 **Ce** Cerium 140.12	59 **Pr** Praseodymium 140.908	60 **Nd** Neodymium 144.24	61 **Pm** Promethium (145)	62 **Sm** Samarium 150.36

Actinoid Series

89 **Ac** Actinium 227.028	90 **Th** Thorium 232.038	91 **Pa** Protactinium 231.036	92 **U** Uranium 238.029	93 **Np** Neptunium 237.048	94 **Pu** Plutonium (244)

154 ■ N

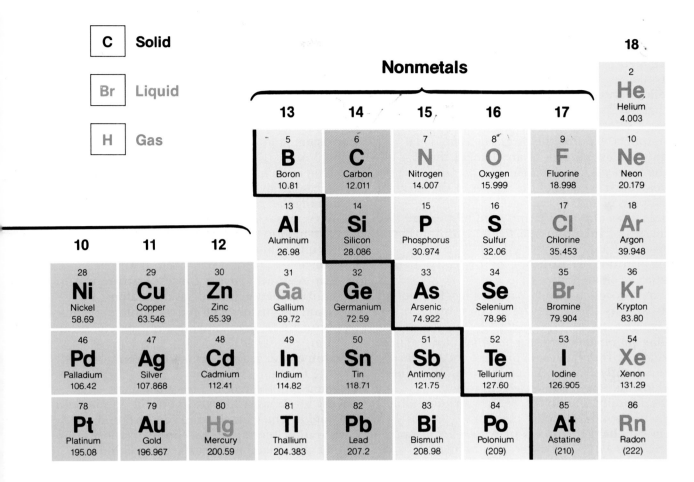

								18
C	Solid							2 **He** Helium 4.003

Nonmetals

		13	**14**	**15**	**16**	**17**	

Br	Liquid

H	Gas

5 **B** Boron 10.81	6 **C** Carbon 12.011	7 **N** Nitrogen 14.007	8 **O** Oxygen 15.999	9 **F** Fluorine 18.998	10 **Ne** Neon 20.179
13 **Al** Aluminum 26.98	14 **Si** Silicon 28.086	15 **P** Phosphorus 30.974	16 **S** Sulfur 32.06	17 **Cl** Chlorine 35.453	18 **Ar** Argon 39.948

10	**11**	**12**
28 **Ni** Nickel 58.69	29 **Cu** Copper 63.546	30 **Zn** Zinc 65.39	31 **Ga** Gallium 69.72	32 **Ge** Germanium 72.59	33 **As** Arsenic 74.922	34 **Se** Selenium 78.96	35 **Br** Bromine 79.904	36 **Kr** Krypton 83.80
46 **Pd** Palladium 106.42	47 **Ag** Silver 107.868	48 **Cd** Cadmium 112.41	49 **In** Indium 114.82	50 **Sn** Tin 118.71	51 **Sb** Antimony 121.75	52 **Te** Tellurium 127.60	53 **I** Iodine 126.905	54 **Xe** Xenon 131.29
78 **Pt** Platinum 195.08	79 **Au** Gold 196.967	80 **Hg** Mercury 200.59	81 **Tl** Thallium 204.383	82 **Pb** Lead 207.2	83 **Bi** Bismuth 208.98	84 **Po** Polonium (209)	85 **At** Astatine (210)	86 **Rn** Radon (222)

The symbols shown here for elements 104-109 are being used temporarily until names for these elements can be agreed upon.

Metals

Mass numbers in parentheses are those of the most stable or common isotope.

63 **Eu** Europium 151.96	64 **Gd** Gadolinium 157.25	65 **Tb** Terbium 158.925	66 **Dy** Dysprosium 162.50	67 **Ho** Holmium 164.93	68 **Er** Erbium 167.26	69 **Tm** Thulium 168.934	70 **Yb** Ytterbium 173.04	71 **Lu** Lutetium 174.967
95 **Am** Americium (243)	96 **Cm** Curium (247)	97 **Bk** Berkelium (247)	98 **Cf** Californium (251)	99 **Es** Einsteinium (252)	100 **Fm** Fermium (257)	101 **Md** Mendelevium (258)	102 **No** Nobelium (259)	103 **Lr** Lawrencium (260)

Glossary

actinoid series: second row of rare-earth elements in the periodic table, which with the exception of three elements are radioactive and synthetic

alkali metal: member of element Family 1 that has 1 valence electron

alkaline earth metal: member of element Family 2 that has 2 valence electrons

alloy: a solution of two metals or a metal and a nonmetal that has the properties of a metal

atom: smallest particle of an element that has all the properties of that element

atomic mass: average of the masses of the existing isotopes of an element

atomic mass unit (amu): unit used to measure the masses of subatomic particles; a proton has a mass of 1 amu

atomic number: number of protons in the nucleus of an atom

boiling: process in which particles inside a liquid as well as those on the surface of a liquid change to a gas

boiling point: temperature at which a substance changes from the liquid phase to the gas phase

boron family: Family 13 of the periodic table; elements have 3 valence electrons

carbon family: Family 14 of the periodic table; elements have 4 valence electrons

chemical change: process by which a substance becomes a new and different substance

chemical equation: expression in which symbols, formulas, and numbers are used to represent a chemical reaction

chemical formula: combination of chemical symbols usually used to represent a compound

chemical property: property that describes how a substance changes into a new substance

chemical reaction: process in which the physical and chemical properties of the original substance change as a new substance with different physical and chemical properties is formed

chemical symbol: shorthand way of representing an element

coefficient (koh-uh-FIHSH-uhnt): number that is placed in front of a symbol or a formula in a chemical equation that indicates how many atoms or molecules of this substance are involved in the reaction

colloid (KAHL-oid): homogeneous mixture in which the particles are mixed together but not dissolved

compound: substance made up of molecules that contain more than one kind of atom; two or more elements chemically combined

condensation (kahn-duhn-SAY-shuhn): change of a gas to a liquid

corrosion: gradual wearing away of a metal due to a chemical reaction in which the metal element is changed into a metallic compound

crystal: solid in which the particles are arranged in a regular, repeating pattern

density: measurement of how much mass is contained in a given volume of an object; mass per unit volume

ductile: able to be drawn into a thin wire

electromagnetic force: force of attraction or repulsion between particles in an atom

electron: negatively charged subatomic particle found in an area outside the nucleus of an atom

electron cloud: space in which electrons are likely to be found

element: simplest type of pure substance

energy level: most likely location in an electron cloud in which an electron can be found

evaporation (ee-vap-uh-RAY-shuhn): vaporization that takes place at the surface of a liquid

family: column of elements in the periodic table; group

flammability (flam-uh-BIHL-uh-tee): ability to burn

freezing: change of a liquid into a solid

freezing point: temperature at which a substance changes from the liquid phase to the solid phase

gas: phase in which matter has no definite shape or volume

gravity: force of attraction between all objects in the universe

group: column of elements in the periodic table; family

halogen family: Family 17 of the periodic table; elements have atoms that contain 7 valence electrons

heterogeneous (heht-er-oh-JEE-nee-uhs) **mixture:** mixture that does not appear to be the same throughout

homogeneous (hoh-moh-JEE-nee-uhs) **mixture:** mixture that appears the same throughout

inertia (ihn-ER-shuh): tendency of objects to remain in motion or to stay at rest unless acted upon by an outside force

insoluble: unable to be dissolved in water

isotope (IGH-suh-tohp): atom of an element that has the same number of protons as another atom of the same element but a different number of neutrons

lanthanoid series: first row of rare-earth elements in the periodic table; soft, malleable metals that have a high luster and conductivity

liquid: matter with no definite shape but with a definite volume

luster: shininess

malleable: able to be hammered out into a thin sheet

mass: amount of matter in an object

mass number: sum of the protons and neutrons in the nucleus of an atom

matter: anything that has mass and volume

melting: change of a solid to a liquid

melting point: temperature at which a substance changes from the solid phase to the liquid phase

metal: element that is a good conductor of heat and electricity, is shiny, has a high melting point, is ductile and malleable, and tends to lose electrons

metalloid (MEHT-uh-loid): element that has properties of both metals and nonmetals

mixture: matter that consists of two of more substances mixed but not chemically combined

molecule (MAHL-ih-kyool): structure made up of two or more atoms

neutron: subatomic particle with no electric charge that is found in the nucleus of an atom

nitrogen family: Family 15 of the periodic table; elements have atoms with 5 valence electrons

noble gas: member of Family 18 of the periodic table; elements have atoms with 8 valence electrons and are extremely unreactive

nonmetal: element that is a poor conductor of heat and electricity, has a dull surface, low melting point, is brittle, breaks easily, and tends to gain electrons

nucleus (NOO-klee-uhs): small, dense positively charged center of an atom

oxygen family: Family 14 of the periodic table; elements have atoms with 6 valence electrons

period: horizontal row of elements in the periodic table

periodic law: law that states that the physical and chemical properties of the elements are periodic functions of their atomic numbers

phase: state in which matter can exist: solid, liquid, gas, or plasma

physical property: characteristic that distinguishes one type of matter from another and can be observed without changing the identity of the substance

plasma: phase in which matter is extremely high in energy and cannot be contained by the walls of ordinary matter; very rare on Earth

property: characteristic of a substance

proton: subatomic particle that has a positive charge and is found in the nucleus of an atom

pure substance: substance made of one kind of material having definite properties

quark (KWORK): particle that makes up all other known particles in the nucleus of an atom

rare-earth element: general designation for those elements in the lanthanoid and actinoid series

solid: phase in which matter has a definite shape and volume

solubility: the amount of a solute that can be completely dissolved in a given amount of solvent at a specific temperature

soluble (SAHL-yoo-buhl): can be dissolved in water

solute (SAHL-yoot): substance that is dissolved in a solution

solution (suh-LOO-shuhn): homogeneous mixture in which one substance is dissolved in another

solvent (SAHL-vuhnt): substance that does the dissolving in a solution

strong force: force that binds protons and neutrons in the nucleus

subatomic particle: proton, neutron, and electron

subscript: number placed to the lower right of a chemical symbol to indicate the number of atoms of the element in the compound

sublimation (suhb-luh-MAY-shuhn): change from the solid phase directly into the gas phase

transition metal: element that has properties similar to other transition metals and to other metals but whose properties do not fit in with those of any other family

vaporization (vay-per-ih-ZAY-shuhn): change of a liquid to a gas

volume: amount of space an object takes up

weak force: force that is the key to the power of the sun; responsible for a process known as radioactive decay

weight: measure of the force of attraction between objects due to gravity

Index